Tales

of the

East Neuk

Nanzie McLeod

THE HYNDLAND PRESS
GLASGOW

Cover painting: 'The Sma' Lines' by John McGhie 1867–1952, courtesy of the Anstruther Fisheries Museum.

First published in the United Kingdom, 2005
by
The Hyndland Press
Glasgow, G12 9QL

The author has asserted her moral rights.

British Library Cataloguing-in Publication Data.
A catalogue record for this book is available from
the British Library.

ISBN 0 9529527 1 8

Printed by
Cordfall Ltd, Glasgow, G21 2QA

Also by Nanzie McLeod
Tales
of the
Arlington

**John McGhie setting off for a day's work
was a characteristic sight for nearly forty years.**

Contents

Introduction 7

The Bowler Hat 11

Early Days 25

An Incomer of Long Ago 33

Tragic Memories 47

Fisher Girl 52

Reen Thomas 66

Village Temptations 74

Notable Characters 92

Babies 106

The Butcher 116

Headland wind 123

First Kiss 125

Ice Cream and Sweeties 145

The Grocer's Flitting 152

Youthful pursuits 162

Destiny 174

The Studio 200

Black Annabell 205

Street Sweeper 207

The Pageant 226

Heading North 234

Festival Haikus. 2004 243

Pittenweem Arts Festival 244

Introduction

MY GRANDFATHER WAS JOHN MCGHIE, the artist, and these stories would not have been written if he had not come to live in Fife in order to paint the rugged coast and the fisher people. It was in 1901 that our family's long association with the East Neuk started.

In 1911 they bought the house at 54 High Street, Pittenweem, which five generations of our family have enjoyed throughout the twentieth century, sometimes as a home, more often as a holiday house.

I have tried to make the stories move consecutively through the twentieth century, but I have indulged myself with the prologue which is not about the East Neuk at all, but about how my grandparents first met.

It was not my original intention to involve my grandparents, but as I wrote, their marriage, their characters and the life that they lived became inextricably interwoven with the tales, just as the house at 54 High Street will always have for me, a strong sense of their presence.

McGhie was born in the small village of Lesmahagow in Lanarkshire and studied art in Glasgow, London, Paris and Venice. His father was a grocer and very much against such a career for his son, however John was obviously talented, very determined. He won prizes and scholarships that made his excellent education possible. In spite of his father's forebodings, John became a very successful artist, part of the Glasgow establishment and for the greater part of the year, lived in the city and painted portraits of wealthy businessmen, notable military men, provosts and even the Moderator of the Kirk. Although portraiture is a remunerative art form, sadly unless the paintings portray very famous people, they are ephemeral, and slip into obscurity when the subject dies. Fortunately my grandfather, early in his career, fell in love with the sea and the East Neuk and painted there practically every summer for at least fifty years. His pictures of the strong, handsome fisherpeople, although somewhat romanticised, are a social comment and a tribute to the East Neuk. They seem to me much more dashing and alive than his commissioned portraits which were expected to keep to narrow conventional straits. He obviously had a great love of the sea and a deep affection for the people of Pittenweem. There are still many people who remember him and who posed for him and this affection is returned. He was known as,

"The laud that kin pent!"

Some of his sea paintings can be seen in the superb Anstruther Fisheries Museum.

He also illustrated several books and was president of the Scottish Etching Association.

In the first half of the century, he spent three months in Fife each year, painting, which meant that my mother Annie and her brother, Willie, attended the local school every June.

My grandmother, Agnes Burns, was nineteen when she married John McGhie and came to Fife. Her father had been a soldier in the Indian army and she was born in Rawalpindi. After the family returned to Britain, her father, like many other soldiers, did not find civilian life easy. With an ever-growing family, they moved from place to place in England and Scotland, never staying long anywhere. Agnes was a beauty and clever, but her education was almost certainly scrappy and minimal. However, she quickly learned the demands of an artist's wife and by the time she was in her late twenties, was not only her husband's favourite model, but his valuable business associate, for very often her persuasive charm might nudge a prospective buyer into being a regular patron. She also worked for charity, organising whist drives and bazaars at that time. There is a postcard from Ellen Terry, the actress, thanking Agnes for her efforts at fund-raising.

In her thirties my grandmother discovered golf and was a very keen player and eventually captain of Hilton Park golf club on the outskirts of Glasgow. She also enjoyed the small but demanding Anstruther course. Agnes had a life-long interest in antiques and loved roups and bazaars and had an eagle eye for a bargain. Most of all she loved to tell a good story, spiced with drama and humour and throughout her life she mesmerised many an appreciative audience.

Some of the stories in this book are based on my grandmother's anecdotes. She was a superb raconteur and I only wish that I could remember more of the things that she told me. Other stories are based on experiences of later generations of the family. The factual articles mention names which will be well known to inhabitants of the East Neuk, but in the stories, events and names are invented and only remotely based on real happenings or people. I have tried to use imagination and artistic licence to make a painting in words of various times that I have heard about or lived through, times that have now passed away. I have worried that the articles and the stories would so blend into each other that the reader might find it difficult to decide whether he is reading fact or fiction so I have layered them alternately, thus each factual piece will be followed by a story and vice versa. The three poems are outwith this pattern but should not be confusing, especially if the reader, like myself, tends to ignore poems.

It would be impossible to give a flavour of the East Neuk without the vivid sayings and unique speech inflections of the locality, but it is very difficult to reproduce speech in the vernacular and success depends almost as much on the reader's familiarity with the accent as it does on the writer's ability to reproduce it. I have no idea how to convey the *song*, which is so much a part of east coast conversation. That must come from the reader's own experience. It is similar to French, with a dramatic rise at the end of each sentence and I can hear it clearly in my head as I write. Please forgive me if my reported speech does not always ring true to the Pittenweem ear, for though I have an unbreakable connection with the East Neuk, I consider myself a born and bred Glaswegian. Apart from the six years which I spent abroad, I have enjoyed every summer of my long life in Pittenweem. I also attended Pittenweem school for most of the war years and have many friends from those days, although I cannot say it was easy to be an 'incomer' in the early forties. By my mid teens, I was more accepted and much of my 'growing-up' was accomplished in the sunny Pittenweem summers, for there is no doubt that the East Neuk is particularly blessed as far as sun is concerned. It seems that the little corner thus designated, sticks out into the North Sea and avoids the clouds and rain. Most of the time at any rate.

When, in 1989, I arranged a historic pageant to celebrate the four hundredth anniversary of the Parish church, some of the congregation were kind enough to suggest that I was ninety percent a 'Pittenweemer', but I think that was over generous.

I was not born a 'Pittenweemer' and these stories are told from an observer's point of view, a loving observer who has shared a great deal of the life of Pittenweem.

I hope that I have recorded some happenings and facts which, though trivial in themselves, will strike a chord of recognition in the reader, for it is amazingly easy to forget. More importantly, I hope to have recreated a small part of the rich and varied social history of Pittenweem, lapped by the economic ebb and flow of the last hundred years.

I want to thank the many local people who have provided such valuable information and so many touching personal memories of the past. I am particularly grateful to the following: Kenneth Adamson, Margaret and Rachel Aitken, Chrissie and Bill Black, Jessie Bowman, Isobel and Andrew Grieg, Bessie Horsburgh, John and Jessie Wilson, Mary Richards, Belle Ryrie, Heather Cunningham and the late Bob Moir, the late Chrissie Taylor and the late Jen Wilson

I am grateful for the help I have received from Jean Reid and Jak Edwards.

I very much appreciate the support and encouragement as well as practical advice which has been given so willingly by each of my four daughters, Kate, Esther, Sarah and Alice.

This book is a tribute to my grandfather, John McGhie who painted the East Neuk lovingly and truly and to my grandmother, Mary Ann Agnes McGhie, who was such a fascinating teller of tales and whose strong character has reverberated through the generations.

The Bowler Hat

As John McGhie walked eastwards along the south side of the Clyde, he admired the fine architecture of Carlton Place and idly wondered if at some time in the future he might achieve success as an artist and aspire to live in a splendid area like that. After years of study it was time to make his way in the world and Glasgow, with its wealth and its strong interest in art, seemed the best place to start. Portraiture was especially remunerative and was his ultimate aim, for he knew that he could make a 'true likeness' but portraits were invariably commissioned and it was necessary to become 'known' in the art world before commissions dropped into your lap and that state of 'becoming known' seemed a difficult and slow process. Perhaps impossible.

In the last seven months, John had taken lodgings in Garnethill, joined the Glasgow Art Club, exhibited at the Royal Glasgow Institute and made several friends, all artists and all, like himself, hopeful of finding success in the city. So far his success had not been great, more appreciated by his penniless peers than by the buying public, but he worked hard and hoped to return to the east coast in the summer.

During the previous summer and autumn, he had painted in some of the picturesque fishing villages strung along the coast of Fife and known as the East Neuk. He was fascinated by the sturdy ancient harbours and breakwaters, the brown sails of the fragile fishing boats, the random clustering houses on the cliffs and not least by the handsome men and women who lived in constant danger and unceasing toil in order to harvest the sea.

John had grown up in the small rural town of Lesmahagow in Lanarkshire and he delighted in this entirely new environment. The problem of how to depict in paint, the animal strength and ever-changing colours and moods of the sea was a constant challenge to him. As a bonus, he found that the sharp, clear atmosphere helped his chest problems and filled him with an energy which he had not previously experienced.

Some of those small paintings of Anstruther, Pittenweem and St Monance had sold and he had plans for larger compositions which would incorporate the fishergirls wearing their decorative clothing and busy at their various tasks. That was for the future though, because there was no likelihood that the hanging committee of the Glasgow Institute would accept a large canvas of sixty by forty inches, when submitted by an unknown painter. These large pictures were what caught the eye and brought attention to a man's ability. It was a vicious circle and very frustrating.

John never left home without his sketch book and today he was walking around the city with the idea that he might find something attractive to paint. He had stopped several times to make drawings but somehow he could not imagine translating any of these scenes to paint. Whistler had painted city-scapes in London and Paris, as had Walter Sickert, who was much the same age as himself but John would always be drawn to nature. For him, the streams and trees of his youth and the ever-changing sea seemed more attractive and more worthwhile to depict than buildings, streets and river industry. And, more to the point, he was sure those beauties of nature would be more saleable! Who would decorate their wall with a foggy dockland or a row of grubby shops? However he continued to note things of interest that he passed, sometimes only a quick but telling scribble of workmen busy at some laborious task, sometimes a more finished sketch of a horse and cart. Sometimes a small rhyme or riddle would pop into his head and he would jot it down on the back page with a suppressed smile, partly amused at the joke and partly laughing at himself for appreciating his own humour.

It was a bright breezy day in spring and the river Clyde was busy with small craft. On the north side the row of warehouses struck John as interesting and he stopped for ten minutes to make a quick workman-like pencil sketch of them. He had no particular aim in view but they had a certain decorative quality which appealed to him and though it was highly unlikely that anyone would want a painting of warehouses or that he would ever make use of the sketch, one never knew. He had gratefully earned a few pounds for designing one or two small pamphlets, invitations, cartoons and a menu card for the Art Club. Perhaps he would be asked to illustrate a book one day. He was at the beginning of his career and was determined to accept all opportunities. With his soft pencil he deftly indicated the architectural detail and the bold lettering across the front of the buildings. Then at the side of the page he described the different colours of the faded walls, the brightly painted boats and water, scribbling the words, pale purple, light ochre, dark umber, slate grey and using lines and arrows to indicate the appropriate places.

The craft were all quite small at this part of the river and John was reminded of his beloved Pittenweem. In his mind's eye he saw the old harbour, the Thell, with its beautiful cream and pink rocks and the gently bobbing boats waiting for the tide to turn. How fresh and sweet-smelling the air would be there. He imagined a tall fishergirl in her heavy striped skirt sitting on a rock and gazing out to sea. He was a romantic young man!

Just then a university rowing boat passed him on its way to Glasgow Green. The young men were pushing themselves to their utmost and the boat moved swiftly up-river. It was a fine sight and John appreciated it but he could not help comparing their pleasurable but unnecessary exertion to the work of the Fife fishermen, who must daily struggle for many hours to earn a meagre living and sometimes battle to save their lives in unexpected storms. Life was strange and unfair.

And what about himself? He hoped and expected to make a great deal of money just for dabbing morsels of paint in the right place on a canvas rectangle. Again he smiled to himself because he had never quite thought about his career like that. He considered adding this thought to his humorous verse but decided it was too complicated to express in a few words and resolved that he would try to bear it in mind when he became rich and famous.

As John turned to cross northwards over the suspension bridge, an unexpected gust of wind blew from the Clyde and neatly lifted his bowler hat from his head. As he stooped to pick it up, the breeze eddied and sent the hat rolling straight across the bridge in a determined manner. Though not travelling fast, the hat seemed to have an almost human sense of purpose in its straightforward direction, which appealed to John and he smiled in embarrassment as he quickened his speed in order to catch it. Unfortunately he was hampered in his pursuit by the people who strolled aimlessly back and forth in the warm spring sunshine. Few even noticed the runaway hat and those who did, stood aside from its path with a smile, as if to give it a sporting chance of escape. With a flustered and hurried step and repeated "Excuse me"s and "I beg your pardon!"s, John zig-zagged across the bridge, dodging the other walkers but the breeze made sure that the hat stayed always just tantalisingly out of reach. He had almost decided to abandon the chase and retrieve his dignity, though he could ill afford the price of a new hat, when he realised that the errant billycock was finally stopped in its course by the small brown boot of a tall young woman. He was half aware that she had taken several quick dancing steps sideways to waylay it. As he came up to her she bent quickly and gracefully picked up the hat and held it out to him.

"I'm afraid it's rather dusty!" she said with a smile. Her voice was pleasant and without any discernible accent.

John stood there, motionless and speechless, for her face was wonderful.

It seemed to him the epitome of beauty.

He had never looked at such a face.

Every era has its own standards and fashions in good looks and John had been trained in the London Royal Academy Schools by Millais, Burne-Jones and Alma-Tadema. Those eminent men had taught him to consider the large liquid eyes, well marked nose and clearly defined Mediterranean mouth of the Pre-Raphaelite beauty as absolute perfection. And here in front of him was a real live, healthy, energetic specimen of that type smiling at him and holding out his hat. Even the mass of glinting brown hair under her straw boater was absolutely right. What a stunning young woman! His mind was fired with the wonderful portrait which he might paint of her!

He stood as if turned to stone and said not a word.

"Don't you want it? Is it too dusty to wear? Shall I just throw it in the river?" She made a playful movement as if to skim it over the parapet of the bridge.

"No no, don't!" he exclaimed before he realised that she was teasing him. "Thank you! Thank you so much for catching my hat, no it's not dusty at all, thank you."

Without looking at it, he jammed it on his head then immediately took it off again in a polite fluster.

"It was awfully quick of you to stop it for nobody else seemed to think of doing that. Thank you again."

"Being tall, I suppose, I can see what's happening more easily than other folk that are small. That's the only good thing about being tall."

"I think it is very elegant and attractive to be tall."

John had not had much practice in making complimentary speeches and he was daunted to hear himself say these words and blushed, though no one could have doubted his sincerity.

The girl seemed to pay no attention and continued, laughing,

"I feel like a giantess here in Glasgow. Nearly everyone is so very *little*. Hardly anyone reaches my shoulder even. Just a *giantess* that's all I am."

"More like a goddess " John thought, but did not say. Perhaps his rapturous regard made words unnecessary.

Until this moment they had stood still but now the girl moved forward to continue her journey across the bridge towards the south side of the river and in a fascinated daze John turned and walked beside her. He was at a loss as to what was the correct procedure. It seemed rude to walk away from this benefactress and to separate himself from her was the last thing on earth that he wanted to do. Yet it hardly seemed right to impose himself on her. He had no idea what the etiquette was in such a situation and he was distinctly uncomfortable. A discomfort which she did not seem to share, for she chatted on in a spritely way as though they were old friends. John was very much afraid that this was what was called a 'pick-up' and it worried him considerably. Yet she was obviously a well brought up girl, neatly though not expensively dressed. She spoke with so very little accent that John guessed that, like himself, she had lived in a lot of different places.

As they made their slow way through the crowds on the bridge, she asserted that this sunny breezy weather was just her most favourite of all. Next she pointed out a pretty red boat on the river and informed him that it was called the "Bessie Miller" and that it was her ambition to have a boat named after her. Before John could find the courage to ask her what that boat would be called, she started to bemoan her young brother Jim, who was such a trial to his sisters and always in trouble at school.

"Always getting whacked by the teacher! And I expect he deserves it too."

Then she enthused about her newly-born baby sister who was "just the loveliest baby you have ever seen and so good". The baby's name was Roberta.

The girl's voice was deep and attractive and her vivacious way of speaking gave a sparkle to the small talk which poured from her lips, while a wide range of expression flitted across her face. Her nervousness would have been apparent to a more objective observer but John was too enmeshed in her magic to notice. He was obsessed by the wish to paint her yet it seemed impertinent to ask her to sit for him when they had just met so casually. He had to admit that he felt intimidated by her. Intimidated by her beauty perhaps? Or was it her presence? For although she was young, she had a commanding manner and seemed to John to be much more in charge of the situation than he himself was. Most importantly, he felt that this was hardly a respectable way of meeting a young lady. She seemed terribly young, perhaps not more than twenty and compared to her, John, at twenty nine, felt like an old man, though certainly not an old man of any great experience with women. His upbringing in Lesmahagow had been religious and strict and he had worked too hard at his craft for much in the way of dalliance. His student days in London and Paris had been spent largely in the studio, for he was ambitious.

John retraced his earlier footsteps along Carlton Place at the side of the tall young woman who talked animatedly and continuously. He noticed that she had beautifully expressive hands with which she gestured dramatically as she spoke. Her stately carriage and her vivacious hands reminded him of the stylish Parisian women. The mixture of innocent girlish chatter and womanly allure was mesmerising. He hardly listened to what she said, yet he was drinking in her looks, her movements and her personality. He was also wondering desperately how he could suggest that he might paint her or arrange another meeting without offending her. He was unwilling to proclaim himself an artist, for so many people considered the breed to be disreputable, if not downright immoral. But he could not deceive her because that was what he was. He hardly recognised that his interest in her was as much personal as artistic

What a duffer he was to have reached this age and still be unable to find out a young lady's name or arrange a future meeting. Where were they walking to anyway? He could not see how to improve the situation. Could he ask her to take a cup of tea with him? But there were no tearooms in the vicinity that he knew of and anyway that seemed much too forward. The young woman solved the problem by suddenly exclaiming, with her charming smile,

"Oh, this is where I am going. Good bye and look after your hat, now!"

AUDITION
Young ladies of advanced musicality, alluring figure and
superior morals required to audition for

FORTHCOMING SPECTACULAR

Dancing ability an asset.
10 a.m. Thursday at Bridgeton
Burgh Halls

Laying the paper quietly down and saying not a word to anyone,
Agnes dreamed all evening of her success at the audition, of how she
would be specially chosen for her high kicks and her fiery dancing.
Her imagination pictured a glamourous and wealthy future, a vista
of beautiful hats and gowns, carriages and admiration far, far from
Silvergrove Street. Esther asked her why she was smiling as she dried
the dishes, but even to her favourite sister, she said not a word.

By Wednesday evening, however, her excitement and nervous
tension had grown too great to hide. The whole family knew that
there was something afoot and her father demanded to know what it
was. All fell silent as she explained, for even the youngest was aware
that the stage was not respectable. Agnes might as well have
proposed robbing a bank and they awaited the immense explosion of
their father's anger. As Agnes blurted out her secret and watched her
father's face turn dark red, her wonderful hopes disintegrated as
quickly and as completely as soap bubbles.

"Aye, if you go to that *owdition* tomorrow, ye'll go with two **broken
legs**!" he thundered and Agnes could only be glad that nothing more
was ever said about it.

She continued to wrap loaves in rustling tissue, count buns into
paper bags and place cakes carefully in fine card boxes with only
infrequent and wistful thoughts of the footlights.

When a girl has once considered the stage as a career, it is seldom
that she will ever completely relinquish the possibility.

And now we return to John McGhie. Unlike Agnes, he could think of
nothing but his meeting on the bridge with this wonderful girl and
how he might find her again, but he had no idea how to tackle the
problem, no experience to help him. He had been nearly two miles
distant from his lodgings when they met and she might have been as

many from her home. Two miles east, west, north or south, the vast tenements stretched in all directions. The impossibility of it all depressed him and for two days he stayed at home, drawing unsatisfactory scribbles and crumpling them up.

Mrs Cramer was quite worried by this behaviour of her favourite lodger and after various pots of tea and sympathetic enquiries as to his health, John took her into his confidence.

"And ye're sure she was a nice respectable girl, Mr McGhie?"

"Oh certainly. Without a doubt. Mrs Cramer."

He was fervent about this point, because he had at times had his worries about whether she should have spoken to him quite so freely, but he had finally and fully convinced himself in her favour.

"There's some awful nice churches thereabout, Mr McGhie. There's the Tron and there's St Andrew's Kirk this side o' the Clyde and Ah can't quite mind the names o' the south side yins but thur three o' them and they're all very well-tae-do churches and maybe if ye went tae some Sunday services, ye might bump into her and jist lift yer hat and efter a few Sundays, ye could speak. an' then mebbe her Mither or even baith parents would be there to make it all respectable-like."

John listened unenthusiastically. He suspected that this was a thinly-veiled ruse to improve his church attendance and he was not entirely mistaken, although the motherly Mrs Cramer did want to help him and could not really think of any other acceptable way of meeting a young woman. It seemed a slow and unlikely process to John and with all those churches to choose from, it was a bit of a lottery.

"It might take a lot of Sundays to find the right kirk that she attends."

"Aye, but ye could go tae evening service, too."

"She was *such* a beautiful girl, Mrs Cramer and I really want to paint her."

"Aye, Ah ken that weel but a nice well-brought up girl might not want tae sit tae her pictur. I know fine ye're a good laddie and a *gentleman* in the making."

Mrs Cramer was more partial to John than to any other lodger that she had ever had under her roof.

"And ye're that hard, hard workin' and such a wonderful livin' likeness ye get wi' yer pencil in just meenutes! And never a drop o' drink from one week till the next and yer faither an elder and teetotal forby. Still an' all, there's funny stories about artists and their goin's-on that she might hiv heard and she might no' like . . . "

"I know that only too well," John said sadly, shaking his head.

"Ye see, if ye met her at the kirk, that would show repectability. Though maybe ye should be crossing the bridge another day about the same time like and maybe jist hang aboot an' dae drawin's in yer wee book for a while an' ye niver know, ye might jist see her again by chance."

You will understand that Mrs Cramer was a romantic at heart.

And now, dear reader, as you are well aware, there would be no story for me to tell, unless these young people did meet again in more propitious circumstances. That they did meet is certainly the case because they would, in the fullness of time, become my grandparents.

Did John follow that last very practical piece of advice from his landlady and find success?

Or did he attend the cold services in the Tron?

Or perhaps in his perambulations around that part of the city, did a young man's hunger suggest a nourishing 'flies' cemetery' and fortuitously direct him to the very baker's shop where he would find Agnes?

Or did he, on an incredulous ramble along the filthy and poverty-stricken Gallowgate, delight in the irony of a side alley named Arcadia Street (for he was well educated in the classics) only to find on turning the next corner that he was face to face with his goddess as she emerged from number five, Silvergrove Street?

It may even be that Agnes, in her quest for adventure, applied for the position of waitress in the Glasgow Art Club in Bath Street and, becomingly decked in her neat black uniform and lace cap, brought a cup of coffee to the astonished young artist one evening.

I must now confess that though the above characters are true to life, the circumstances are sheer speculation and I only know for sure that they did meet and after slightly more than two years were married.

It was by chance, quite recently, that I bemoaned to a friend that I did not know how my grandparents, with their disparate ages, tastes and backgrounds could ever have met.

"Why," she exclaimed, "Bruce always said that they met on the suspension bridge."

Bruce was my father, now dead for many years and better known for an accurate memory than for an imagination. I myself had never heard him make this statement, but my friend's word is absolutely reliable and the idea was so romantic that I felt bound to pursue it.

Perhaps most simply and obviously, my grandfather was not such a 'duffer' on that very first encounter. I know that he was a shy, retiring man with little personal vanity and it was probably most improper to 'pick up' a young lady in those days, but nevertheless, folk do not change with the centuries and if the two tall young people both liked what they saw and the sun was shining, they may very well have walked off together along the Clyde, with Agnes ignoring her waiting duties in the baker's shop.

That is, if she ever worked in a baker's shop.

Early Days

IN 1901, WHEN THEY WERE first married, my grandparents Agnes and John McGhie, rented a small house in Kilconquhar, or to be more precise, the outcrop of Barnyards.

John had worked for short periods in the East Neuk of Fife for years and it must have seemed sensible to settle there amongst so many paintable scenes. No doubt the modest rent was also appealing for, though in his early thirties, he had not yet attained any degree of success in his profession. Agnes was a city girl and probably found the quiet rural life rather strange but at nineteen she was resourceful and energetic, tall and strong. Her father had been cursed with the wanderlust and she had lived in several different cities in her nineteen years and was well able to adapt to a new environment. Besides, she had her bicycle and loved the freedom of the empty country roads. They had chosen to take a bicycling honeymoon which must have seemed quite daring at the start of the century. It was a strange and daunting sight for the locals to see the young woman bowling along on her two wheels. Each morning in those first months, the couple explored the many pretty roads of the area on their bicycles, visiting the small inland villages, the wealthy and self-sufficient estates of Grangemuir, Balcaskie and Balcarres when they were open to the public, and the picturesque fishing towns of St Monance, Pittenweem, Anstruther, Cellardyke, Crail each with its own individual plan and personality. Each indeed with its own accent, though that was a subtlety not distinguishable to 'incomers' like the McGhies.

John was always on the lookout for anything that he might incorporate into a picture and would stop and make a quick sketch of trees overhanging a stream or fishermen busy in their boats at the harbour or perhaps a pretty child wading at the waters edge.

As so often happens, the splendid summer of 1901 was followed by a severe winter, a fact which delighted the enthusiastic curling fraternity of the East Neuk and John would make many studies and at least two large paintings of a group of curlers on Kilconquhar loch.

Meanwhile Agnes had her knitting with her to pass the time while waiting for her first child, my mother Annie, who would be born in 1902.

They had bought only the absolute basics to furnish their rented home, for they intended to collect antique furniture. John had become interested in antiques when he had lived in Paris and Agnes was delighted with the idea of the story behind each piece and had a very good 'eye'. Many of their bicycle expeditions took them to 'roups', furniture auctions where ancient and amazing articles of china and furniture were to be had for pennies. It was like a treasure hunt and Agnes adored it, searching and burrowing amongst the carelessly piled objects until she had found just exactly what they needed. The more ancient and filthy the article was, the cheaper it would be sold and the more fun she would have later, lovingly cleaning and polishing it. The best part was when the obviously precious article would be produced and her friends amazed by how little it had cost. This was a hobby which Agnes would pursue for the next seventy years with unfading enthusiasm. Probably one of her outstanding bargains was her first purchase to furnish the Barnyards house. For thirty shillings she acquired four nice old chairs, a solid kitchen table, two heavy brass fenders, a brass bed *and a piano!* The piano was a square pianoforte dating, she would later learn, from around 1790. Unfortunately it was not in working condition and someone offered to tune it for another thirty shillings, but Agnes decided to use it as a sideboard, for it was a handsome Georgian piece of furniture and when closed, it gave no indication of its musical identity.

When the baby arrived in September, mother and infant were incorporated in the large painting "The Harvest-Field" which shows a group of harvesters resting amongst the stooks with the baby at its mother's breast. Perhaps this painting, exhibited in the large annual exhibition held in Glasgow, helped to establish my grandfather as a painter worth watching.

At intervals, they would return to Glasgow for a few weeks and take lodgings of the simplest and cheapest, while John had an exhibition or perhaps ordered frames for his latest work. My mother had a very early memory of sleeping in a drawer.

By 1904, they had moved to Croft Cottage in Pittenweem where William, their second child, was born.

Agnes had a very bad time at the birth of her son. I cannot vouch for the medical accuracy of this story, for although I heard it several times I was young and busy with my own life. How one regrets youthful inattention and forgetfulness. As we grow older, we wish that more questions had been asked when it was possible to obtain the answers!

Willie was a large baby, nearly eleven pounds according to the midwife's spring scales, although Agnes would always aver that Annie had been even larger though there was no record to substantiate such enormity.

Soon after Willie was born, Agnes became very unwell and the doctor pronounced that she was suffering from the dreaded puerperal fever and she should no longer feed her baby or he too would be in danger. However she was suffering so much that the sturdy baby was put to the breast and, although he too became ill, they both eventually recovered, although my grandmother was very thin and fragile for the next year or two. I have noticed that mothers of sons often have a heightened dramatic devotion to their male babies and I believe Agnes always felt that she owed her son a debt of gratitude for risking, however unconsciously, his own little life to save hers.

There are sketches of Agnes by my grandfather at this time in preparation for a classical painting of the deserted Ariadne, kneeling amongst the rocks of Naxos. John has sketched various back views of his wife and unusually, for she was very modest, she is somewhat undraped, although still highly respectable. It is obvious that she is very thin and delicate. I do not know if this picture was ever painted because John McGhie made his name with portraiture and the realistic depiction of the sea and its fishermen, but it may have been a commission to illustrate a book or perhaps it was a last look back to his nineteenth century training when mythical compositions were fashionable. I mention these sketches because by the time that Willie was walking, Agnes was less willowy and had gained enough weight to be the fashionable deep-bosomed shape of the first few years of the century. She would continue to gain weight and become a 'fine figure of a woman' for the next fifty years, only becoming gradually slender again as she approached old age. In spite of her opulent figure, she was stylishly dressed and always very active and swift, golfing, swimming, gardening and scrubbing floors. She was a dominant, determined, impatient and rather spoiled woman and yet she had great charm and kindness. She could tell a good story with drama and humour. Her timing was excellent and I often thought that she might have had a wonderful success as an actress. She was a perfect complement to her quiet, scholarly husband and was a great help to him in the business of selling paintings. She could enthuse about his talents to possible buyers. She could help a shy fishergirl to relax and in later years, when John had important and famous people to paint, she was able to greet and entertain them when they came for a sitting. She had enough confidence to chat with Lord Provosts and millionaires. When the Moderator of the Kirk, who was himself a well-known raconteur, came for his portrait-sitting, the conversation and laughter was so *immoderate* that John eventually had to send Agnes from the room. Their vivacity was making the artist's job impossible.

In 1905, it was apparent that John's career could not progress in the East Neuk, for portrait painting was the most lucrative part of an artist's output and John McGhie could produce very competent work in this field. They decided to move to the city and spend most of the year in Glasgow. They rented a large flat in Blythswood Street in the centre of town and a separate studio next door. My grandmother was greatly delighted with the location of this flat for a particularly macabre reason. From the living room could be seen, just across the street, a basement window which had figured fifty years previously in a notorious murder trial. The accusation was that from this window, the gently reared, middle-class Madeleine Smith had handed a cup of poisoned cocoa to the penniless but insistent lover whom she had jilted for a much wealthier suitor. Although the verdict at the trial was 'Not proven' her uninhibited love letters to the murdered man, plus her several purchases of arsenic, painted a suspicious picture. Although this incident was so much in the past my grandmother was enthralled by the basement window, and the drama of murder trials would fascinate her throughout her life.

For the next few years they returned to Pittenweem for the three summer months and rented the house at 58 High Street, where John worked hard producing his favourite work, pictures of the sea and fisherfolk.

The move to the city was very successful professionally and by 1911 my grandfather had a large painting, an east coast scene, purchased by Glasgow Corporation to hang in the Kelvingrove Art Galleries. This was an acceptance by the establishment and would lead to great things.

In Glasgow they moved to another large flat, one which had been specially designed for an artist and had its own studio. John had a successful show in this new flat and it must have seemed the right time also to buy a house at the sea. John had painted extensively throughout Scotland, on the west coast as well as the east and had seen a modestly priced house in the Maidens, a small town in Ayrshire. He and Agnes travelled by train to view the little villa. It was a cold, dreich day and John could see that the rain-drenched view of Ayrshire flying past the window did not impress his wife. She made no secret of her dislike of the place.

"No, no, I could never live here, John. It's really miserable and not a bit picturesque. And look at the women! They're not nearly as good-looking as the Pittenweem girls."

They returned to Pittenweem where Mr Lawson suggested that they look at 54 High Street as a possible summer residence. From the outside the house looked very dilapidated and was in fact 'condemned' with no water or gas installed and several of the windows broken. Agnes declared that 'she would not be seen dead staying there' but once they walked through the house to the sheltered, south-facing garden overlooking the sea, and realised the privacy and the possibility that the large carpenter's workshop next door would make an excellent studio, they decided to invest the necessary money in restoration. I do not know how much money was required for the extensive improvements which were carried out by Mr Lawson, but the basic cost of buying the two buildings was one hundred and twenty pounds, exactly the same sum as Glasgow corporation had paid for my grandfather's painting.

Agnes joked that they should call the house 'Corporation Cottage'.

This house has remained in our family ever since and my grandchildren are now the fifth generation to enjoy its low-ceilinged rooms and that splendid little garden with its ever-changing view of the sea and the opposite coastline.

Interestingly, from the title deeds, it seems that number 54 was owned for the hundred years previous to 1911 by only one other family, the MacCalmans. I am not aware of anyone of that name in Pittenweem now, but presumably Calman's wynd, which is almost adjacent to 54, was named for the last owners.

Of course John McGhie was not the only one to delight in the clear light and picturesque quality of the East Neuk fishing villages. Many came to paint and a colony of his fellow artists would descend on Pittenweem each summer. Every year the big annual art exhibitions in Edinburgh and Glasgow were crammed with views of the East Neuk. The whole area was a magnet to some very fine painters and their signatures can still be seen in auction rooms, on heavy, gold-framed paintings of the harbour and the small old-fashioned brown-sailed fishing boats.

Particular friends who visited the East Neuk to paint were Gamley and Dowell, both fine watercolourists, Coventry, Eadie and Macdonald, who lived permanently in Pittenweem. And there were many others, both professional and amateur, who regularly rented accommodation every summer. On a typical bright August day, I believe that one could often count twenty or thirty busy painters scattered along the shore. Like my grandfather, most preferred to paint a scene on the spot, then work at it later in the studio. Generally the size of the first painting would be quite small, twenty-four inches by twenty. In the studio it would be transferred to a bigger canvas of thirty-six inches by twenty-eight, or perhaps even larger.

John McGhie never left the house without a sketch book in his pocket and I still have many of them. They are filled with a wide variety of style and subject, from exquisite tiny watercolours to hurriedly scribbled scenes in pencil with directions as to colour written in the margins. These books show his close observation and need to capture everything that he saw around him as he walked about Fife and their spontaneity and immediacy bring his presence very close to me.

Compared to the comfortable and affluent town that we know today, Pittenweem at the beginning of the twentieth century was primitive and poverty-stricken. The high ideals of cleanliness still to be observed in the area must have been painfully difficult to maintain where gutting fish and baiting lines with raw shellfish were daily procedures, not to mention the cleaning and drying of the heavy clothes worn while performing these tasks. The sand on the shore was hidden under a deep layer of discarded mussel shells, also ashes and household rubbish was deposited there, to be carried away by the tide. This habit was continued well into the fifties, long after civic rubbish collection was established.

Then the messy and smelly business of 'barking' sails and

equipment was a regular occurrence, with the brown liquid boiling for several days in the backyards.

Modern sanitation was hardly known and wynds and quiet corners were polluted with human ordure.

My grandfather told a story that he had witnessed at the Thell, the old harbour, a favourite location of his for painting. Another artist had arrived after him and exclaimed in disgust when he found that the spot where he had painted the previous day, was now defiled by excrement. Summoning two little boys who stood nearby, he offered them sixpence to clear the offending pile away which they did and duly collected their reward.

Later my grandfather saw the two boys in the distance, dancing about and shouting joyfully,

"We'll kaki there the morn, we'll kaki there the morn."

Even the fresh sea breezes cannot have been quite able to blow away the pungency of the town, with its many smoke houses. When the gasworks provided cheap tar and a thick layer was used on boats, seawalls, outhouses, practically every surface was plastered for protection. On a hot summer's day, it bubbled and added its own aroma to the atmosphere.

Each small town along the coast was a narrow, self-sufficient community with little idea of the world outside. Although many did leave the area and succeed, those who were left travelled little and strangers were viewed with suspicion.

Mr Goodall was the minister at that time and he was a tall commanding man of six feet or more. Another tale of my grandfather's, which took place at the old harbour, depended on his unusual height.

The rock formation around the 'Dubs' or puddles at the Thell make them like miniature lochs and mountains and they are perfect for sailing boats, jumping and clambering. All children that have grown up in Pittenweem have found long hours of delight at the 'Dubs'. There is one particularly large and long dub and my grandfather heard two boys passionately arguing about it one day.

"Yon dub's twal' feet lang!"

"*That's* no' twal' feet lang!"

"Aye, it's *twal' feet*."

"It is *nut!*"

"It is *sut* twal' feet!"

"*It is nut!*"

"It is sut!"

"Yer no' tellin' me it's twal' feet, *that dub's niver dooble Goodall!"*

There seem to have been a plethora of small outlets for drink as well as the several public houses for no doubt alcohol was used to relieve the harsh lives. I have been told that one such place was hardly bigger than a large cupboard.

There were certainly many bakers' shops for the population of one thousand people, for these were working women and just as involved in the fishing industry as their men. They needed to buy scones and pies, the equivalent of modern 'fast food', for as well as preparing and maintaining the equipment, gutting the fish and keeping their homes scrubbed to the expected high standard, there was long underwear, socks and jumpers to knit, those warm garments required for the cold nights on the boats.

Conversation was always accompanied by the click of knitting needles.

Although the east coast race have proved themselves intelligent and full of potential and many have travelled far and carved successful careers in other parts of the world, the unremitting toil and the constant struggle for survival was the only life that most of its inhabitants knew. Many had little idea of life outside their own small sphere, although fishermen often sailed further afield and young unattached girls followed the herring fleet south down the coast to gut and salt.

The small towns immediately adjacent were within walking distance and St Andrews was perhaps visited once a year for the Lammas Fair, but for many the concept of a city was virtually unknown. Edinburgh and Glasgow were only names, as remote and unreal as Moscow or Shanghai.

When my grandparents took Reen Thomas back to Glasgow as a maid, her reactions to the loud, busy, dirty city were astonished and disbelieving, though she quickly adapted.

Apart from three summers partly spent in Iona and one summer in Perthshire, the McGhies returned to Pittenweem each year for the rest of John's life, and from June till September, John would paint his beloved seascapes.

An Incomer of Long Ago

MEGGIE WAS FORTY MILES from her home at Inver and on holiday for the first time. The journey had seemed long and arduous to her, for as well as several changes of vehicle, she had crossed the Dornoch Firth by ferry on a breezy, choppy day and she had been astonished and terrified by the strength and size of the waves. Although she had seen the sea often enough when she had climbed the hill beside her father's farm, distance had made the water look smooth and flat, like a large pond. Although it changed colour, sometimes blue and sparkling and sometimes grey, the ocean seemed remote and unexciting. Even on days when small drifts of white were scattered over the grey, it was far enough away to give no feeling of motion. But now, as she stood on the jetty, the water seemed alive and angry to Maggie, like a raging animal. She trembled and could not understand how other passengers laughed and chatted as they boarded the frail, swinging craft, apparently unaware of the tumultuous monster at their feet. In spite of her fears, they had reached the other side safely and after another two rattling rides, she was welcomed by her Aunt Bessy.

All her life, Meggie had heard of the luxuries of Aunt Bessy's house in Embo. There were certainly very nice carpets, ornaments and pictures on the walls, but what seemed most delightful to the girl was the peace and quiet that filled each room and the gentle calm way that Aunt Bessy accomplished her tasks. Maggie's mother, with her large family and the farm work, was in a constant storm of activity, always rushing 'to beat the clock' and trying to finish one job before it was time for the next. Meggie was at that stage of filial criticism that disapproved of her mother's determined push through the day, with its accompanying impatience, the sharply clicking heels and the untidy hair.

Meggie felt that she had been searching all her life for the tranquil atmosphere of Bessy's house.

Bessy delighted in spoiling her pretty niece. Her late husband, manager of the local gasworks, had left his widow with a fine home and a comfortable little pension.

There were cakes and a custard for supper, with flowers and a lace tablecloth and the elegance delighted the girl. No time for luxuries like that at home with six children and two farmhands to feed!

"I thought we might go to the draper's shop tomorrow and buy a length of cotton for a summer dress for you. There are some awful bonny prints just new in. Would you like that? Then we could make it up together. They have pretty ribbons and laces just now, too. It is a long time since I gave you a present."

Meggie's glowing smile made a reply unnecessary.

For a week there would be no cows to milk, no floors to sweep, no furniture to polish, no hens to feed or chase into their shed at night, no brothers to tease her and, most important, her mother's critical eye would be absent. Lingering and careful dusting of the various precious gewgaws would be her only duty. Blissfully, she would sleep alone in her own bedroom *in a feather bed*.

It was a sort of Heaven.

"There is a wee dance in the halls tonight, Meggie. Will we go along? I'll see my friends for a blether and I'm sure you'll meet some young people and have a bit of a dance. Would you like that, my darling? I'm sorry we have not finished your new dress yet but your blue one is lovely. It is not a swell affair at all."

It seemed an excellent idea to Meggie. She always enjoyed a ceilidh.

Bill was a fisherman and had asked her to dance almost before she had taken off the new shawl that Bessie had decided she might need 'if the night grows chilly'.

The fact that the man earned his living on the sea undoubtedly added a glamour to him in Meggie's eyes. How brave he must be to venture far from land on that terrifying, unknown element and stay out for hours or days even, in all that heaving up and down. She still shivered when she remembered that she must return on the ferry next week.

How unimaginable to spend all day, and sometimes nights too, with only wooden planks between you and those fierce waves!

There was excitement, almost danger in his company because he was so very different from the stolid farm boys that she knew. He was far more active in the dance than they were and his laugh was louder. His eyes and teeth sparkled in the light of the oil lamps as he whirled her round to the wild fiddle music, sometimes jumping in the air in absurd yet graceful leaps that made her laugh.

Meggie liked the way that Bill danced and the tender way that he looked at her and how differently he spoke! They often had trouble understanding each other and it made them both laugh.

Meggie spoke English with a gentle, educated accent and only the slight lilt betrayed the fact that her first language was Gaelic. Bill came from Pittenweem in Fife and not only was his grammar far from perfect, but he pronounced every vowel in a different way from Meggie. His speech was sprinkled with old Scottish words and phrases that were unknown and mysterious to her and in every sentence, his strong, deep voice careered up and down from heights to depths, almost as though he were singing.

She loved it and his incomprehensible words seemed foreign and exotic.

Before she left Embo she had promised to marry Bill Taylor.

It was a beautiful sunny day and the sea was like a mill pond for her return journey and Bill accompanied her in order to meet her parents. Meggie gazed at the fascinating expanse of water and laughed at her previous fears.

It was only natural that her parents were unhappy that Meggie should choose a husband from such a distant and unknown place as Pittenweem, when there were so many fine young farm lads in Bonar Bridge. Who had ever heard of Pittenweem? And what did they know of Bill Taylor?

After meeting Bill, Maggie's mother wailed,

"That man is never a Scotsman with such a foreign accent. I cannot understand a word that he is saying with his voice going up and down like the waves of the sea. Indeed I think he must have sailed here from Scandinavia."

However Meggie was determined and besides, she was twenty, certainly old enough to leave home and make room for her brothers and sisters.

So Meggie was married and left her family and farm behind without an inkling of the hardships of her new life. To be fair, neither could Bill appreciate the terrible difficulties of the work that awaited his new bride. She was a strong, sturdy farmgirl, obviously a good worker, and he had no worries that she might find problems in adapting to the role of fisherman's wife.

After a long hot dusty train journey, the half mile walk from the station, laden with boxes, baskets and parcels seemed almost too much for Meggie.

As they passed small neat cottages on their right and more imposing villas on their left, she paused.

"Are ye tired, ma sweetheart?"

"I hope your mother likes me."

"There's nae worry aboot that, ma lovely lass. Hoo could she no' like a bonnie wummin like yersel'"

"Where will we stay tonight, Billy?"

"Thur's a surprise fur ye. Ah've goat oor ain wee hoose waitin'. Jist twa rooms in the Barracks but it's cosy and the rent's no' dear."

She plodded on for a few steps then asked in a small voice,

"Will the soldiers not be awful noisy?"

Bill roared with laughter,

"Na, na ma lassie. Thur's nae sojers. That's jist whit it's cried, the Barracks, for thur a wheen different faimilies livin' in different hooses there. Mibbe it wis hooses fur the airmy at wan time. Ah dae ken. But no' the noo, no' the noo. It's a' fisherfolk livin' in the Barracks nooadays. Awfy freendly like."

They left the more modern and genteel villas at the back of the town and came to the South Loan, where Maggie cried out in delight,

"There's a byre there. I can hear the cows snuffling inside . . . "

"Aye an' smell thim an a'."

"I like cows, Bill. I might even get a job milking. I'm a grand milker."

"Ye'll no' be needin' tae get ony job, ma darlin', ah'm tellin' ye. Ye'll be helpin' me. Fishermen's wives hiv tae work hard."

"Oh that will be fine, Bill. I will be proud to help you."

It was the first that she had heard of the necessity of helping, but she was very pleased. She thought of her ferry trip and wondered if she would be expected to go to sea, but she did not like to ask, in case she sounded stupid. Whatever he wanted, she was ready to support her wonderful husband in any way that she could.

They turned into the High Street and Maggie exclaimed over the shops. She had never seen so many shops together in her life before.

"It is more like a city! Just look at that big shop over there! It's three stories high!"

"Aye, that's the emporium that Mr Birrell keeps."

"Now what on earth is a numporium, Billy?"

"Ah weel, Ah'm no' shair but Ah suppose it's jist a big shoape that sells a'thin'."

"Look, Billy it's all written on the end wall, all the different things you can buy there and is that the name the 'emporium'. Is that what you said before?"

"Aye, come oan lassie, dinnae stand an' stare. We're needin' tae get hame."

But Meggie was amazed at the shops in the High Street.

"And there's *another* chemist's shop and there's the *third* draper's that I've seen."

"Aye, ye kin buy onythin' ye're needin' in Pittenweem. Ye niver need tae gan oot the toon. It's jist findin' the money that's the worry."

"There's a boot shop and there are *two* bakers *shops side by side.*"

"Aye, the wives haveny the time tae be bakin'!"

In spite of her fatigue, Meggie laughed heartily at this joke. Baking was surely one of the basic tasks of a housewife, the criterion by which a housewife would be judged and Meggie was well known at home for her excellent scones and light hand with pastry and looked forward to impressing Bill with her domestic excellence.

Next moment she found herself descending a very steep narrow road at the foot of which lay the harbour. It was high tide and she had never seen so many fishing boats bobbing together.

"It's so much busier than Embo!"

"Aye Ah'm gled tae be back. We hud'nae ony luck up north, but Pittenweem's thrivin' the noo. The Firth's jist teemin' wi' fish. Lang may it last!"

They entered a pend opposite the harbour and in the corner of the courtyard, Bill opened a blue door. Although it was dim, Meggie could see that they had entered a circular space with stone floor and walls. It was unlike any place that she had seen before, for a curving staircase spiralled around the wall to the next floor and as they climbed it, Meggie avoided looking up or down. They walked along a landing with three doors then climbed another spiral flight, passed another three doors and finally reached the top of the building by a straight flight. There was only one door on the top landing which Bill opened it with a flourish and they walked into a small over furnished sitting room.

It was all so foreign to Meggie that she could say nothing.

There was no one to greet them and his face showed his disappointment but a pot of hot soup sat on the embers of the fire.

"That'll be ma Mither's left some kail fur us."

Maggie did not even ask what kail was but ate it hungrily. It was a very different flavour from her mother's soup, but comforting nevertheless.

The following day was Sunday and after church, where Maggie's new hat, new dress and shining boots had been scrutinised by the congregation, they walked around the town, Bill showing off his bride to the population. He was also proud to show her his home town.

"The kirk's auld ye ken, awfy auld an' these hooses in the High street, some o' them are jist *awfy* auld, hunners o' years auld."

Maggie said nothing, believing that this was a young man's boasting.

"They folk that live up the toon here think they're the toffs, ye ken, an' they look doon oan us that live doon the shore. But we're the yins that catch the fish an' Pittenweem widnae be much wi'oot her fish."

He sounded quite angry and Meggie stole a glance at him but he smiled back at her.

They descended to sea level by a different twisting wynd with several flights of stairs. Halfway down they passed yet another bakehouse and shop for Maggie to exclaim over.

"Aye they mak awfy grand pies. We'll hae yin next Setterday fur a treat, ma lass."

Maggie decided in her own mind that there would be no bought pies in her kitchen but said nothing.

"It seems such a big town. I'll never find my way around these different streets, Bill."

"Och, it's easy, ma lass. Ye jist gan doon ony wynd, that's whit we ca' these wee hilly streets and there y'are east or wast o' the herbour. A clever lass like yersel! Ye'll soon learn."

Strolling westwards beyond the harbour, Maggie asked,

"Why is the beach not sandy like Embo, Bill?"

"Aye it's sandy, Meggie."

"I see no sand."

He looked over the wall and scratched his head.

"It's saundy, Meggie. The saund's jist unnerneath the mussel shells, ye cannae see it, but it's there a' the same."

The discarded, blue mussel shells, detritus of the never-ending baiting of lines, lay two feet deep on the shore. Spring tides piled the empty shells even higher and at other times they were washed out to sea to be ground into sand by the relentless waves.

"What sort of shells are you calling them, Bill?"

"Mussels!"

"They're a bonny colour but what are they and where did they all come from, there's so many?"

"D'ye no' ken whit a mussel is?" Bill's voice was higher than she had eve heard it. Ye'll get tae ken a mussel fine whin ye stert baitin' ma lines fur me. Aye we'd be loast wi'oot the mussels. They cam doon frae the Eden mooth at Leuchars an' thur awfy dear the noo."

She shook her head and looked at him blankly. Bill had a sudden horrible realisation of the ignorance of his new wife and of the many new skills which she must learn to make her a suitable partner in his never-ending struggle with the sea. Every woman that he knew, from her earliest girlhood had been deft at shelling multitudes of raw mussels daily to bait the lines for her father or husband, as well as all the other skills of filleting the fish, mending nets, and knitting the thick socks and underwear that the job demanded. Poor Meggie would soon find out what mussels were.

"There's another big grocer's shop, Billy! And a drapers and a bakers. There's nearly as many shops on the shore as there are on the High Street."

"Aye there's anither big grocer's further oan. Plenty shops. Jist the money ye needin'. There's never enuff o' that."

He laughed as he pointed out a little red door.

"That's the wee-est pub in Fife. Jist five or six folk and it's fu'. It's an awfy squash but it's grand 'n warm oan a cauld nicht!"

The sun had come out and Bill guided his bride west along the shore, past the pretty west bay to the gaswork.

"Ye get a grand pail o' taur there an' it's no' dear."

Maggie did not need to ask what the 'taur' was for, as every sea-wall and every outhouse was coated with a thick black layer.

On Monday morning, Billy somewhat hesitantly told his wife that Mary and Phemie Reekie on the ground floor were going to teach her how to bait the lines that day. Meggie had planned to bake that morning and give the house a good going over, perhaps explore the town in the afternoon and bake for tea but the honeymoon was over and her husband's word was law.

"Ah'm gaun oot wi' Sandy Black's boat the morn's mornin' an' Ah hiv tae gan tae Cellardyke the day, tae get a bit net bit. Ye should come wi' me sometime an' see they lassies workin' the big net machines in the factory. They hiv tae dance aboot wi' their feet as weel as workin' wi' their haunds. They're niver still fur a meenit. It's awfy coamical. It wid mak ye laugh an' they're a' as thin as rakes wi' the jumpin' aboot."

"It sounds like very hard work, Billy and I do not think I would like to be laughed at while I was so busy working."

"Aye, richt enough it's mebbe no' fair tae laugh . . . weel but ye'll be fine wi' the Reekies. Thur grand lassies. Ah wis at the skill wi' Mary. My, but she wis an awfy talker, whit a blether that lassie wis, aye talkin'. She talked hersel' hoarse."

He felt he was talking a lot himself, for Meggie said nothing but bit her lip and looked at him with a an unhappy expression.

"Ye ken the sooner ye learn tae bait the lines the better it is fur me, ma lass."

"I understand that and I'm very willing to start but I've never done anything like that before. Is it difficult, Billy? Is the knife very sharp? D'ye think I'll manage it?"

"Even wee lassies at the skill dae it, Maggie!"

"I am sure I can learn but I don't know these women downstairs, Billy."

"Aw ye'll soon get tae ken them weel, they're oor neebors an' 'body's awfy freendly in Pittenweem. Thur's nae worry aboot that, ma darlin'."

As he spoke these words, dark memories of the hard times that other incomers had suffered crossed his mind, the jeering, exclusion, bitter jealousy and malicious gossip, but he suppressed those thoughts.

"What will I wear, Billy?"

"Nane o' yer new fancy stuff. Nae flooers nor frilly bits. Jist a plain skirt an' a big apron. It's no' a verra clean joab."

Yes the honeymoon was over.

The two women were sitting on kitchen chairs outside their front door in the yard, their hands and tongues busy. An older woman sat slightly apart. A deep round basket of wet shining mussels was beside them with another shallow basket of dry grass which the children had gathered before going to school. On a piece of canvas on the ground to the left of one of the women, the carefully wound coils of dark brown cord showed the hooks glinting in their depths. Each girl had a tin container of shelled mussels in her lap and while one placed the mussels on each hook, the other continuously shelled and replenished her partner's can, also helping to place the grass between the layers of baited line which were carefully laid in a large shovel-shaped wooden box, which was placed between them. Their cooperation and long practice made it appear a rather leisurely and pleasant occupation.

The sun was shining, a tortoiseshell cat sat on the window sill, some marigolds grew in front of the house and the bright scarves about the women's shoulders made a charming scene that would have delighted any one of the many artists who were just beginning to discover that picturesque corner of Fife.

The two younger women smiled as she approached.

"Aw here she is! Hiv ye come tae learn tae shiel? Aye come an' tak a seat, Meggie. I'm Phemie an' this is Mrs Gairdiner an' this is ma sister Mary."

The older woman was sitting knitting and looked up but did not smile.

Meggie sat on the empty chair which was waiting for her and meekly folded her hands in her lap.

Phemie was in her mid thirties, a small square woman with strong black hair springing back from her brow and well marked eyebrows. She gave an immediate impression of eager energy and intelligence. Her sister Mary was very different, tall, slender and blonde with large protuberant blue eyes. In spite of her employment, she seemed more languid and less focused than her sister. Maggie knew she must be twenty four or so if she was at school with Billy.

Mary spoke first.

"So, ye're from the north? Whaur aboots is it ye cam frae?"

The sharp tone of voice was not as friendly as it might have been and Meggie paused before she answered because she needed a moment to analyse the question. It was confusing, what with the strong unfamiliar accent and Mary's voice did have a strange hoarseness, as Billy had said. It made Meggie feel stupid and slow and she had not yet even touched a mussel.

"I come from Inver, well near to Inver. I lived on a farm."

Phemie immediately commented,

"Ye're awfy thin fur a fairm lassie. Ah thocht they wis a' grand 'n plump wi' the butter 'n eggs an' a' . . . "

Mary broke in with her rough aggressive tone

"Whaur's Inver? That's a funny name shairly. Whauraboots is it? Is it near the sea? Ah've niver heard o't at a'. Hive you heard o' Inver, Phemie? Ah hivnae. An' up there, div they speak different? Div they a' speak 'la-de-da' like you dae?"

Before Meggie could reply to any of these questions, Mary spoke again,

"Wis it yer faither wis the fairmer? Wis it a big fairm? An' did you dae the mulkin'?"

Then Phemie, who smiled and seemed more kindly disposed, asked,

"An' tell us, hoo did ye meet up wi' Billy Taylor? Wis it at a dance? It must shairly hae been at a dance. He's an awfy grand dancer, isn't he. He fairly *whurls* ye roon'."

With a determined effort Meggie spoke,

"Yes, I did all the milking and yes I met Billy at a dance . . . At Embo . . . He is a wonderful dancer . . . but please tell me how many mussels do you need to shiel for that line?"

Mary broke in again in her strange strangled voice

"Six hunnert mussels fur six hunnert hooks. Aye, Ah've heard o' Embo. They were at the fishin' at Embo last year, tae. An' if ye lived at Inver, whit were *you* daen' at Embo? Wha wis mulkin' the coos whin you wur at Embo?"

Suddenly the old woman put down her knitting and spoke in a loud deep voice, a voice that had shouted over many an east coast gale.

"Are you twa tryin' tae speer the een oot the lassie's heed? It's *her* should be askin' the questions like *hoo* tae open a mussel shell wi'oot jabbin' her haund, an' *hoo* tae fix the bait and *hoo* tae lay oot the lines wi' gress, so thull no fankle. Hiv ye fergoat she's here tae learn an' no' tae answer yer silly speerin'."

Then turning to Meggie, she continued her reproaches,

"An' did ye no' bring nae knittin' wi ye tae dae whiles ye wur watchin'? Ye ken there's nae time tae be sittin' wi' yer haunds foldit here, ma lass. Yer man'll aye be needin' socks an' guernsies, an' long drawers an' a'. Ye kin shairly knit, can't ye lassie?"

"Oh yes, I learned at school." Maggie quickly unfolded her hands, unsure then what to do with them but grasping each side of her apron in the meantime. "I'm better at sewing than knitting."

"Ah weel, thur's no' muckle need fur shewin', best ye get up the toon this efternin an' get some wool fur socks. He'll aye be needin' *them*. An' you twa better gie yer tongues a rest an' get oan wi yer sheilin' and show the lassie whit she hus tae dae. She'd best watch fur a wee while then she kin pit oan a gag an' try it hersel'"

Meggie looked startled at the idea of a gag, but Phemie saw that she did not understand and held up her hand with the leather guard and pointed to it, nodding encouragingly.

The work restarted and the questions stopped, much to Meggie's relief, although the two sisters spoke continuously, loudly, quickly and with much laughter. Meggie could follow little of it, nor could she learn much from their flashing hands as hundreds of mussels were broached, scooped from their shells and firmly impaled on the never-ending hooks. It was all too quick and skillful for her to follow. Then, the moment that she dreaded arrived and Phemie held out the leather hand guard and the sharp little wooden handled knife with its leaf-shaped blade.

"Wid ye like tae hiv a shoat at it noo, Meggie? That's ma gag an' ma sheilin' blade but we a' like oor ain. Ye get intae the wey o' yer ain baitin' knife, but try it the noo' if ye like."

But the look on Meggie's face caught Mrs Gardiner's sympathy.

"She's no' needin' tae try it the day. She's niver seen it done afore in her life an' she' needin' tae gan slower than you twa. Ye're faur ower quick fur her tae see whit ye're aboot."

Mary was ready to be indignant.

"Well we hiv tae get thae lines ready fur ma faither or he'll be ragin' an' Ah think he's reddin' anither line fur us the noo. We cannae afford tae gan slow fur *her* sake."

"Naw richt enuff, yer no' the best yins tae be teachin' her. It's no' easy, cos ye're baith *real experts*," the note of sarcasm was ignored by the girls, "And verra quick, ower quick fur hur tae follow. Aye an' ye've goat tae get yer work done, Ah ken that fine."

Mollified, the girls smiled at each other and at Maggie.

Mrs Gardiner continued,

"Ah'm thinkin' she'd be better wi' a young lassie tae help her get sterted slowly. There's wee Jessie Broon, jist left the skill an' lookin' tae mak a penny whaur she kin. Ah'll send her roond tae yer door the nicht, Meggie. She's a grand wee hard-workin' lassie."

After many pennies worth of tuition from Jessie, who was a good friend as well as a good teacher, Meggie learned to bait lines. Meggie was very slow at baiting and found it best to get up two hours earlier than the other women. It was the only way that she could be finished and have everything 'redd up' at the same time as the other wives. When she had her first and only accident with the knife, Jessie was there to take over and get the line ready for Billy.

Fortunately the skills of filleting fish and mending nets never seemed so difficult to acquire and Billy always had beautifully knitted socks and long drawers.

After the first baby was born, they left the Barracks and moved to the middle flat of a large three storey house at the foot of the Cove Wynd. There were fewer stairs to climb but secretly she had longed for a house at shore level. Though the flat was brighter and more spacious and had a wonderful view of the harbour, Meggie found it a mixed blessing as all the other residents in the building were related to Bill and she felt that her shortcomings and slowness were under even closer scrutiny.

However she had a beautiful baby boy, she was in love with a kind helpful husband and she was young and strong and optimistic that things would improve, although she had little time to think or plan quite how they might do so.

Sometimes she thought of the old life on the farm and smiled to herself at how she had grumbled at the early rising or the necessity of bringing the cows home when she would rather have been sewing. It had certainly not been an idle life, but it had been a calm, slow-moving life where only one task was tackled at a time. It had seemed to her then as though more were asked of her than was fair, but there were plenty of people to deal with the various jobs. Of course she had just been a girl. Now she was a woman and must learn and accept what hard work was.

There was always a pressure to complete the work as quickly as possible for so many other tasks lay waiting. She remembered her mother's continuous bustle, but surely she had a harder and lonelier life than her mother, who was always within reach of her own family while Meggie more often encountered suspicion and aggression, rather than friendship, amongst the other women. She would always be an 'incomer' and speak differently. It is possible that Meggie's Highland pride and independence did not invite sympathy.

However life was too busy for much self-pity. The lines must be ready for the tide and the baby must be cared for. Fortunately he was a good baby, for while other women had sisters or nieces to help feed and pacify, Meggie must manage on her own while Bill was at sea. Bill's mother, who might have helped, suffered from arthritis and was practically an invalid.

Each day required a continuous and relentless struggle to get through the work, for she shared the obsessive cleanliness of the Pittenweem housewife and her scrubbed floors, shining brasses and crisp curtains could compare with those in any other house on the shore. She held out manfully against the baker's shop and made scones each week and occasionally a pie, but only at Christmas or on Bill's birthday did she search out her recipe book and produce a fruitcake.

Though the work was hard and she was sometimes lonely, these were not her greatest problems. Always at the back of her mind was a terrible fear of the danger that her husband faced each day in his work. That first dread impression of the sea at the Dornoch ferry had stayed in her mind but now she would learn how innocuous the sea had been that day compared to the unpredictable power which it could exert. A beautiful blue calm sea could change to a grey tumultuous monster in half an hour. Danger had never been a part of her life on the farm. An ill-tempered bull that could be locked up and avoided was the only real danger she had faced at home. Now when the wind blew and the sea was choppy or worse, she felt terror as she watched Billy walking away from her towards the boats. If he were already at sea she suffered terrible pangs of fear and worked all the harder at her tasks to fight off panic.

Of course her fears were not without basis. Only weeks after her arrival in Pittenweem, a young man was lost overboard one night, leaving his widow to bring up five children as best she could.

It was a Sunday in October that a terrible storm suddenly and unexpectedly blew up. The waves dashed against the harbour wall and soared thirty feet into the air, crashing down and foaming back into the raging water in the outer harbour. Maggie, almost paralysed with fear but held by a terrible fascination, watched the magnificent scene from her window.

"Billy, you would never go out if it was like that, would you?"

"Na, na ma lass, but it's Sunday an' we're no' gaun oot the day onywey. But ye cannae always tell when a storm's comin' up."

"I know. I worry so much. Do you not worry, Bill?"

"Ach, ye'd niver dae the joab if ye wur aye worryin', ma dearie. Jist try no' tae think aboot it."

By the second year Meggie's skills were improving although her speed could never match that of a woman who had baited from girlhood. But with the arrival of a second baby and the increasing mobility of the first child, Meggie's workload never seemed to lessen. Each year the babies kept arriving. Bill was a wonderful husband, peeling potatoes, washing dishes and putting children to bed, tasks that most fathers saw as women's work. His garden produced potatoes, cabbages, beans and kail.

It would be thirteen years before Meggie returned to visit her family and sadly by that time her mother had died. In those thirteen years, eleven children were born, ten of whom survived.

Jock, Billy, Tommy (who died when very young) Alec, Tom, Fergie and Jim were the boys and Jessie, Maggie, Chrissie, Lena were the girls. They slept head to tail like sardines and according to Chrissie, who was my grandmother's friend, they were always, "Awfy happy and close, though we were aye poor. My faither was good wi' his gairden and we always had plenty fish. We complained richt enough whin it wis 'fish again', but there was aye plenty."

Although I have used imagination and artistic licence, this tale would not have been written if it were not for the stories that Chrissie Taylor told me in her fast, fluent Pittenweem accent. She had a wide vocabulary, never repeating herself and she was never boring. She used many old words and expressions that I heard from no one else and are sadly lost now.

She was the most articulate of talkers, perhaps her mother's careful Highland speech helped.

Many people have told me that in her youth, Chrissie Taylor was the best dancer in Pittenweem and knew all the latest steps and taught them to her friends and that must have been an inherited skill from her father.

Tragic Memories

IT IS IMPOSSIBLE TO DO JUSTICE to the rich verbal history of Pittenweem but I would like to record a few of the dramatic stories that I have been told. I am indebted to so many people for their memories that I cannot mention them all. First of all my grandmother of course, then the late Chrissie Bowman, her son John, Andy Grieg, Jessie Bowman, Bessie Horsborough, Dr Kennedy, the late Bob Moir, George Bremner, Belle Ryrie, John and Jessie Wilson, still impressively energetic in their later years and with spectacularly good memories and lastly Bill Black, a natural and charming raconteur who can fascinate for hours with his stories and whose wife, Chrissie, is just as entertaining.

Many of the stories that I have heard were of course light-hearted, but in this article, I shall deal with the darker side. Human misery can never be avoided and poverty plus a dangerous occupation adds its terrible weight to the wrong side of the scales.

Accidents at sea were always a threatening possibility.

Fishermen purposely did not learn to swim, as there was little hope of saving themselves. The thigh-length leather boots that they wore would be filled immediately with water and drag them down to a swift death.

My grandmother was visiting a friend who lived at the shore. The window framed a perfect scene with a blue sparkling sea and small clouds hovering over the Bass Rock with the distant shore a hazy purple.

"What a wonderful view you have!" my grandmother exclaimed.

"Ah *niver* look at it, Mrs McGhie. Ah've loast ma faither an' twa brithers oot there an' ivery day ma man an' ma son are awa' an' they micht no' come back. It's no bonny tae me, Mrs McGhie an' Ah *niver* look at it."

Apart from the loss of life at sea, which in spite of modern communications sadly still occurs, there was also the deep despair born of poverty and the constant struggle for survival which led some to choose suicide. Garrets were equipped with tempting beams and fatal ropes. Others chose to drown themselves, first attaching themselves to an anchor in the harbour, in order that the body might be recovered when the tide went out and given a decent burial. Gas ovens were also a temptation to those at the end of their emotional tether.

At the beginning of the century, mental derangement was accepted as something that the family must live and deal with, unless there was extreme violence, which no doubt sometimes occurred with tragic results.

My grandmother spoke of a woman who walked around Pittenweem all day, muttering and carrying a sharp carving knife. At intervals, she would stop and whet the knife on a windowsill, regarding its sharp edge with great concentration, and then continue on her way, talking to herself. Although the knife was never put to use, it must have been an uncomfortable moment as she passed close beside you on the pavement.

Poverty was a terrible driving force for some. One young unmarried woman abandoned her newly born baby on a roof behind her home, thinking in her temporary madness that it would not be discovered. However the sweep was working there the next day and saw what he thought was a doll lying in the gutter. It was said that he took many months to recover from the shock of his find.

Poverty could also act as a stimulant to the morally strong and many heroic acts were performed to protect the welfare of families in those harsh days.

During the years of the second world war, a widow, left destitute with three little daughters to bring up in one room, was able to provide for them by working incredibly hard. Before the children were awake, she milked cows at the other end of Pittenweem, returning in time to make their porridge. After that she collected the laundry from the Polish soldiers who were billeted in Pittenweem at that time and very particular in their dress. In a tiny washhouse, with its own little coal fired boiler, she washed the heavy flannel shirts (usually twenty-seven) and then dried and ironed them. Quite how she managed the drying, if the weather were damp, I have no idea. The one room with the two built-in beds must have been draped around with all those shirts. She also went out 'cleaning' sometimes.

No doubt she knitted in the few moments that she was not employed making money. Her daughter told me that there was always a grand pot of kail waiting for them every night. The daughters were all smart girls who worked well at school and grew up to have good jobs and marriages. Their mother was one of the many unsung heroines of Pittenweem.

Another was a young woman who worked in a shop and, unaided, nursed an ailing mother, an invalid father and a brother who suffered from multiple sclerosis and was almost completely helpless, having to be lifted and fed.

"The house was like a hospital sometimes!" she confessed to me. "I was just running from one to another but I could never have done it without the help and sympathy of Dr Kennedy. He was just wonderful and realised how much I had to do and gave me support."

By the time she reached her forties, she was forced to leave her employment. The government did give some small financial help in the seventies and eighties, but certainly not enough for adequate maintenance.

She is one of the many strong determined women that did an absolutely necessary job for love and because there was no one else to do it. She was a 'carer' long before that word was invented or the role recognised.

Although she was such a devoted and busy person, she had her personal ambitions and always yearned to travel, though it seemed an unlikely dream. However, since the death of her relatives has freed her to live her own life, I am delighted to say that she has realised that dream and visited Canada and America as well as all the main countries of Europe, some of them several times. She has seen Vesuvius, Paris, Berlin, New York and all those other exotic places that she read about and longed for. I take my hat off to her.

She never married.

Marriage did not necessarily make life easier. There were husbands who drank and there were wives who got into debt. My mother heard about one woman who had spent twenty five pounds on 'awfy braw velvet curtains'. This was an enormous sum at that time, perhaps equal to three months' housekeeping for the family. When it came time to pay the same sum to the income tax, there was no cash left in the box!

"What on earth did she do?" my mother asked with a horrified expression on her face.

"Och, she jist took tae her bed, that's a' she cud dae. *Jist took tae her bed.*"

I remember thinking, as a child, that this did not seem very helpful and I could see from my mother's face that she agreed with me.

To marry a fisherman was to sign a contract for hard work and it was toughest on the girl who had not grown up to the baiting of lines. Many of those who were used to baiting also admitted to hating the cold relentless grind which ruined hands with chaps and cuts and chilblains in the winter. The herring gutting and salting was another cruel occupation. One friend, a fisherman's daughter, told me how she was determined not to marry into a life of toil, as her sisters had done. She found a job as a cook and succeeded in her career, working abroad in good hotels and never marrying.

In 1939 when the war started, it was decided that my mother and I would live in Pittenweem as Glasgow was a likely industrial target for German bombing. The first ten months of the war strangely passed without incident, although it must have been a stressful time of waiting. Ironically the first enemy action of the war took place in the Firth of Forth and was visible from our garden. My mother was talking to our neighbours, Mr and Mrs Brown, as a convoy of ships made its way towards Leith. Planes were circling around the ships and my mother was watching anxiously as small puffs of smoke appeared here and there.

"Aye, it's just practice, Annie," said Mr Brown comfortingly and his wife echoed,

"Aye jist practice."

There had been months of practice manoeuvres in the Forth and people had become used to them. Also there had been no air raid siren warning.

Just then one plane burst into flames and dived into the water.

"That's not practice, that's the real thing!" exclaimed my mother, "And we had all better go inside."

My mother was badly upset by this happening practically on our doorstep.

A fisherman, Mr Hughes was out in his fishing boat and very close to all the action and while he was not injured, he was very much affected. He returned home shocked and ill and went to bed where he died three weeks later.

The suave appearance, good manners, bowing and heel-clicking of the Polish soldiers who were stationed here during the war, brought temptations with them. The perfumes and manicured hands of these strangers in town must have exerted a fascination over girls used to fishermen and farm workers. Some girls lost their heads and paid the price. Some girls married respectably and their husbands settled locally. One or two married women left their homes and families and 'ran awa wi' a Pole'. It was a destructive and tragic choice to make, but it may have seemed that the unknown life with a stranger was bound to be easier than the unremitting slavery which had burdened their lives so far.

I learned of another tragedy, a very modern one, from an old swimming friend. In her youth she was an excellent swimmer and while still in her teens, dived into the harbour to rescue a small child who had fallen in. Now in her mature years she had tried, but failed, to rescue her grandson who had fallen into the muddy depths of drug-taking and had died before he was twenty.

How sad that each different era has its dangers, temptations and tragedies.

Fisher Girl

THE TWO OLD LADIES SAT on the bench in the sunny market place. The smaller had a mane of white hair and a solid foursquare build that had battled against a thousand east coast winds. She was the first to speak.

"Oh aye, he was awfy kind, yer grandfaither. Awfy gentle an' kind."

"Aye, awfy kind," her slightly younger companion echoed.

"An' he wis an awfy grand penter."

"Aye, he wis the laud that cud pent."

"He wis a gentleman, wisn't he?"

"Aye he wis a gentleman."

They were talking of my grandfather, John McGhie, who for the first forty years of the twentieth century, painted the picturesque scenes and handsome, hardy fishing people of the East Neuk. The taller lady who wore thick glasses and was blessed with an impressive bust continued.

"He used tae gie ye hauf a croon fur sittin' tae 'm. That wis an awfy money! An' jist fur sittin' still a' efternin."

"Aye, an awfy money."

"Aye, mair than ye'd mak in a week o' baitin' lines."

"Aye an' if it wis yer faither's lines, ye didnae get onythin'."

"Aye an' Mester McGhie aye gied ye a bar o' choaclit an' a'. Fry's Cream choaclit it wis."

"Aye, an' the first day Ah kept mine in ma haund till it meltit, Ah wis that frightened o' spilin' the pictur."

They both laughed heartily, nudging each other with meaningful elbows.

Jen, the smaller of the two was in her eighties but every part of her from her strident black eyebrows to her brown muscular forearms spoke of the strength, energy and decisiveness born of a long hard-working life, a life where each day was a struggle for survival. She had cut her grass that morning and just finished painting the walls of her bedroom last week and was now about to start on her brother's house. With her fiercely white hair and the clear modelling of her features, Jen bore strong traces of Mediterranean ancestry and might easily have been French or Spanish. Pittenweem was an important trading centre from the eleventh century onwards and European and Scandinavian genes are still evident in the local faces and figures.

Jen smiled proudly and informed her friend,

"Ye ken Ah've goat yin o' his pentins. *Everybody admires that pictur*. Ah wish't ah'd goat mair. They aye ask hoo auld Ah wis in it, but Ah dae ken. Aboot sixteen mebbe. But he pented Aggie mair nor me. He wis awfy fond o' oor Aggie's face. She wis the bonny yin. No' me! Ah wis jist the hard worker!"

Again they chortled.

"He wis aye doon at the door in the moarnin' whin we wis baitin' the lines, wonderin' if Aggie cud sit tae him."

"Ah first sat tae 'm whin Ah wis jist a wee lassie aboot nine."

But Elsie, deep-bosomed and stately, was more reticent than Jen and allowed the conversation to be steered away from her own experiences of those far off days to a typical market-place dialogue.

I admit that my interest dwindled as unknown names were bandied about.

". . . Aye, noo Jessie's mither cam hame then efter the bairn wis born . . . "

". . . Ah but she didnae *bide* wi' the granny, did she?"

"Aye, she did, efter Mary deed an' then thur wis an awfy row whin Wullie left the sea . . . "

"Aye, ye're richt enough. Ah remimber it a' noo . . . aye, oh it wis an awfy row . . . richt enough."

At a suitable moment I interrupted and encouraged Elsie to talk about her first sitting as an artist's model.

"Weel, Mester McGhie saw me at the shopes wi' ma mither an' Ah wis wearing this helio an' black checkit dress, awfy faded it wis, an' he askit ma Mither if he cud pent me an' she cud come an a'. Tae keep me comp'ny like. So she said yes an we went hame and she said we'll need tae get ye cleaned up if ye're gettin' yer pictur taen! An' she washed ma face till it wis stingin' and tied ma hair up wi' a braw white ribbon and Ah goat tae wear ma Sunday dress. Ah wis awfy pleased aboot that. It wis an *awfy* braw froack. A lovely pink wi' black butterflees oan it. But then whin we cam tae the hoose, eh, Mester McGhie lookit disappinted like an' said it wis the *ither* frock that he wantit, the auld faded yin that Ah'd hud oan before. So we went hame an' took it oot the dirty claes baskit an' Ah hud tae wear it an' Ah wisnae best pleased, but he gied me tuppence tae gan tae the sweetie shope, that wis Mrs Reekie's wee shope, ye ken, an' get a quarter o' pineapple chunks tae keep me sookin' fur Ah had tae sit still fur a lang time. An' he didnae want the braw white ribbon bow neether, he jist wantit ma hair hingin' a' aboot ma shouthers. Richt enough, Ah believe Ah hid bonny hair! Fur it wis thick an' fair an' curly then."

It is fourteen years since this scene took place. Those two ladies have now been gathered to their fathers and I who would then have hardly admitted to middle-age am now in my own turn approaching old age, if not yet quite as old as they were. I am so very delighted that we had that short conversation and that I magically captured it on video. It brings my grandfather and his work and that almost unrecognisable world of the hard-pressed Pittenweem women so very close. Up until the 1950s, the wives and daughters of fishermen were working women. Housework and child-rearing must be slotted in with their important role in the business of catching fish. Daily, the men faced danger and still do, but the women were mainly responsible for the infinite toil of opening mussels, baiting lines, mending nets and gutting the fish when caught, all cold unpleasant relentless jobs which could not be rushed or skimped. The immense amount of bread, scones and pies sold by the six thriving bakers' shops (for a population of one thousand) testifies to the fact that take-away food is not an absolutely modern invention but a necessity for the busy housewife.

There are always regrets in life and if I look back to nearly fifty years ago there was an even more evocative encounter which I foolishly avoided. What an ass I was! There was the possibility for me to meet the heroine of the most romantic of stories, a story in which my grandfather's paintings and a fishergirl from Pittenweem played the lead parts, a story infinitely superior to the bland, little romances that I used to read in Woman's Own every week.

And I muffed it!

What did I do instead? I probably went swimming or met a friend for an ice cream or walked into Anstruther with the gang to have a turn on the dodgems at the fair. Our amusements were simple and cheap in those far off days. Most probably I went swimming and paid my thruppence for a changing box unaware that my grandmother's visitor, a tall elegant old lady with a North American accent was very well worth listening to. But when did twenty year-olds prefer to spend time with sixty year-olds rather than their peers?

I remember the summer afternoon that she knocked at our front door and asked to speak to my grandmother who had fortuitously just made a batch of her superior pancakes. I had no idea who this stranger was and I could see that, just at first, my grandmother was also puzzled. However when a particular name was mentioned, the lady was immediately welcomed with such enthusiasm that I wondered if she were a relative. I was given the task of making a pot of tea, dusting the special china, buttering pancakes and then serving it all in the sunny garden. This was almost a daily routine and the price I must pay before I escaped to my own youthful pursuits.

I was introduced to the gracious old lady, as she seemed to me, and astonishment was expressed that Mrs McGhie was old enough to have such a grown-up grand-daughter. Then I quickly and foolishly took my leave.

As I left I heard the words. 'more than forty years' and '*impossible, surely*'.

But we must move away from Pittenweem to Glasgow to tell this romantic tale properly and from the beginning.

In 1907 my grandparents were staying in Glasgow, where John was making a name for himself as a portrait painter. He was a successful and competent portraitist, but I believe that his real delight was always in painting the sea and the everyday lives of the people who struggled with its strength and beauty. Each summer the McGhies returned to Pittenweem with their two children and rented a house for three months. The pictures that were painted in that time would be exhibited and hopefully sold in Glasgow in the Autumn.

In the city, my grandparents were a social couple, theatre-goers and members of clubs. They golfed and played bridge and entertained.

John had been a member of the Glasgow Art Club since before his marriage and played billiards there each week.

Fifteen years previously, when John had first joined the club and before he was married, he had become friendly with Alfred Rosier-

Morton, a humorous and carefree young man, son of a very wealthy father. Alfred was a lay member of the club but aspired to be an artist, though he displayed rather less than the necessary talent and none of the required energy and application. Though from very different backgrounds, they had become firm friends and had sketched together and played snooker and Alfred had joined John in Paris for a few months in 1895, when John studied there. However Alfred had appreciated the bistros and cabarets more than the hard grind of the studio and they had lost touch since those Parisian days. John was surprised one evening in the Spring of 1907 when a shabbily dressed and heavily bearded man greeted him in the billiard room of the club.

"Is it Rosier Morton? It can't be! Man, it's good to see you but ye're a lot hairier than the last time we met. How are ye doing these days?"

John secretly wondered what had happened to the dandified and almost effete fellow that he remembered, but he clapped his friend on the shoulder and shook his hand while Alfred laughed self-consciously.

"It's me right enough, John an' I guess we're all pretty hairy in Canada. It helps keeps you warm in the dreaded winter."

"I believe I did hear that you'd gone abroad. In fact I remember you came to see me when you first considered going. Doing well, are you? Great opportunities out there I suppose, aren't there?"

"Well . . . some folk are lucky enough. I aint been very lucky so far but I think I've got a break at last. The post office at Medicine Hat is mine to run . . . if I go back . . . it's a hellish climate in the prairies . . . but the Royal Mail shouldn't let me down the way some other things have . . . but what about yourself? I hear great things about you! Married to a beautiful wife, two kids and selling pictures right and left. You always were a worker, McGhie. You deserve success."

John made the proper deprecatory noises but he felt the man was very sad. Failure seemed to be written all over him. What had happened to the extravagant, light-hearted boy of ten years ago?

Later, John heard the whole story from the club gossip. Apparently when Alfred's father had died suddenly, his assumed financial position had not been as solid as everyone supposed. There was little capital and many debts. His widow and three children had been left almost penniless, the house and furniture sold up, the carriage, the riding horses, everything had to go. Alfred had two sisters and fortunately they had shown energy and enterprise and started a private school for girls in the West End of Glasgow which was flourishing. Alfred had shown less adaptability and, rather than fall into debt, had been packed off to Canada where he had had a rough time of it by all accounts. His gentle and affluent upbringing had not prepared him for the hardships of the climate or for the manual labour by which he earned his bread.

John told his wife the sad story that night.

"Oh John I expect the experience has made more of a man of him. What age is he?"

"Much the same as myself. Hitting forty, I suppose."

"And he's not married?"

"No, I'm pretty sure he's not."

"That's what wrong with him. He's needing a wife. I'll bet he's come home to find one."

"Och, woman, ye're an awful romantic. He certainly didn't say so but maybe you're right. I'll tell you he doesn't look like much of a catch at the moment. He used to be so particular about his linen and his trousers but now a visit to the barber would be the best investment if he's looking for a wife. He looks like a desperado. He's worse than the wild, wild man of Borneo."

Soon after this, John had an exhibition in McLure's Galleries and Alfred walked in on the second day.

"McGhie, these are wonderful paintings! Just look at that glittering sea and those waves splashing on the shore! How do you do it? I can feel the breeze. I can even smell it. My God, how you miss the smell of the sea when you're on the prairies. The sea is more than a thousand miles away in any direction. You long for it! Some folk think the prairie looks like the ocean, it's so very flat and vast but the smell isn't there. Oh no."

He shook his head sadly and clasping his hands, sat morosely down on a chair, paying no more attention to the paintings.

John felt infinitely sorry for his friend. He had no idea how to cope with this depressed withdrawal but awkwardly he invited comment on another of the paintings, one of an old man mending a basket in an attic.

"What d'ye think of this one, Alfred? I'm worried that it's a bit gloomy but I found the subject interesting and I painted it."

Once Alfred was on his feet again he seemed fine and he walked around the large room exclaiming and enthusing over each picture. There was one of a young fishergirl holding a basket of herring that he returned to several times and peered closely at the detail of the fish and also the girl's face.

"That's a marvellous looking girl, John, isn't she. Surely she's not a fisherlass?"

"Yes. She lives down the shore with her parents and baits the lines, guts the fish and mends the nets just as all the other girls do. They're brought up to be hard working all their lives, poor souls. Even the young children have to gather grass to layer between the hanks of the baited line so it doesn't tangle and can be paid out smoothly. Grass is at a premium! Sometimes you see the wee things walking away out of town, half way to St Monance, to get what grass they need."

But Alfred was not listening. He was gazing at the girl in the painting.

Just then, Agnes arrived, beautifully dressed in a dark green velvet gown. Her hat, fashionably outsized, was decorated with pale pink roses. Alfred was introduced and, in spite of his massive beard, assumed a charming and suave manner to the artist's wife and John, for the first time recognised something of the sophisticated fellow he remembered.

In a moment he was horrified to hear his wife say,

"John doesn't agree with me, but I believe you've come back from Canada to find yourself a wife! Am I right?"

Even with his beard it was obvious that Alfred was blushing.

Agnes smiled her charming smile and said no more and they walked around the exhibition together, Agnes and Alfred enthusiastically agreeing about what a marvellous painter John was. When they came to the painting of the girl that Alfred had so admired, Agnes said,

"That's Ellen Hughes, a very pretty girl, isn't she?"

"Absolutely lovely!"

"And that is such a good likeness. John, did you know she was going into service? That big house up at the back of the town. I wonder how she'll like that."

"Perhaps it will be easier than the life she has now?"

"I daresay! Still, a servant! She's bound to miss her freedom."

Alfred was silent for a few moments then shook his head and murmured

"It seems incredible that a girl who looks so . . . marvellous, should have to work so hard. She is so delicate and so lovely . . . she could be a duchess."

Agnes smiled archly.

"Mr Rosier-Morton, I believe you would like to meet that girl!"

"Yes I would and I'd like to marry her if she'd have me."

As John regarded his friend in astonishment, he seemed to see the old optimistic, devil-may-care and unpredictable boy that he had known in Paris, for Alfred's face was alight with pleasure, his shoulders were square, his excellent teeth shone out from their hairy jungle and even the beard did not seem so uncontrollably large. John was speechless but his wife was not.

"Of course Ellen is only a simple uneducated girl, you know, but her parents are very respectable and well thought of. I know her mother well. Why don't you come to Pittenweem and meet her?"

"I'd certainly like to do that, Mrs McGhie. Thank you. When are you next going through to Fife? You know I don't have all the time in the world before I must get back across the Atlantic."

"We hope to go at the end of next week. Just give us a day or so to settle in, air the beds and cut the grass . . . you could come through on the Tuesday, if you like."

"I'll be there on the Tuesday. I sure will."

John nodded and smiled his welcome but remained speechless.

"But Mrs McGhie, we dinnae ken onythin' aboot this man! An' him wi' a double barrelled name an' a'. Ah dae ken if Ellen wad be interested. Mebbe there's a Pittenweem laud . . . but she niver tells me onythin'."

"Oh, Mrs Hughes, he's a very nice fellow. Mr McGhie has known him for twenty years. He's a gentleman and he went to a very good school in Glasgow. His late father was a wealthy Glasgow businessman."

"But whit's a man like that daein' seekin' a fisherlass fur a wife?"

"Well as I told you, he just fell in love with Ellen's picture as soon as he saw it! He was just completely entranced because she is a particularly beautiful girl. You know that yourself, Mrs Hughes."

"Aye, she's a bonny lassie. Ah ken that."

"And I don't think he is quite as well off as he used to be but he is living in Canada now and will probably do very, very well eventually, I daresay. It would be an excellent match."

"An' ye say he's in his late thirties? Ellen'll be thinkin' that's an auld man. Her faither's only forty-fower."

"Why don't you and Ellen come up for a cup of tea on Thursday afternoon and meet him, anyway. Nothing needs to be said that day."

"Aye, but we'll a' ken why they're meetin' each ither. It micht be awfy awkward like."

"You just come along and I'll bake a scone and we can chat and you can see Mr McGhie's latest painting."

On Tuesday Alfred arrived with his battered leather valise. He stood in the garden and took deep breaths of the sea air.

"Wonderful, wonderful to be in Fife again, beautiful Fife. We came here when I was a child and a young man too. I look back at that curled darling that I was and think what a useless wastrel I was brought up to be. Such a silly ass! Dear, dear, how things change. But those holidays at Elie were great, just magical."

In bed that night, Agnes chided her husband,

"Why did you not get him to a barber in Glasgow and get rid of that abomination on his chin! Did you see how the wind blew it about and made it wilder? Ellen will be horrified. Maybe it's different in Canada but even the ancient worthies here don't wear beards like Methuselah."

John protested that one fellow could hardly make another fellow trim his beard.

"Don't you worry, *I'll trim his beard for him* before he meets that girl. He hasn't got a chance otherwise."

And Agnes, who was a determined woman, did trim Alfred's beard for him the next day. She sat him in a garden chair with a sheet wrapped around him and for the first time in her life, trimmed a beard. She used her dress making scissors and she made a very good job of it and enjoyed herself.

"He looks years younger!" she thought to herself, but refrained from saying it out loud, for Agnes herself was only twenty five and he did seem quite mature to her.

Although Alfred was nervous about the meeting with Ellen on Thursday, he seemed happy to sit in the garden, gazing out to sea and sometimes amusing the two McGhie children with simple tricks. Annie was five and Willie was three and they were fascinated by the big stranger.

When John started to chop firewood in the morning, Alfred said that he would like to do it,

"You better get on with your painting, John. That's your speciality. I've had plenty practice with an axe."

After he had chopped an impressive pile of sticks he showed the children how to build a log cabin. Annie was particularly delighted with the little model.

"All we need now is a wee horse to stand outside the wee house!"

"A wee horse, Annie? D'ye like horses?"

"Oh, yes I love horses. Do you have a horse in Canada?"

"Well, I've looked after a lot of horses and ridden a lot of horses, but they all belonged to other people, I'm afraid."

"Did they gallop like this, uncle Alfred?"

Annie galloped round the small garden several times, jumping over any small object that was lying around. She was breathless when she returned.

"Yes, they galloped just exactly like that, Annie. I think you'd like to *be* a horse!"

The child gazed seriously at him for a moment.

"*Everybody* would like to be a horse, Uncle Alfred."

On Wednesday evening, the two men strolled down to the harbour. The breeze had died away and it was a perfect June evening. The sea was like a silken sheet and the small boats looked like toys.

Five fishermen were smoking as they walked their eight steps back and forth in a tightly knit group, three facing in one direction, two in the other so that they could look into each others faces as they walked and talked.

"That looks like a sort of dance that they're doing, John!"

"It's a ritual, certainly, just the length of the deck, back and forth."

They were silent for some minutes.

"The Canadian prairies seem very unreal to me just now."

"I daresay they do."

"Sometimes I dread going back."

"Must you go? Could you not get some position here?"

"Nope, I doubt it. I have to get back. There is a fascination about those vast spaces. I suppose the fishermen feel the same about the sea. But my goodness it is idyllic here. Why don't you live here all the year round, John?"

"No big commissions in the East Neuk, I'm afraid, no Lord Provosts or Brigadier Generals needing their portraits painted. Got to go where the money is. And I expect Agnes would find it too quiet here in the winter."

Neither man spoke of the real reason that Alfred had come to Pittenweem.

Next morning there was a sharp knock at the door and Agnes answered it. It was Mrs Hughes.

"Oh, Mrs McGhie, last nicht we saw Mester McGhie and yon man walkin' past the windae an' Ellen's sayin' if that's the man, she's no' interested at a', an' she's no' comin' up the day an' Ah'm awfy vexed fur Ah kin see he's an awfy braw man, hansum an' weel built but mebbe jist that wee bit ower auld fur a young lassie o' nineteen. Ye ken, Ah'd tak 'im masel' if Ah didnae hiv a man a'ready! But Ah shouldnae joke because the puir fellow is expectin' tae see her. Ah dae ken whit tae dae, Mrs McGhie. Whit shud Ah dae?"

"I'll come down and speak to Ellen."

And whatever magic the determined Agnes worked, Ellen was persuaded to come up that afternoon.

At first, the children were the centre of attraction and each recited a small poem. Then their outfits were admired and Agnes admitted that she had made all their garments herself. When the children were sent out to the garden with their scones, the sitting room seemed very small and terribly overcrowded and an awkward silence descended which Agnes and Mrs Hughes bravely but unsuccessfully tried to shatter. John was never much of a conversationalist and Alfred was nervous as a cat.

Agnes found her glance kept returning to Alfred's beard and she wished that she had chopped it even shorter when she had the chance.

Ellen took no part or interest in the conversation but gazed steadily out of the window at the children playing in the garden.

When Agnes brought in the tea things, Alfred offered to hand round the scones and cake though Agnes would have preferred him to sit quietly in his chair. He seemed so very big as he moved around. However he caused no damage to the many knick-knacks and it was through this offer to help that the breakthrough came.

Alfred had been splitting more wood that morning and in spite of his boast of previous practice with an axe, he had been slightly injured on the back of his hand by an unexpected jumping piece of wood. It was a graze and a minor cut and it had not seemed worthwhile to put a plaster on it. Ellen had determined not to take a scone but as he held the plate towards her, she noticed the injury and exclaimed involuntarily, for she too had hurt herself that morning. In a moment of carelessness with the mussel knife, it had slipped and her wound was in almost exactly the same place on the back of the same hand.

Hardly anything was said but sympathy for each other and amusement at such a coincidence can be conveyed without many words. Her deep blue eyes looked into his brown ones for long enough to read the adoration and shy yearning there. After she took a scone, they smiled to each other, each displaying very beautiful teeth and again exchanging a long glance.

The eyes of Mrs Hughes and Agnes met in a brief flicker of relief and triumph, then Agnes looked across at her husband with a look which he knew only too well. Soon she started to tell one of her skilful anecdotes and as always the company was soon dissolved in laughter.

When Mrs Hughes and her daughter were leaving, Alfred boldly asked Ellen if she would meet him the following evening for a walk and she agreed.

The following evening, Agnes said to John how sorry she was for Alfred.

"*Sorry!* Now why is that, my dear, when he seems to have got exactly what he came here for?".

"Well, he used to live in a mansion, himself, with all those servants and now he's got to go to the backdoor of that house and collect the maid on her night off. It just seems such a come-down."

"I don't think he'll feel it's a come-down when he puts his arm round Ellen's waist."

"I hope he's not too forward to frighten her."

"I daresay he has as much charm and sophistication as the Pittenweem lads."

But truthfully John felt confused by the speed with which everything had happened. Throughout the week, he asserted several times that he felt like an actor in a play.

When Alfred called at the back door of the imposing mansion, Ellen still had some duties to attend to and the cook, large and fat as cooks should be, invited him to wait in the kitchen. To be polite he complemented the cook on her 'fine big kitchen' but was silenced by her rejoinder,

"Aye, it's a grand big kitchen for coughs and colds and snotty noses!"

But this snub was soon forgotten as he and Ellen, hand in hand, wandered slowly along the seashore towards St Monance in the bright June evening.

By the following week, when they had exchanged many

confidences and Ellen had discovered how easily Alfred could make her laugh, there seemed to be no doubt that Ellen's answer would be "yes" to the great adventure of marriage in an unknown country.

One happy evening, they took supper with John and Agnes and Alfred was about to accompany Ellen home. After saying her farewell to the McGhies, Alfred, in order to snatch a goodnight kiss, not the first by any means, pulled Ellen into the small back room which he thought unoccupied. But unknown to him, or perhaps forgotten, there was a built-in box bed in that room in which Annie slept and their kiss was interrupted by a small voice warning,

"Mind! I'm not sleeping yet!"

Their courtship was necessarily brief as Alfred must return to Medicine Hat before August. Ellen shed many tears at the thought of leaving her family but her mother bravely kept her own tears till after the departure. She felt that her daughter had made a splendid match and gave her and Alfred every encouragement and blessing.

Mrs Hughes had no idea of the Canadian prairies and the terrible extremes of weather and other vicissitudes which her girl might face there, but she knew the alternative, the harshly demanding and insecure life of a fisherman's wife, only too well. And with one daughter gone, there would be a little more for the five children still at home and perhaps more yet to come.

Within five weeks Ellen was married and had left the small fishing village to start her new life. She would not return to Fife for nearly fifty years and she would never see her mother again.

And Ellen was the lady that I avoided! Foolish girl that I was to miss the story that she had to tell.

I might have heard of some of the hardships that she and Alfred had suffered. The fierce, bitter winters when they awakened to find his beard white and solid with frozen breath and when the snow piled eight feet high and animals in the barn died in the deep and terrible cold. I might have heard of the summers of parching heat when streams dried up and the scorching sun was the daily enemy. I might have heard of homesickness for the sparkling seas of the Fife coast and of moving from one town to another, of lost jobs, missed opportunities and dishonest partners. I would also have heard, for this is what she told my grandmother, that eventually they had made money and had been very comfortable in a beautiful clapboard house where three tall healthy sons had been born, all of them now successful professional men. Alfred had always been wonderful, a kind, loving and perfect husband and father and their love had never faltered.

Sadly, last year Alfred had died, a very old man, but Ellen believed that she had been terribly lucky and had had the most wonderfully happy, adventurous life possible.

Reen Thomas

By 1910 THE NAME OF John McGhie was beginning to be noticed in the art circles of Glasgow and my grandparents had moved from their modest lodgings in Renfrew Street to a large gracious flat near Blythswood square. It was rented, as all tenement properties were at that time.

There was a nearby studio where John painted, but potential buyers regularly visited the house to look at pictures. Nowadays, the art dealer takes over the business management of an artist's career but at that time it was more of a 'one-man' concern and a helpful wife and an attractive home were very important. As well as being charming, Agnes was a good business woman. John just needed to paint the pictures and leave the rest to his very competent wife!

Agnes, with two young children, needed some domestic help. That summer in Pittenweem, a local girl, Reen Thomas, came to work for the McGhie family. Reen was a good worker and Agnes suggested that she might like to come back to Glasgow and 'live-in' for a month or two and see if she liked it. Reen had possibly not been further afield in her lifetime than St Andrews or perhaps Kirkcaldy. It is difficult for the restless mobile people of today to appreciate how little travelling there was in the first part of the century. The fishermen and gutting women, at certain seasons, travelled south to other fishing towns or through the canal to the west coast, and a few Pittenweem inhabitants did make the brave leap of 'leaving home for foreign parts'. Many of the latter were very successful in their lives. However these journeys had a purpose and the idea of travelling any distance for pleasure was outwith the experience and finances of most folk of the East Neuk. For the first half of the last century, Pittenweem was an amazingly self-sufficient town with shops which were able to provide practically any article that might be required, household or otherwise.

Agnes was anxious that Reen should not be too overpowered by the change that she was contemplating.

"Are you quite sure, now, Reen?" Agnes asked anxiously. "It's a very, very different place from Pittenweem, you know. It is a big, dirty city with busy streets and we live on the top flat of a tenement that's much higher than any of the buildings in Pittenweem, with lots of stairs to climb when you carry home the messages. It's a big flat, too, with big rooms to clean and big floors to wash. And it rains a lot. Are you really sure about coming through?

Reen, who could form no mental picture of what was being described, paid little attention to the warning.

"That's a'richt Mrs McGhie. It'll be an adventure fur me. Ah'm fair seek o' the cauld winds here an' aye baitin' the lines. An' Ah kin aye come hame if Ah divnae like it."

"Of course, of course you can, though I hope we will suit each other and you will stay till next summer at least."

"Aye well, we'll see whit happens, Mrs McGhie."

Nothing had prepared Reen for the size of Glasgow. First of all, after the interminable train journey, there was Queen Street station with its choking mixture of steam and smoke, the deafening noise and the soaring, grimy glass roof which made such an enormous, frightening space above her head. It bore no resemblance to those quiet, flower bedecked platforms of the East Neuk stations, where only the arrival of a few small trains each day disturbed the cows in the nearby field for a brief, noisy interval. Reen almost considered jumping right back on the train again. Then there was the hot, uncomfortable journey, crammed into the dusty cab, rumbling through busy streets where buildings rose high on either side and cut off any sight of the sky. Lastly there were all those stairs to climb when they finally reached Blythswood Street! Reen, who was a comfortably built girl, would never find those stairs easy.

Then the McGhie's home bore no relation to Reen's perception of a flat. Her aunty lived in a flat at the bottom of the Cove Wynd and her Granny lived an another in the Barracks, but if you put the two of them together that would hardly make what Mrs McGhie called her sitting room. That seemed more like a town hall to Reen. An enormous table-shaped piano, bigger than a double bed though fancier in shape, stood in one corner of the vast room. And the high windows! How would she polish the top panes of the windows? The entrance hall was big enough for a horse and cart to walk in and there were three bedrooms, each with a complete bedroom suite. The bathroom had a beautiful bath with a shower and the WC had blue swans and bulrushes on it. Although it was like a palace, Reen was a practical girl and immediately saw the drawbacks.

"Ah'll be at thae floors frae mornin' tae nicht," she thought to herself.

However Reen had a nice big kitchen to work in, with a bed in the recess and plenty of good food always available. The enormous black range demanded daily maintenance, but it provided plenty of hot water which flowed from the tap at the sink. In Reen's eyes, this was probably the most wonderful feature of the whole flat.

After the luggage, together with many large paintings and Mrs McGhie's treadle sewing machine, had been manhandled upstairs by Mr McGhie and the grumbling cab-driver, they all had a cup of tea in the kitchen. Then Mrs McGhie showed Reen round the flat with pride. To be truthful, Agnes was almost as impressed by the flat as Reen. She had not been the mistress of anything quite so grand or gracious in the first years of her marriage and she now delighted in it and in finding the bargains in antique furniture and old Persian rugs with which the Blythswood Street flat was furnished. She herself had made the blue-patterned cretonne loose covers on the chairs and sofa and the cream curtains with the bold border of deep blue. It was a lovely room and she was justifiably proud of it.

"But d'ye know one of the things I really like about this house, Reen? Come over to the window a minute. D'ye see that house across the road, with the basement window? Well, a long time ago, more than fifty years, a young woman handed her lover a cup of cocoa out of that window," Agnes opened her eyes wide and dropped her voice to a slow and dramatic whisper, "and the cocoa was laced with arsenic!"

"Oh, Mistress McGhie, did he dee?"

"Yes I'm afraid he did. You see the young woman had met someone else, a much wealthier man, that she wanted to marry, so it seems she got rid of the first one.

Then, taken aback by the intense look of horror on Reen's face, Agnes smiled and tried to lighten the moment by adding in a sprightly tone,

'Off with the old before you're on with the new!' I suppose."

Reen continued to gaze across the road.

"Oh, she wis a bad bitch, wisn't she. Did the polis no' get her?"

"Yes, they arrested her and she was tried, but found 'not guilty'. They weren't able to prove that she had done it, though there was a lot if incriminating evidence, but she was young and beautiful and wealthy and I suppose the jury was sorry for her . . . "

"*Sorry fur her!*" and her expression showed the harshness of the life she had known, "Ah'd've gi'en her sorry, she wis awfy wickid if she did that tae her man. Whit wis her name, Mrs McGhie?"

"Madeleine Smith. It was a very long time ago.

Only afterwards did Reen start to think about what a strange thing her mistress had said. Mrs McGhie *had seemed to like the idea of a woman across the road committing murder!* She puzzled over this quite often and never found an answer for she was not to know that Agnes had a great interest in the morbid and sensational and enjoyed reading reports of criminal trials of the past and present.

Because of helping out in the summer, Reen knew that the McGhies were kind, although Mrs McGhie was quite demanding and had an eagle eye for overlooked dust. Reen was yet to learn that Agnes had a very quick temper which had not been apparent in the summer time. However she was also generous and sympathetic and made chicken soup for Reen when she caught a bad cold and never a day passed but she made Reen laugh.

In the first week Agnes had come into the kitchen one day as Reen was on her knees, washing the floor. Perhaps the girl was feeling a little homesick for Pittenweem where the floors were smaller and her friends were nearby. As Reen washed, she sang the hymn, "Abide with Me," in a slow lugubrious voice and her scrubbing brush kept time to the rhythm of the music.

"Jump up a minute Reen, please."

Agnes took the scrubber from her then knelt down in her place.

"Now I don't want any of this "Abide with Me" stuff" and Agnes mimicked the maid's mournful song and languid movements. "What I want to see is 'The Campbells are Coming, Hurrah, Hurrah'."

As Agnes sang, she wielded the brush with a swift and vigorous motion to match the new tempo. Then she jumped up, handed the brush back and left the kitchen.

Reen stood there with her eyes round and her mouth slightly open and told herself that not many people had such an unusual mistress.

Reen's first Saturday out in Glasgow was a great success. She took the two children, or rather they led her through the canyons of dark tenements to the zoo and moving pictures in New City Road. A notice outside proclaimed it to be,

The Cheapest Attraction in the Civilised World

Inside Reen gazed disbelievingly at a camel and an elephant, as well as monkeys and a rather shabby lion. The subtitled film was shown on a free standing screen and could be viewed from either side, tuppence for the right side and a penny for the wrong side, where you soon learned to read the simple subtitles backwards. The trick photography of the films bedazzled the Pittenweem girl as people jumped on and off tables, repeatedly chased each other through the same door in impossible permutations or even flew about like birds. Lots of white paint was spilled everywhere and Reen's loud, hearty laugh resounded again and again. Annie, at eight years old found that laugh very embarrassing and would never learn to care much for Reen. The feeling would be mutual. However, four-year-old Willie and Reen adored each other from the first moment.

"Now did the children look after you all right, Reen?"

"Oh, but Mrs McGhie whit a grand time we've hid! Thon animals were that big! Ah've seen picturs o' wild animals but Ah niver expectit tae see them in real life an' Ah niver kent they wur *that size*. An' the movin' picturs an a'. Ah wiz lauching til Ah wiz greetin'. An' the *streets* wur *that busy*, wi' a' they hoarses, we kid hairdly git across, thur wur that many hoarses 'n cairts, whaur div they a' gan tae at nicht, Ah wunner? An' wee Willie wis a richt wee gentleman the wey he lookit efter me an' held ma haund . . . an' Annie wis fine tae," she added, as Annie looked at her, unsmiling.

The Saturday outing had certainly cheered Reen up, for the first week had been a great culture shock to her.

On the second Saturday, Reen and Willie went out alone as Annie was at a party or perhaps, being a determined child, she had opted out of accompanying them.

That day was a great success too.

"Oh mistress McGhie, Wullie took me oan the subwey the day. Whit a grand wee train it wis wi' real leather seats an' we jist went roon' and roon' *aw efternin*. Oan the wan ticket, tae! Naebody niver asked us fur ony mair money. It was really jist awfy grand an' a' they stairs gaun awa doon the wey, deep intae the grund an' thin up again. My it wis fair excitin'."

For once Agnes was struck dumb.

On the Saturday that the family were to visit John's sister in Lanarkshire, Agnes spoke seriously to Reen.

"Now we'll be away all day. I hope you'll be all right by yourself, Reen. Will you go out?"

"Oh aye, Ah'll be jist fine, Mrs McGhie, Ah'm findin' ma wey aroond easy noo. Ah micht gan shoppin. Aye, Ah'll tak the blue tram doon tae Argyle street where you 'n me went oan Wednesday last, fur Ah'm needin' shoes an' thur wis plenty shoapes doon there, grand and cheap."

"Well, I just want to tell you to be careful because it is a big city with some strange men in it and you're young and attractive and if you're walking alone . . . " Agnes was not finding it easy to say what she meant but she did feel responsible for the girl, ". . . a man might speak to you and . . . he might even be a married man . . . " she finished lamely, but she was only a few years older than Reen.

"Na, na don't you worry, Mrs McGhie. Ah kin look efter masel' richt enuff."

"I'm sure you can, Reen. We'll be home on the late train tonight."

The following morning after breakfast Agnes asked Reen how she had enjoyed her day in town.

"Did you get your shoes, Reen?"

"Aye, Ah goat a nice pair o' broon yins for Sundays but d'ye ken whit happened tae me!"

"Nothing bad I hope." Agnes looked dismayed.

"Weel, Ah wis staundin' at the tram stope an' a man cam along and stood a bit close tae me, sae I moved sideyweys awa frae him and then he spoke, an' he said,

'"You're a nice-lookin' lassie. I expect ye're from the country," an' Ah said,

"Ah'm frae Pittenweem! An' Ah expect you're a mairrit man," an' he said,

"Well as a maiter o' fact, Ah *am* a mairrit man, but circumstances alter cases," an Ah jist said,

"An' broken noses alter faces."

An' Ah lookit the ither wey, an' then he jist walked awa doon the street."

"Well done Reen! I think you'll look after yourself all right."

Then they both had a good laugh and that conversation was often quoted in the family.

Reen stayed throughout the winter and returned with the family to Pittenweem in June, where she lived with her mother and came in daily to work.

The relationship between Annie and Reen never blossomed.

Reen said to Agnes one day,

"D'ye see that Annie, she's aye lookin' oot at me alow her eebrees, but Wullie's a dear lamb."

I am unsure how many years Reen returned to Glasgow to work for my grandparents but I know that, after she married in Pittenweem, she continued to give some domestic help in the summer for there were many visitors to the house. Some of her pithy sayings have remained in the family's vocabulary and still surface after all these years.

One visiting English couple had a four year-old son dressed in a Lord Fauntleroy suit and displaying characteristics to match. Standing in the garden, he would lean in at the open sitting room window where his mother was and wave a limp little hand and say adoringly,

"Hillo Ma-ma."

And she would return the wave and greeting equally sentimentally,

"Hillo darling boy."

This cloying exchange occurred frequently throughout the morning, interrupting the conversation and irritating Agnes. Sometimes the mother and son blew kisses to each other.

When Agnes went through to the kitchen to see about lunch, she grumbled to Reen,

"That boy gives me the pip!"

Reen immediately answered,

"Aye, an' he gies it tae me an' a'!"

For some reason, this exchange has always been a favourite catchphrase in the family.

Another visitor, a foolish woman who had an impressive array of diamond rings, was in the kitchen washing the diamonds to make them sparkle. As she replaced them on her fingers, she took it upon herself to speak to Reen, who was peeling potatoes.

"Do you know, Reen, that these rings are worth more than your husband could earn in several years."

As she spoke she spread out her hands to show the rings, but Reen just glanced cursorily over her shoulder before commenting,

"Ach weel, Ah jist think they're coammon. *And* they disfeegur the haunds."

There is no doubt that Reen could look after herself.

Village Temptations

"WHITTEN ITHER COLOURS hiv ye goat?" Lizzie asked in a serious tone then broke into helpless giggles as she looked at her friend Aggie.

Mrs Duff, the fat and cynical shop owner, looked stonily at the two pretty girls.

"Thur's the cream, like these yins . . . an' pink an' blue an' beige." She pronounced it 'beej' with some importance.

Aggie stroked the silky knitted fabric of the large bloomers which lay before her under the hissing gas lamps.

"Thur awfy big!"

"That's the sma'est size available."

"Whit are they made oot o'?"

"Celanese! It's the finest sort o' artifeecial silk an' it's knitted up like."

"Kin we see the ither colours an a'?"

The shop was small and crammed, with every possible cubic inch of space utilised to display an astonishing variety of goods. Delicate lace-trimmed baby wear was arranged on stands. All types of underwear and nightwear were folded and tightly packed in glass-fronted drawers. Sheets, towels and dusters hung from the ceiling like medieval banners. On several surfaces were piles of brightly patterned cotton 'pinnies', uniform of the local housewives, each with a cross-over front and a binding of bias tape. Wools of many colours and thicknesses were piled on shelves or bulged from paper sacks on the floor and all the appurtenances of embroidery were obviously available, while more mundane necessities such as buttons, tape or elastic were stowed away in battered cardboard boxes piled in swaying towers. Embroidery was Mrs Duff's speciality. The five other drapery stores in the town were each known for one particular section of the soft goods trade although each kept a wide selection of stock. The largest draper could supply linoleum, rugs and even furniture, another would provide suits and shirts for funerals or weddings, another sold the high boots and heavy clothing required by seamen. The two smallest shops relied strongly on babywear, toilet paper and sanitary towels. However all the shops sold wool for it was a time in which every female was dedicated to productivity from an early age. Women knitted as they stood at their doors and gossiped and little girls in the school playground crouched over knitting, crochet or 'ratstails'.

Though the population of the village numbered less than one thousand, there was little travelling done in the penurious thirties and such a plethora of drapers, while not exactly thriving, continued from year to year in business.

Mrs Duff brought the three other pairs of knickers and threw them down unceremoniously. From experience she knew it was unlikely that these girls would buy anything. On a Saturday afternoon there was little else to do in the small town but trawl around the shops. They had not even asked the price. The tall girl worked in the post office and to Mrs Duff's certain knowledge, was a cheeky besom.

"That's the *beej*!" Mrs Duff laid a heavy hand on the fourth pair. "Very smart."

She turned to the next customer and the girls snorted with pent-up giggles.

The elderly lady on Aggie's left was buying a piece of linen with the design to be embroidered already printed in blue. She had many examples laid out in front of her, three tray cloths, five tea cosy covers, several handkerchief sachets and an anti-macassar, all adorned with extravagant possibilities of decoration, a large bunch of flowers tied with a ribbon or a crinoline lady with unlikely bonnet, a garden full of hollyhocks or even a three masted schooner sailing proudly on billowing waves. Really the choice was much too great and she hesitated and dithered interminably, rearranging and holding each item high in the air. Beside her an ingenious folding box displayed the tempting hanks of jewel bright embroidery threads and she longed to reach that supreme moment of purchase when the delicious colours were selected. The linen articles struggled for space with the silken underwear on the small counter and Aggie good-naturedly helped the old lady when some pieces fell to the floor.

Jostling Lizzie on the other side was a young man who had put his well-worn valise on the counter and opened it with an assertive flourish. He was a travelling salesman from Glasgow and Mrs Duff had given him a very bitter look. He should have remained quietly waiting until she was finished with her customers, but James Turner was a small energetic man who had found that remaining quiet got him nowhere and he was certainly determined to get somewhere. As he unpacked his bag, Lizzie, who was almost a head taller than Jimmy, turned and looked at him. She was an exceptionally good-looking girl with large brown eyes and a figure of Victorian voluptuousness. He smiled up at her with obvious appreciation and winked. A wink from a local fisherman would have been coldly rejected but because of his well-trimmed moustache, his sparkling shirt and his tightly knotted tie, Lizzie smiled back and then looking away slightly, blinked in return.

"Mrs Duff, I huv a similar but supeerior article here," Jimmy called out in his alien west coast accents, almost bouncing in his eagerness. "Jist look ... maybe the young ladies would prefair these ... and thur not ... too roomy, mair suited for they ladies wi' less embongpong ... Ah mean."

Raising his dark eyebrows, he looked knowingly and appreciatively at Lizzie's well-shaped but neat behind, then produced a pair of pink knickers with a flourish and covering up the larger and more practical garments already displayed, he draped the pink drawers artistically on the counter.

"See, a wee touch o' embroidery makes them dead glamorous," He indicated a small rose. "Extra strong elastic, too, *very* reliable and a *double gusset*, ... "

His voice dropped to a dramatic stage whisper on the last phrase.

The girls looked at each other and started to laugh again while Mrs Duff looked very stern.

"Mr Turner, wid ye be so guid as tae remove thae goods which are no' pairt o' ma stock frae ma coonter and allow me tae deal wi' ma ain customers."

Though the words were simple, the tone and delivery would not have disgraced a Shakespearean actress, but Jimmy smiled engagingly and continued,

"Or maybe the young ladies would prefair the French style of pantees and I have them here."

He delved into his bag once more but it was too much for Aggie who rushed from the shop, hooting hysterically with Lizzie close behind her, shrieking just as loudly.

Jimmy Turner would pay another seventy five professional visits to the East Neuk village before the electric spark which had flowed between him and Lizzie with that first wink, would finally ignite and Lizzie, in spite of her mother's tears, would join him on the train to Glasgow.

But that is only part of our story. First, Lizzie must experience some of life's pains and payments.

Perhaps less obvious than in the city, but even in a village, it is plain that rewards and pleasures are unequally divided in society and Lizzie brooded about this inequality more than most.

No one could work harder than her mother who seemed at fifty, to be an old wizened woman, constantly 'scraping the bottom of the pot' and with never enough money to pay the most necessary bills. There had never been a father in Lizzie's life and she had always lived in the small damp house, redolent of the potted meat which her mother made for a living. Underneath the heavy meaty smell was a faint stale aroma of burned sugar as tablet was made at the weekends. After cooking, the hot liquid sweetmeat must be stirred continuously until cool, to achieve the desirable fine texture. If Lizzie were about, she would be expected to stir until her arms ached. In spite of her sympathy for her mother, Lizzie generally found some outdoor occupation to save her from stirring.

Her home environment seemed to be one of continuous, grinding work. Lizzie hated it and she hated the smell. She longed for a house where one sat down in a nice dress and read a book or did some fine lacy knitting and she determined that as soon as possible she would find this ideal.

She was only ten when she visited a school friend, child of a fisherman, and realised the toil of line-baiting, net-mending and gutting that was the lot of a fisherman's wife. That life seemed even harder than her poor mother's! At that tender age, Lizzie determined that the husband who would give her a nice dress and a chance to sit at lacy knitting was not to be found in Pittenweem. From then on her dreams and fantasies centred around a future when she would have left the small fishing town.

Lizzie looked smart and was good at arithmetic and found her job in the Post Office, much lighter work than any other available in the village might have been. The post mistress was Mrs Furniss, a rather indolent widow from Kirkcaldy, who had come to Pittenweem the previous year. Lizzie saw very little of Mrs Furniss, who was happy to leave the daily demands of the office to Lizzie, which suited the girl very well for it was seldom busy.

However working in the post office revealed even more clearly to Lizzie the great gap between the rich and the poor.

There was wee Miss Bascombe for instance, a relative of the local aristocracy and in charge of the Pittenweem contingent of Girl Guides and Brownies. She spoke in a high giggling English voice that was often difficult to understand. Each week she bought lots of postage stamps, she must always be writing letters and postcards. Sometimes she bought four shillings' worth! Then she would present a ten-pound note. Ten pounds! It happened all the time, Miss Bascombe never learned. Where was Lizzie expected to find change of a tenner? There was never more than two pounds of silver in the drawer and three or four single notes at most. What could she do but ask the old bat to wait while she nipped next door to the grocer's who could always oblige, it being licenced and thriving. Lizzie was disobeying rules because she should not have left a customer unattended on the premises but there was nothing else that she could do. Mrs Furniss was upstairs, probably deep in a novelette and would certainly complain about being disturbed. Though Lizzie enjoyed the freedom to run the office on her own, she considered Mrs Furniss a lazy bitch.

Then there were other folk from up the town, where the big houses were. They came regularly with large badly-made parcels. God knows what was in them and they cost a fortune in postage. Lizzie took some comfort from the fact that the parcels would probably have disintegrated before they reached their destination

But the worst of all were the summer visitors. Not the 'Glesca keelies' of course, who came on the train and swamped the town for a fortnight, eating fish suppers in the High Street and pushing up the profits of the six pubs. The keelies spent their money freely, though not in the post office where their only purchase would be a couple of stamps for postcards or maybe a postal order for the football coupon. It was the young swells, the 'Toffs' she called them, that arrived in their cars and motor bikes in August and played tennis in white outfits and golf in tweeds and fairisle pullovers. Lizzie hated them and their loud confident voices and all the telegrams that they sent. There were not even twenty of these toffs but they were noisy and the Post office never seemed free of them. They were forever sending wires to Perth, Edinburgh or St Andrews with invitations to meet for a game or a meal and the hairs on the back of Lizzie's neck stood up when they crowded up to her counter with much laughter and conversation amongst themselves as though she were invisible. Most would be smoking and Lizzie would long for a cigarette but this was a strictly and utterly forbidden luxury for Post Office employees.

The toffs took ages to compose their telegrams, consulting and advising each other with whispers, nudges and giggles, scribbling and scoring out and wasting several forms before they handed one over the counter. The money that they spent on telegrams seemed utterly profligate to Lizzie. Money did not matter to them at all, she realised bitterly. They had no need to count sixpences and plan ahead. Their money flowed from their purses like water from a tap and mostly there was no real information in the wire, certainly nothing of importance. Sometimes the same person came several times in one day to the office with stranger and stranger messages. They were like children playing a game but the money spent on this game was shocking to Lizzie.

"Looking forward to our midnight swim. Be sure to bring your towel this time, fathead. Ha ha ha. Hairy Neptune."

"Wear your green costume on Tuesday, I am wearing blue. Unfortunately Beatrice will probably be there. Don't dare to be late. Your devoted friend."

"Cannot wait to see the new vehicle, it sounds just dandy. Please, please, please bring that naughty book you were talking about. Betty Boop."

"Cream cakes, kisses and lemonade on the lawn, dinner at Rusack's later. Just longing to see you, Dizzy Blonde."

This was the sort of rubbish that they paid to send by wire and sometimes the message was much longer and cost as much as Lizzie earned in a day.

Lizzie had nothing to do with the telegraph machine though she was responsible for all the rest of the Post office business and she must call up the stairs to Mrs Furniss to come down and send wires off. Mrs Furniss would descend with a bad-tempered look as though it were Lizzie's fault that these stupid messages must be tapped out and Lizzie would brood over the unfairness of it all. Mrs Furniss getting a big pay and doing practically no work, grudging the work she did do. And then all that good money thrown away on useless telegrams by those loud, overdressed young folk while Lizzie had to mend her old stockings, curtail purchases of comforting chocolate and cigarettes and walk home from dances for the lack of a few pennies. It was all just so unfair.

By September all the summer visitors had departed and there was very little business in the small post office.

Jimmy Turner had been in town ten times since that first meeting in Mrs Duff's shop and he had taken Lizzie for an ice-cream each time. How had they met? Jimmy was enterprising and energetic and presuming that Lizzie worked during the week, he had made sure that his next visit to Pittenweem was again on a Saturday. With his swift lope and sharp glances into the drapery stores he quickly surveyed the two main streets from end to end, then galloped down to the harbour and up and down the several steep connecting wynds. It was a small town with nothing to do but stroll about and on his third speedy circuit, Jimmy caught sight of the tall beauty and her friend sitting on a bench at the harbour and invited them to a cafe.

His third visit was an arranged tête-à-tête with Lizzie. Though Lizzie wore flat shoes and even bent her knees slightly, she would always be inches taller than this determined suitor but he fascinated her with his energy and gusto. His naughty, suggestive conversation was more attractive than the crude jokes and swearing of the local boys and his Ronald Colman moustache held the promise of adventure, romance and even a touch of danger.

For though the exigencies of the railway timetable had so far limited their outings to the ice-cream parlour, it seemed to Lizzie that the nice dress and the lacy knitting were that little bit more attainable since meeting Jimmy Turner.

There were no telegrams sent for weeks until the Monday that old Mr Tait, the owner of the big fish smoke-house suddenly died and there was a whole day of telegrams coming and going. Lizzie was kept busy delivering them while Mrs Furniss sat for hours at her table, tap-tapping furiously.

On the Friday of that week, Lizzie received permission from Mrs Furniss to sell her mother's tablet at the counter. This concession had been requested several times previously and always refused.

"She's wantin' some favour aff ye" Aggie said to Lizzie.

The following week, Mrs Furniss announced that she would be taking a holiday to visit her sister and would be gone for three weeks.

"Three weeks!" Lizzie gasped. "But whit if thur's telegrams? Ah cannae dae them!"

"Ah doubt they'll no be mony telegrams fur a whiley. The machine's near rid-hoat wi' last week. Niver you mind, ma lass. Ony yin wantin' telegrams sent 'll jist have tae hop oan a bus and gang tae Anstruther or they can walk if they want, it's only a mile. You'll dae fine. Ye jist hiv tae hiv the books richt and the money in the drawer richt when the inspector comes in a fortnicht. Ye'll manage jist fine, ma lass. Ah ken ye wull."

Mrs Furniss had never spoken so sweetly to Lizzie before.

Lizzie told Aggie about her new responsibilities.

"Ach she's richt, ye'll manage jist fine, Lizzie."

"Aye, Ah hope so."

For twelve days everything went very smoothly. There were few customers, in fact many of them had come to purchase tablet, and they tended to stay longer and chat. For the first time, Lizzie really enjoyed her job. Two days before the inspector was due, the situation changed. At mid-morning there were several big parcels, three of them registered, which always flustered Lizzie slightly. One lady had forgotten that registered parcels must have sealing wax on the knots and Lizzie had to search for the small piece of red wax and matches and a candle to melt it and then write out the special labels and receipts. Next garrulous Mrs Reekie wanted five postal orders, all for different amounts and as Lizzie made out the postal orders, the old lady described her individual grandchildren, the lucky recipients of her bounty and the exact reasons why each child would receive a different sum. Then paying for the orders with a cascade of threepenny bits, she started a complex explanation of how she had been saving these tiny coins for years.

Next, an unknown woman asked questions about dog licences and Lizzie must refer to the book of regulations before she could help her.

Then two children brought their post office savings banks to be emptied. These banks looked like small red books and were very heavy. Sadly the weight was all in coppers which meant a great deal of counting for Lizzie and disappointment if not disbelief on the children's faces when they learned the modest sum which would be added to their savings account.

When Miss Bascombe rushed in and produced a twenty pound note for half-a-crown's worth of stamps, assuring Lizzie that 'she was in a most fearful hurry' and 'could not wait a moment' Lizzie was aghast. She had never *seen* a twenty pound note before and wondered if it were legal tender and if even the affluent grocer could help her this time. As she stood holding the large note, Miss Bascombe, who seemed more nervous and rushed than usual, tapped the counter impatiently.

"What are you waiting for? Hurry up you stupid girl, I'll miss the bus. Hurry up, do."

Lizzie felt fury added to her confusion and was about to reply in an entirely unsuitable manner, when a tall important-looking old man came through the door.

Lizzie felt sure it was the inspector, two days early, with nothing ready for him. She turned away from the small irate member of the nobility and asked in a faint voice.

"Kin Ah help you, sir?"

"I require to send several telegrams. Where are your forms, please?"

After Lizzie had explained the unfortunate situation and directed him to the bus stop for Anstruther and he had expressed his anger and disgust at the shocking inefficiency and inconvenience, he stormed out of the shop,

By then Miss Bascombe was beside herself and her speech was incomprehensible to Lizzie, who still held the twenty pound note in her hand."

"I shall certainly report your conduct to your superiors. Return my note to me, immediately."

And the note was snatched from Lizzie's hand. It was five minutes before Lizzie realised that Miss Bascombe had acquired her stamps for *nothing.*

That night she and her friend sat close together on a bench overlooking the harbour.

"Ah'll need tae pit ma ain hauf croon in the drawer, Aggie."

"Ah suppose ye wull."

"It diznae seem fair."

"Mebbe the nixt time she comes intae the shop, ye kid ask her fur't. She micht gie it tae ye."

Lizzie looked at her with a small twisted smile.

"Mebbe aye an' mebbe hooch-aye."

The half-crown seemed a terrible sacrifice to Lizzie but she saw no way out of it. The drawer would be 'short' unless she added her own money to it.

The following day after the shop closed, Lizzie reluctantly brought out the account book and brought it up to date. The parcels and postal orders had practically doubled the usual amount of business but she was neat and quick and her figures and writing were an improvement on those of Mrs Furniss. There should be exactly fourteen pounds, two and six in the drawer. Of course there would only be fourteen pounds for she must provide the two and six herself from her own money.

She emptied the drawer and laid out the cash. There were three pound notes and a ten-shilling note and she made neat piles of the change, first the pennies and ha'pennies, then the different silver coins, thruppennies, sixpences, shillings, florins and finally the satisfyingly solid half-crowns. She rather enjoyed the task until she came to the last pile of coins. There were only three of those and she would have to add another, her very own money. How unwilling she was to lose that precious amount. Oh she felt bitter. That screechy, old brute, she'd never serve her again!

Reluctantly but exactly she placed her own half-crown on the pile and added it all up.

It came to nine pounds two and sixpence! It was five pounds short! She totalled it once more and it came to the same result. She felt she was going mad. How could five pounds have disappeared? She searched the drawer thoroughly but it was empty. She looked on the floor and in all the corners. Nothing. What was she going to do?

She was finished! Done for! The inspector came tomorrow at ten o'clock! The loss of her half crown faded to insignificance beside this immense tragedy. She lay for many hours that night wondering how five pounds could disappear and weeping tears of frustration and misery.

But when Lizzie wakened next morning she had a brain wave. If she could just act like normal . . . and she was a good actress.

She opened the post office and as usual there were no customers in the first half hour which gave her the chance to organise everything in the shop and compose herself. Then she popped next door to the grocers and spoke in a loud tone as soon as she set foot inside the shop.

"See that Miss Bascombe! She's the limit! Ah'm jist fair fed up wi' her! She's in again wi' ain o' her tenners an Ah've enough oan ma plate the day, Jessie. Ah'm jist waitin' fur th' inspector tae arrive. D'ye think ye kid oblige me . . .thur's plenty silver in the drawer, it's jist a fiver Ah'm needin'. Oh ma Goad, an' Ah hivnae even brocht the tenner wi' me. Jist wait' er the noo Jessie, Ah'll be back' er the noo.

"Jist tak the fiver the noo, Lizzie an' bring it back when ye get a meenit! Yer fair trimlin', ma lassie. Jist tak yer time, noo, tak yer time!"

Lizzie sped from the grocers with the note in her hand. She was breathless but triumphant. How easy it had been!

The inspector arrived promptly, checked everything and complemented her on her neat accounting and the exact amount of fourteen pounds, two and six."

"Sometimes there is a shortfall of a penny or two," the inspector confided, "Sometimes as much as sixpence and it is *such* a nuisance. So nice to find it *absolutely exact*. Now I won't take any of your change away today, I think every office should try to have a float of at least twenty pounds to be business-like and you seem a very business-like young lady."

Lizzie smiled a demure smile though her heart was thumping.

The helpful fiver was returned to the grocer within the hour. Lizzie was ready to explain how very busy she had been but Jessie seemed to need no exclamation and took the returned fiver with polite thanks.

Lizzie regretted that she could not have borrowed the half-crown too but decided that could have been unlucky.

When she described her adventure to Jimmy the following week, he was full of praise, but he pointed out a fact which Lizzie, in her triumph, had overlooked. The five pounds was still missing and must at some future date be accounted for.

She was appalled, but Jimmy assured her he had faith in her.

"Ye niver know, hen. Ah might hiv some luck wi' the ponies an' Ah cud mebbe help y'oot."

"Div ye bet on horses, Jimmy?"

"Aye, noo'n then."

"Whit div ye hiv tae dae, tae mak a bet?"

"Ach ye jist pit yer postal oarder an' the name o' the horse ye fancy in a ninnvelope and pit it wi' yer ain name an' send it aff tae the bookie afore the race is run. S'easy"

"Div ye win much?"

"Naw, but ye see Ah'm no' too greedy. The greedy yins lose thur cash a' the time."

After a short interval of kisses, Jimmy smiling fondly, suggested,

"Why d'ye no' take ower the books, yersel? Then ye cud aye work the same wee scam wi' thon inspector. He duzzny soun' a cliver bloke. It wid gie ye time before the auld bugger finds thur a fiver missin'.'"

It was chilly when Aggie and Lizzie met at the harbour the next night to smoke a couple o cigarettes and catch up on the town gossip. They huddled close together on the bench and pulled their skimpy skirts as far over their knees as they could.

"Ah doot ye'll niver see yer hauf croon again, Lizzie."

"Ah ken that fine but why are ye gaun oan aboot it the noo?"

"Well thon woman his goat hersel a wee caur an' she'll be tootin' intae Anster a' the time noo. Ye'll niver see her in the shoape."

"A caur, Aggie! She's goat hersel' a caur?" Lizzie's voice, normally rather deep, was high and disbelieving.

"It's no' a real caur, ye ken. It's a kinda wooden thing wi' jist three wheels. Mair liker a wee boat oan wheels than a richt caur."

"*A wee boat oan wheels?*" Lizzie's voice reached new heights.

"Aye, she maks it gan wi' pedals like a bicycle."

"She'll no' gan verra fast in that, dis she."

"No but she hud three lauddies pushin' her along the High Street yesterday an' they wur makin' her gang faster. She wis fair stoorin' along."

"Ah widnae trust they young lauddies, they'll hiv her doon a wynd an' intae the herbour if she's no' carefu'"

"An' ye'd *niver* see yer hauf croon then, Lizzie."

"Ah'll niver see it onywey."

"But here Ah'll gie ye a laugh, Lizzie, whin thur no' pushin' her an' she's jist peddlin' hersel, it's gey hard wark an' her skirt flees up an' ye see her big broon bloomers!"

The two girls went into uncontrollable giggles at the thought of this vision.

"Wur they '*beej*' like the yins we saw at Duff's?"

"Aye, 'beej' an *awfy* baggy."

After more hoots of laughter, Lizzie went home in an optimistic mood.

When Mrs Furniss returned, refreshed and cheerful after her holiday, she invited Lizzie upstairs to her parlour while she checked the books.

"My, whit a nice writer you are, Lizzie and the figures are a' that neat an' the total's balanced jist fine. Ye didnae hiv ony trouble did ye?" She looked closely at the girl as she spoke.

Lizzie shook her head.

"Nae telegrams?"

"No, Mrs Furniss, nae trouble, well thur wis an auld gent no' pleased whin Ah tellt 'im tae gan tae Anster fur telegrams. But a' the rest wis jist fine. Ah enjoyed masel and ma mither's taiblit has been awfy popular."

Lizzie hoped that no word of that terrible afternoon would ever reach her superior.

The smiling postmistress nodded and patted Lizzie on the shoulder, much to the girl's displeasure.

"Ye'd think Ah wis a wee dug," she thought to herself but aloud she said meekly,

"Ah kid aye dae the books if ye likit. It wid save ye the boather."

Mrs Furniss, a languid woman with little energy was always pleased to find extra time to devote to her novelettes. Besides, there was a mystery here which she could not fathom.

"Noo, is that no' a grand idea, Lizzie. Yer feegurin's that neat. Aye, Ah think that's jist whit ye should dae. Ah'll leave it a' wi' you, ma lass."

Mrs Furniss smiled widely, showing the pink bakelite of her false teeth but as Lizzie left the room with her usual stately walk, the older woman watched her with a puzzled thoughtfulness.

Lizzie accomplished her new tasks neatly and efficiently and the inspector checked the books another four times. On each visit, Lizzie would borrow the fiver from Jessie and she no longer dramatised her request with breathless haste or excuses now, for Jessie would produce the note from the till automatically as soon as Lizzie entered the grocer's shop. Lizzie even wondered if she guessed her guilty secret.

One result of the 'Awful Afternoon' as Lizzie always referred to it in her mind, was that Miss Bascombe, for whatever reason, had never returned to the Pittenweem post office. Lizzie was grateful for that, she even wondered if the peculiar woman had realised that she had not paid for the stamps. Probably not. What was half-a-crown to the likes of her?

"She'll ken fine!" was Aggie's opinion.

But the knowledge of the missing five pounds was a terrible and constant burden to Lizzie. Her thoughts constantly returned to the question of what would happen to her if someone found out? Each time Lizzie opened the drawer, the situation jumped to the forefront of her mind and she would feel herself flush. She would lift out the wooden change cups, with which the drawer was fitted, several times each day but of course it was hopeless. The drawer had been thoroughly searched in every corner. She had no feelings of personal guilt for she had committed no sin. It had been some sort of horrible accident that the money had disappeared. She had not stolen a penny, in fact she was short of half-a-crown and it was really unfair that she also had the responsibility and worry of the five pounds. She had a vague belief that money was worth nothing in itself. It was made to go round and round and at the moment, thanks to her own cleverness, nobody felt any loss. Lizzie sometimes wondered how an immense and impersonal public service like the Post office could possibly suffer much from the loss of such a sum. What would the inspector have done if the drawer had been short of five pounds? They must lose money and articles every day, all over the country. Oh, unfair, unfair that she should have to worry!

Lizzie had no intention of working in the post office for ever and she knew that before she left, the five pounds must be replaced.

Before the inspector returned for a sixth visit, an opportunity to solve her problem presented itself. It was Lizzie's own idea and it was spectacularly simple though only feasible because Aggie, too, had recently found employment with the post office.

Lizzie still needed two vital pieces of information from Jimmy and fortunately Jimmy's visits were now much more frequent than his profession required of him.

What was the address to send bets to?

How little could you place on one bet?

When Jimmy heard the reason for these questions he looked very serious for a moment and then burst into loud laughter.

"Ma Goad, ye're a wee humdinger, so y'are. Whit a wumman! Rimember tho', jist *doan't* be greedy!"

And so the plan was put into action.

Aggie worked at Arncroach a small village inland from Pittenweem. There, in a cramped corner of a tiny shop, she would, as well as purveying stamps and postal orders, date-stamp the letters from the Arncroach pillar box. These letters were picked up at 11 a.m. by the bicycling postie after he had finished his morning delivery in the country and then brought to Pittenweem, where Lizzie sorted them into two groups, one bundle for local delivery and the other for the van collection, which whisked them away to distant and unknown sorting stations for nation-wide distribution. There were two van collections, one at 11 a.m. and the second at 2 p.m.. The arrangement was that Aggie in Arncroach would address an unsealed envelope to the bookie and date-stamp it for the 11 a.m. collection The postman then took it with the rest of the mail to Pittenweem, where Lizzie located the empty envelope and made sure that it was not part of the bundle for the 11 a.m. van. Using the wireless in the back shop to ascertain the winners of the midday race at Doncaster, York or some other centre of equine endeavour, Lizzie wrote down the horse of her choice and placed it with a half crown postal order in the envelope which she then added to the second post bundle of letters, which was to be picked up by the van at 2 p.m.. The letters in that bundle should be stamped for the second collection at 1 p.m. but because the postie with the country mail was occasionally late, it was often a mixture of first and second post and no one seemed to bother. The important thing was that the recipient, the bookies in Glasgow, should believe that the letter had caught the early post, well before the race was run.

Jimmy had given her a crash course on betting and she was determined to follow his advice and not be greedy. The very first time that they tried it, the winning horse was not a favourite and the odds were high against it and Lizzie, in a sudden fit of timidity, decided to name the second horse for a place instead. It meant that she won a shilling or two instead of pounds but she felt a certain power in making this choice. Besides if someone found out what she and Aggie were up to, she felt it was better to have made only a small win. It was in this way that Lizzie quelled her conscience.

When her winnings arrived later in the week, Lizzie longed to share the news with someone but must wait until evening when she and Aggie, seated on their favourite bench at the harbour giggled uproariously as they shared out the small sum.

However when Lizzie explained how she could have won more by choosing the first horse but decided to be moderate in her expectations, she could see from Aggie's face that she totally disagreed with such a Quixotic attitude.

"*D'ye mean we kid o' won mair nor twa punds*, if ye hid pit it oan the richt *horse*?" The last word was pitched high even for the east coast dialect.

"Aye, but Ah didnae think that wis sensible. Ah thocht it wis greedy-like."

"*Greedy! Greedy!* Wid it no' be better tae get as muckle money as we kin, as fast as we kin an' mebbe *no' dae it that oaffen?*"

"Na, it winnae."

"Weel Ah'm thinkin' ye'll niver gether yer five pounds in wee dribs 'n drabs like that."

Lizzie said nothing but was determined to stick to her high-minded principles and made sure that she would not discuss her decision-making in future. After all it was Lizzie's idea and she was the one taking the risks. No one could censure Aggie for sending an empty envelope.

Several times a week the girls arranged to send the unsealed envelope and Lizzie made her decision on which horse to choose. Sometimes she was a little bolder than others but at no time did their winnings exceed one pound. As the winnings were always equally divided and as Lizzie often found it hard not to buy some little treat for herself as Aggie was able to do, the actual amount of cash towards the lost five pounds grew slowly. Lizzie kept this fund in a small knitted purse in her bedroom and continued to borrow the five-pounds from Jessie when the inspector paid his visit. Unfortunately the purse was too tempting on occasions when a really good film came to St Andrews and bus fares, sweets, coffee and chips must be paid for. Then there was the beautiful petticoat that Jimmy was able to get for her at cost price. And also her mother's birthday present.

Never mind! She found she had lost all feelings of wrong-doing, for surely she was the victim of bad luck and should not have to repay the post office, though eventually of course she would. Inklings of martyrdom and virtue started to banish her fears and feelings of guilt. Meanwhile she really enjoyed the skill required for calculating which winners would be remunerative without feeling herself greedy and the money in the woollen purse alternatively grew and dwindled in a most natural way.

She now looked forward to the inspector's visit, too. He was such a nice man and had hinted that he would put in a good word for her and promotion was quite possible.

Then of course smart, funny and sophisticated Jimmy was madly in love with her.

Life was great! Lizzie knew herself to be clever, attractive, desirable and lucky.

Sadly there was only one pound ten shillings in the purse when the flat racing season came to a sudden and unexpected end.

Lizzie was bereft but philosophically realised that she must just wait for the next season to begin.

"It'll no' be lang afore they're runnin' again," she assured Aggie.

The following week, however, two policemen and a man from Ladbroke's arrived to question just why the young lady in the Pittenweem post office was such a consistent, if not particularly lucky, winner. Bookmakers tend to be unpleasantly suspicious of consistency, especially when it applies to winning.

While Lizzie was in Cupar, helping the police with their enquiries, the post office inspector arrived and Mrs Furniss, when faced with the fact of the missing five pounds, showed no loyalty to her staff.

"Ma Goad! Ah'm tellin' ye. That Lizzie's been dippin' intae the till. An' Ah thocht she wis sich a grand lassie. An ye ken! The wee besom's been had up for cheatin' the bookies an' a'. Jist fancy, she's a richt bad yin that, an Ah niver thocht, *Ah niver thocht . . . "*

The inspector listened to her coldly for he could remember two other occasions, before Lizzie worked there, when Mrs Furniss had had a cash shortfall. Both times, fortunately, the money had astonishingly reappeared by his next visit with the explanation that it was found on the floor below the counter.

"See they lassies! They divnae even ken hoo tae sweep the flair richt . . . "

Her indignant complaint had cut no ice with the inspector. On the previous occasions he had accepted her story as the simplest option. This time he frowned and spoke severely,

"Mrs Furniss, I think I will wait until my next visit before I report this large missing sum . . . but this would be the third and *positively the last time* that I could accept such carelessness."

Happily the inspector was not disappointed on his next visit, for Mrs Furniss had given the office a very thorough cleaning with the miraculous reappearance of the fiver but shortly after that, she left Pittenweem and returned to Kirkcaldy.

While Lizzie served her four month's sentence, she learned to type, to cook and to use an electric sewing machine, all useful skills.

She returned to her mother's richly scented little house for only a short period before leaving Pittenweem forever, in the manner described at the beginning of my story.

In future years Lizzie would produce an infinite amount of exquisite lacy knitting and Jimmy would brag to his clients that his wife was a woman he could always look up to and her efficiency, good looks and extra inches fully justified his claim.

Notable Characters

THERE IS A SAYING THAT if you want to remain unknown, live in a city, if you like to be known, live in a small town and there is no doubt that a small town is the best place to study the quirks and traits of humanity. Although every personality is unique, the unconventional passes without notice in the large, busy population of a city. In a small town, the unusual is more obvious and attracts more attention, for the inhabitants have a greater interest in each other than is possible in an urban situation. Villagers are more inclined to store up and share knowledge about their neighbours. By repetition and sometimes embroidery, some of the stories become part of the local mythology, something which would only happen to the famous or notorious in a bigger town.

So how can I possibly pick out which notable Pittenweem characters to write about?

There have been so many!

Any Pittenweem citizen could tell of thirty or forty outstanding personalities that I do not mention: however the following are personal memories and I have limited myself to a few, otherwise there might be no room in the book for anything else.

In the years before the first world war, my mother and her brother attended Pittenweem school in June and September while their father was painting there each summer. The school building at that time would later become the cinema and is now the scout hall.

Bella Anderson was one of my mother's teachers. Tall, slim and good-looking, Bella must have been quite young at that time but my mother remembered her as severe and terrifying and everyone that I have spoken to agrees with that description, although they also qualify it by saying that she was a very good and thorough teacher

My mother remembered two particular things about her. First of all, the wonderful knitted petticoats, which could be glimpsed at story-telling time when Bella would perch herself on an empty desk and put her feet on the seat belonging to it. Her long flowing skirts were hitched up to accommodate this informal position and several multicoloured petticoats were visible to the entranced children, as she read dramatically from a large book. Her ankle-length undergarments were knitted in a lacy 'feather' pattern which formed a scalloped edge along the hem. My mother said she wore many, all in different vivid stripes, but that might have been childish exaggeration. Those lacy knitted layers must have been cosy as well as fascinating.

Secondly, much of the teaching then was accomplished by the class parroting facts in an sing song drone endlessly repeated. One favourite which my mother often quoted was,

"Bronze is a mixture of copper and TI—IN."

With the word 'tin' hitting the two highest and loudest notes and gaining the importance of two syllables.

Thirty years later during the second world war, I attended Pittenweem school and I too was a pupil in Miss Anderson's class. My first week was blighted by my ignorance of her strict rule that every child must sit with arms folded when not writing. Presumably this helped suppress noisy fidgeting and pencil dropping in a class of fifty pupils.

"Come out to the floor those whose arms are *not folded!*" How tall and frightening she looked.

I went out with a few others and was belted. I was generally a well-behaved child and it was one of the few times that I was so humiliated, for the shame of a belting was worse than the pain.

It was a proud moment for me on the day that she asked if anyone in the class knew what bronze was and I alone knew! She commended me on my 'gumption' and it was with difficulty that I resisted the temptation to sing song the phrase with a double beat on 'tin'.

No doubt many Pittenweem families had three generations taught by Miss Anderson. Possibly some had four.

Intimidating as she was, she always had a group of pupils waiting to walk back to school with her after the lunch hour and she seemed very jolly and human on those short walks.

Two fisherwomen from even earlier days have a place in the folklore of Pittenweem. They had a terrible quarrel, then a stupendous physical fight. What could it have been about? A man? Money?

Perhaps only the boundary of a garden? At any rate they rowed and screeched at each other for some time before it became violent and then they started to fight like cats, slapping and scratching and ripping at each others clothes. The story goes that

"... they feuch and they feuch, frae the herbour tae the midshore an' they feuch richt roond past the Thell an' richt alang the wast shore, greetin' 'n skirlin' a' the time!"

I wonder who was brave enough to separate them or if they stopped eventually from sheer exhaustion.

A less dramatic story of the shore always makes me smile. A fisherman who wore a fine gold earring had, after a successful season, treated himself to "an awfy braw ring wi' a muckle dimant." Earrings were not unusual amongst the fishermen but a diamond ring was something special. However after a few weeks, a friend noticed that the diamond was missing from the ring,

"Och Fergie, whit's happent tae yer braw ring?"

"Ach weel, Ah wis daddin' open a partan an' Ah knoackit the dimant oot o't, but it's nae matter, nae matter."

A partan is the local name for crab, that most gourmet of all seafoods and I never eat one without thinking of Fergie's diamond.

Another story that I enjoyed was about a potato merchant of long ago, known as Totty Ecky, no doubt because of his calling. Totty Ecky was fond of a drink and came home late one night the worse for wear. He was trying to slip noiselessly into the house, not to awaken his wife and her wrath. Unfortunately he knocked over a brush and a pail and the crash disturbed the hens, who woke up and made sleepy hen noises. At this point it would be better to be telling the story by word of mouth, for it is possible to imitate the hens by repeating 'totty ecky, totty ecky' several times and putting the emphasis on the vowels, while letting the consonants disappear down your throat. Try it for yourself.

At any rate, Ecky is said to have flown into a rage at the birds and shouted,

"You ken Totty Ecky tae, div ye. Totty Ecky! Ah'll gie ye Totty Ecky!"

And he *thrawed* all their necks.

Jean Hughes was a friend of my grandmother's and was liable to drop in at any time of day, any day of the week and sometimes two or three times in one week. I admit I found this irritating as it meant that cups of tea and bread and jam must be hospitably laid out, just as I was getting ready to serve lunch or supper. Regular meal-times make it easier for the housewife and dropping in unannounced is not so much a city habit. However Jean was always welcomed by my mother and grandmother. She dressed in shapeless and shabby garments and seemed an old, old lady to me but was perhaps not many years different from my energetic grandmother.

Jean had a fund of old words and phrases.

One day my mother was sitting in the garden, although there were heavy clouds flying overhead. Jean looked up at the lowering sky and said,

"Whit's it gaun tae be the day? It's makin' awfy faces!"

Sometimes she would come in the door with a small pot of jam or some shortbread for us and she in turn would be presented with some small tasty bite as she left. Her saying then was,

"Giff gaff maks guid freends."

Her general speech was much as it must have been in her youth and often beyond my understanding. Now I wish that I could remember more of her quaint sayings.

As she left our house, most probably with the intention of dropping in somewhere else, my grandmother would likely give her a few newly baked pancakes or a bunch of flowers. Jean would smile her thanks and murmur,

"Aye, a gaun foot's aye gettin'."

Jean Hughes was certainly a 'gaun foot'.

Another very different visitor requiring my unwilling efforts with the best china was Gertrude Murray. Her visits would be pre-arranged, for Gertrude was very correct, very genteel. She was tall, large-boned and handsome although she always carried rather too much weight. There was something portentous about her dignified carriage as she sailed up the High Street.

Her mother and brother owned the thriving draper's shop in the High Street, but it was seldom that Gerty, as her mother called her, was seen behind the counter. Gerty looked after 'Abbey Lodge', which was the very nice villa in its own lovely garden where she and her mother lived. She kept both house and garden beautifully, it was her life and it may be that this superior home gave Gerty an inflated idea of her position in the town. While her mother and brother were down to earth folk, Gerty tended to take on the role of Lady Bountiful and she seemed to me to have an unattractively condescending and affected manner. That may be only the harsh judgement of youth but I know that my mother, who was the same age as Gerty, was irritated by her constant use of long words which she could not pronounce and also by her ladylike determination to avoid the use of the pronouns 'me', 'him', her', thereby flying in the face of the rules of English grammar.

The day that my mother could stand it no longer and corrected a wrongly pronounced word. It was the last day that Gerty visited 54 High Street while my mother was in residence.

Gerty was much more my grandmother's friend.

Abbey Lodge was one of the first houses in Pittenweem to have a television set and I accompanied my grandmother one evening to visit Gerty and view this new marvel.

I observed that Gerty shared a vice with many other of the early owners of TV that I had come across. This bad habit was probably nervous in origin and it took the form of talking almost non-stop throughout the programme that one had been invited to watch, assuring the guest that last week it had been so much funnier or more interesting than the present one and regretting the fact that they had not seen the other infinitely superior programme last week. As the screen was small and fuzzy and required all your concentration, the verbal overlay of some other entirely different show was confusing. It all seemed like very hard work to me.

I did have an inner chortle at one point.

On screen were three lithe young acrobats cartwheeling, leaping, walking on their hands, doing the splits, very impressive.

Suddenly Gerty spoke,

"Oh, Mrs McGhie, I just do not think I would *ever be able to do that sort of thing.*"

As she must have been well into her fifties and nearly fourteen stone at the time, it was certainly an unlikely pursuit and I avoided my grandmother's eye.

Although Gerty never married, she acquired a gentleman caller in her mature years. This man, whose wife was in a nursing home, lodged in Anstruther but arranged to come to Abbey Lodge for dinner each night. I suppose he was lonely and it seemed sensible for him to come along earlier in the afternoon and watch TV. I am sure no one

John McGhie in his early twenties.

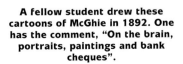

A fellow student drew these cartoons of McGhie in 1892. One has the comment, "On the brain, portraits, paintings and bank cheques".

A travelling photographer took this picture at the door of 54 High Street in 1912 shortly after it had been purchased and renovated. John is paint-bespattered; Annie barefoot and grubby, Agnes is smart as always. Willie could not be found but was probably down at the 'dubs' with Willie Lawson.

Below: "The Fisherman's Garden." This etching is the view from the garden at 54 High Street showing the Old Harbour, the House on the Rock and Calmans Wynd all practically unchanged in the hundred years since it was drawn.

"Mother's Helper."
The strong breeze depicted in this etching is all too familiar to those who live on the east coast.

"A Toiler of the Sea."
Here John has chosen a mature and characterful face to paint rather than the young, good-looking women which we find in most of his pictures.

This scene has all the magical McGhie ingredients, a bright sunny day with a beautiful woman, children, rocks, a basket, and a sparkling sea. I am sure that the model is Agnes although the child is not her own, but one of the handsome blonde Pittenweem children.

With its distinctive shape and colourful rocks, the Old Harbour at Pittenweem, also known as the Thell, forms the background to many of McGhie's paintings. It is used on the cover of this book. He was a familiar sight, standing there at his easel.

An exhibition held in the McGhie's home in 1912.
All the paintings are of Pittenweem.

An exhibition held in Warneuke's Galleries in Glasgow in the late twenties. Again all the paintings are of the East Neuk. John Has spent some weeks painting in Volendam that year, but it is likely that the girl in Dutch costume is from Pittenweem.

A family group of 1916 with Agnes, Annie and William after a swim. The older lady is Martha McGhie, John's elder sister.

A street photographer snapped the McGhies in South Street, St Andrews with Annie and granddaughter Nanzie in 1938.

1941 and Nanzie sits between her grandparents. She has just won a prize at the fancy dress parade, which was part of the War Effort fund-raising.

John McGhie was eighty when this picture was taken in 1948, Agnes was twelve years younger.

really believed that their friendship was anything but very innocent. However such is human nature that there were comments in the town and I believe scurrilous rumours about Gerty were to be heard from fishermen on the ship to shore radio.

I am sure that Gerty's own rectitude and innocence must have protected her from any inkling of the possibility of gossip concerning Miss Murray of Abbey Lodge.

Mrs Clark was my grandmother's particular friend and partner in antique hunting. She was the widow of the headmaster of Pittenweem primary school. They had built a bungalow to the west of Pittenweem, above and beyond the gasworks. It was the only new house there at that time though it is now lost in a sea of modern building.

Pittenweem rumour had it that the Clark's bungalow was cold,

"Oh! It's an *awfy* cauld hoose, awfy drafty an' cauld. They hiv tae sit wi' thur feet in the gas oaven, it's that cauld!"

No doubt this was an exaggeration but when Mrs Clark's family left home, she moved unexpectedly to a cosy little house on the west shore. This was at a time when most shore houses belonged to fishermen.

Both Mrs Clark and my grandmother loved a roup or a church jumble sale where their rivalry to pick up the best article for the smallest possible price sometimes threatened to end in a quarrel.

Mrs Clark was small and very quick and also particularly short-sighted, while my grandmother was tall and long-sighted. It was educational to see them both at a bazaar counter where one, towering over the crowd, could espy and reach for the furthest objects with her long arms, while the other, nipping between less quick customers, would bag the nearer treasures. Mrs Clark would then remove her glasses and hold the find about three inches from her nose to inspect it!

Before I had a family, I was the chauffeur and porter at these bazaars and not only ancient artefacts, but wonderful vegetables, home-baking, knitting at knockdown prices and marvellous flowers filled my car on the road home. The smell of sweet peas seemed to pervade every church hall and that strong sweet perfume will always remind me of those dutiful expeditions of my youth.

After returning to our house, the various purchases would be produced, compared, judged, dusted or even polished to find out their true worth. My grandmother once bought six heavy silver teaspoons for two shillings, much to her friend's chagrin and sat and polished them lovingly and somewhat maliciously, in front of Mrs Clark's envious eyes.

One summer's day, they were at an auction in a Pittenweem house and I was sent to see if I could be of assistance. I was wearing a new and rather smart dress, white with blue spots, and no doubt was quite happy to saunter along the road to show it off. My return journey was direct and swift because my grandmother had bought a dusty, five-foot long stuffed alligator, with fearsome teeth and scratchy claws. Clasping the horrid reptile to my bosom, I walked home very smartly, hoping to meet *nobody*.

Mr and Mrs Clayton ran the Pittenweem cinema, 'The Picture House' as it was advertised in the *Observer*, the two sheet local newspaper (also known as the 'two minutes' silence'). It was a small cinema, only opening in the evenings and it had three changes of programme in the week. The films were old, often films which one had never expected to see again. Unlike the Regal in Anstruther it did not offer 'chummy seats' for courting couples. However it provided an important slice of entertainment in the town for many years.

I suppose that I often gave my money to Mrs Clayton at the box office, but I cannot say that I knew her. She had a busy time of it as the front rows of children were often obstreperous and she must subdue them without disturbing the other patrons. At the interval she would walk along spraying the front rows with disinfectant. I was sitting further back, beside my mother and was awfully glad to avoid this humiliating christening.

During the war, there were regular breakdowns in the programme leaving us in complete darkness while the film was mended. The torches which were carried by many people in the blackout, were then brought out to while away the waiting moments. I was always impressed by the ingenuity of those who had prepared for such an emergency with cut-outs stuck over the glass of the torch and the familiar shapes of Mickey Mouse or Pluto were projected on to the blank screen.

Just recently I heard that in the daytime Mrs Clayton was a skilful dressmaker. My friend Jessie Bowman had been well-trained by her. Evidently Mrs Clayton had only three or four basic patterns to work from, but she found her inspiration in the suits and gowns of the

Hollywood stars whom she watched night after night.

She would carefully note each exotic line or smart little detail designed by Irene for Joan Crawford or Betty Grable and thus have a selection of suggestions ready for her next customer. I think that was brilliantly clever and it is no wonder that there was always an elegance about the female population of Pittenweem.

Last year Bob Moir died. He had lived most of his life in Pittenweem and with his interest in people and his astonishing memory, he was a repository of facts and local information. He was specially interested in farming and knew every Fife farm and its owner's history and could probably have given an accurate estimate of their crops and animals. It is a great pity that he would never allow himself to be taped or filmed. He painted some wonderful word pictures for me. One was of the continuous stream of cartloads of mussels going from Anstruther railway station down the steep hill to the harbour with the heavy horses steaming and slipping on the brae, while the empty carts were on their way up again. He was particularly fond of horses. He also kept pigeons and hens at one time. I often suggested he should have a cat or a dog, for he was very fond of both, but he just shook his head. He was a great High Street talker and it would be unusual if you did not see him several times a day, deep in conversation with some crony but he was much more than a quidnunc and his knowledge should have been stored on a database

A tragedy happened to Bob when he was still a very young man. As he was driving past a side street, a young boy came hurtling out on his fairy cycle, which was a small but speedy children's bike. The child crashed into his car and was killed outright. There was nothing that Bob could do to avoid it. It must have had a profound effect on the nineteen year-old.

When Bob was in his early thirties, he garaged his car in my grandmother's shed and often popped in with the newspaper or to see if she required any shopping and no doubt to give her the latest news about town. He would never sit down, nor would he ever take a cup of tea, but would stand there for an hour or more, chatting. When my grandmother had made soup or scones, he would be given some for his mother who was housebound. He was a very regular visitor for more than ten years and very helpful to my grandmother as she was in her seventies at that time.

Although he had a very fine car, he seldom drove. The car was carefully draped with several rugs to protect it from my cat's dusty feet or possible scratching. Perhaps twice a week he would unveil the automobile, start up the engine and allow it to run for ten minutes, with an occasional gentle revving, then switch off and replace its covering.

My grandmother said to us,

"It's a beautiful car but it's just a toy. It never leaves the garage except for a pint of petrol now and then."

However he did take her and his mother out for a few very short and local runs in his car.

He was a sleeping partner in the local coal business where we bought our coal which was normally excellent. However the time came when a bad batch had been delivered to his firm. My grandmother had, as usual, bought a ton of this poor coal. Each time we visited Fife, she would poke the fire and complain bitterly about what rotten coal he had sold her. Several pieces of chalky white stone lay in the hearth and she would hit it with the poker and say,

"Look at that! Supposed to be top quality coal, it's a *disgrace*, a whole ton of stones that's what he sold me. But I'll tell him. Top price too, supposed to be the best coal! But *he must know fine* what rotten stuff it is. I'll let him know what rubbish he's given me and I've a whole *basinful* of stones to prove it and I'll show it to him, too. See what he says then! Selling me coal like that. *Disgraceful!*"

She lashed herself into such a fury that I did not dare suggest that he would probably have been quick to replace it if she had spoken earlier.

The final confrontation took place in our shed, beside his car. She held the incriminating enamel basin full of ashy stones as she complained bitterly to the astonished Bob. Finally with a dramatic flourish, she scattered the offending material across the flagstones at his feet and marched back into her kitchen, slamming the door.

At this very moment I was sauntering back along the High Street, having been shopping for the lunch. I was taken aback to see Bob's three protective car rugs fly, one after another, out of our garage door. I did not inquire what was happening but hurried into the house. Then I heard Bob's car driven out and along the street at an unaccustomed speed.

Before I heard the full story, I was sent back out to buy a little brandy to calm my grandmother's nerves.

Bob and my grandmother never spoke again.

In later years, after my grandmother's death, when Bob made much better use of his car and drove all over Scotland, he told me,

"Ye ken I wid have done onythin' for her."

It is a sad tale but there is no doubt that my grandmother's temper was fiery and implacable.

George Bremner, builder, is another great fund of local knowledge. He has a quirky sense of humour and many of his stories are designed to create laughter. From an early age, George was interested in old things and his trade has enabled him to acquire an enviable and eclectic collection of objects ranging from antique agricultural machinery to historic films.

One of his finds was in the garret of a West Shore house where George and his friend Andrew Bowman, the joiner, were working on the roof. It was a very old dusty tile hat. I did not see it but he described it as 'waisted', that is smaller at the brim than at the crown, which makes it very old, Dickensian probably. George popped it on his head and the two men climbed to the roof and proceeded with the job in hand. After half an hour, Andrew glanced upwards at the higher road which runs parallel to the shore and exclaimed,

"George, look up yonder! Look at a' they folk!"

There, above them, was a crowd of nearly thirty people, gazing down. Others were arriving. Some had cameras. One shouted down,

"George, Ah'm awa fur ma camcorder an' Ah'll no' be a meenit, noo dinnae tak that hat aff, wull ye, til Ah get back again."

Last summer I had washed my hair and was drying it in the garden. I had just unwrapped the towel from my head and without using a brush, was enjoying the breeze blowing through my wild locks. My garden is so private that there is no need to worry about the niceties of appearance.

Suddenly my blood froze. There, walking along the roof ridge of my neighbour's three-story house and looking down at me was George. He was carrying what was obviously a heavy pailful and his body was cantilevered to one side to offset the weight of whatever the pail contained. One slight slip to either side would have been certainly serious and very likely fatal. Nothing could have stopped his descent down the steep roof and onwards to the concrete beneath.

I held my breath, I was paralysed. George however shouted jauntily to me,

"Aye, aye, Nanzie. Haven a bad hair day, ur ye?"

I suspect that my hair had raised itself another two inches in height at the scene before me.

Bill Black is another wonderful teller of tales. I first met him in Pittenweem primary school when we were both seven. He did not shine at school. He says himself he was a 'late developer', and he seemed to be a trial to most of the teachers. I expect he was not well suited to the educational methods of those days. As a child, it seemed to me that he was punished unfairly and far, far too often and I could not understand why belting might improve bad marks in sums or spelling. It may have been a case of 'give a dog a bad name' for he was the scapegoat of every teacher. However at fourteen, in his first job at sea, he found a mentor, the mate of the boat, who took an interest in the boy and taught him about the engine, about cooking and best of all started him reading. Bill's latent potential was realised and by the time that he was sixteen, six feet tall and very good-looking, he had saved enough money to buy a share in a fishing boat.

With his attractive and supportive wife Chrissie, who was also in my class, he has carved out a successful career, first as a fisherman, then as a fish merchant for nearly sixty years. A highly respected member of the community, an elder of the kirk, he has a family to be proud of, although sadly tragedy has touched it more than once.

Bill is a born story-teller. His vivid memories of his days at sea are fascinating as he talks of his youthful journeys through the Forth and Clyde canal, when the boats went to the west coast to fish. Then he describes most poetically the more exotic scenes of icebergs and whales which were to be seen in colder waters.

I must admit that it is the day to day details that I love to hear about.

"Aye, we had guid feedin'. Afore a voyage, Ah'd be sent tae buy twenty loaves. Mind ye they were getting gey stale before they were feenished, but when they goat a bit past it, ye jist put yin in a pail o' sea water, fur a wee while, jist a meenit, then in the oaven fur ten meenits and it was *grand,* jist like a fresh yin. Mind ye by the end o' the voyage, the last loaf was gettin' gey green!"

He pointed out the interesting fact that there were no heart attacks in those far off days as beef with its high cholesterol was only eaten on Sundays.

"Aye we had herrin' in the mornin' for breakfast an' boiled cod for lunch an' fried haddock at night for supper. Oh aye we ate verra well. We had tae, we worked hard."

When Bill was a tearaway child and the Pittenweem gasworks were still in existence, he accepted a challenge from a friend which might have had serious consequences.

The gasworks were located at the extreme west end of the shore and as there was only a footpath to that area, the coal was delivered from the High Street, at a point immediately above the works. The coal, brought by a horse and cart, would be unloaded into the large bunker at the top of the hill and would then hurtle down a long shute, fifty or sixty yards in length, to the coalyard at the foot of the hill. I have no recollection of seeing this process but I seem to remember the particular noise that echoed around Pittenweem on delivery days. Bill says that the shute was lined with metal and this would certainly be practical as a wooden structure would have needed constant maintenance. How many thousands of tons of coal must have thundered down that steep hill in all those years since 1831 when the gasworks was first established?

One day some irresponsible child suggested to Bill that he should slide down this shute and, never able to resist an adventure, Bill immediately did. He entered the bunker as a normal, possibly slightly grubby little boy and very speedily emerged at the foot of the hillside utterly and completely black. Even his mop of blonde curls was inky black.

In spite of his sooty disguise, the man who saw him pop out at the foot was quick to say,

"Ma Goad, that cannae be onybuddy else but wee Billy Black."

Such was his reputation.

Bill was lucky in escaping without injury, for any damaged part of the metal lining might have ripped or sliced his skin on his headlong descent.

I forgot to ask him if it remains as one of the most exciting or enjoyable experiences of his life.

On another occasion, when he was even younger, a neighbour was up a ladder tarring his dyke. The inquisitive Bill touched and possibly shook the ladder slightly and the pail of tar was inadvertently emptied over him. All the butter available on the West Shore was needed to clean him up!

He paints a graphic picture of the work that was done late at night by the fishing community.

Sometimes the all-important mussels were not delivered from Leuchars until 9 p.m. and each wife would be watching jealously in the dark to make sure her basket was filled as full as her neighbour's. Then the nets must be treated to preserve them. Nets were boiled once a month in a great communal vat of bark which gave them their rich brown colour. Bill remembers watching this late at night as a small boy and enjoying the warmth and the pleasant smell. The white nets for cod and herring were treated with alum which left them white and powdery and the dust from them spread throughout the house when nets were being mended in the garret. After their week of hard work, each fisherman must take his turn at this late Saturday night treatment of the nets and the unlucky ones might finish shortly before midnight, only just in time to stop work for the Sabbath.

In later years when he was a young fisherman Bill had many adventures.

Once when they were fishing on the west coast they decided to treat themselves to the delicacy of tinned fruit pudding, known affectionately as 'duff'. Bill's friend Billy Boyter was cook and he had heated the tins first in boiling water, as usual. However the two boys were going out shopping and Billy thought he would just put the tins of duff in the oven to keep warm until they returned. It was a lazy morning and the other men were relaxing in their beds, reading the papers. The two young men decided to have a pint and were much longer away than they had expected to be. What a scene of devastation greeted them when they returned! The oven must have been hotter than they thought and one tin of duff had exploded and burst the oven door off its hinges, spraying scraps of raisin dumpling over everyone and everything in the cabin. Someone carefully removed the other tin on a shovel and threw it into a small locker and closed the door where it sizzled away but did not explode. The anger and indignation of the men was understandably extreme against the careless young cook.

"We wur nearly killt! Nearly killt in wur beds!"

The phrase was hurled at Billy Boyter's head for weeks.

Bill laughed as he described the scene,

"Aye, when we cam back, they were a' sittin' aboot, pickin' the lumps o' duff aff thur hairy legs."

Bill's grandfather had a brother, Davy, who went into the navy during the first world war and whose nickname was Fly Jack. In the navy he had learned the wonderful intricate footwork of the sailor's hornpipe and, especially after a little encouraging whisky, he would perform the energetic dance as well as singing the tune to accompany it. To accomplish both must have been a rare feat of breath control and delighted his friends and neighbours for he was known as an 'awfy grand dancer'. One time he danced from the harbour and continued dancing right along the West Shore, singing all the time. How I wish I might have witnessed that scene, with admiring children and knitting women standing at their doors and watching him as he whirled and leaped past.

Bill's stories could fill a book on their own and must await another time.

Babies

IT WAS THE SUMMER OF 1930 and there were three pregnant women living in the High Street and a fourth down Calman's Wynd.

Only one of these girls was married and she sometimes wished that, like the others, she only had a baby to worry about, for her husband was a fool. Each time that he opened his mouth, which was often, some stupid self-satisfied remark dropped out. When he had heard about the other three girls, he had smirked and hoped that he 'wouldn't get the blame for all of them'. Dorothy had looked at him with the cold expression of dislike which was becoming habitual with her. As well as his asinine remarks, he was a great 'kidder'. Dorothy never knew where she was with him, for he covered up his hurtful comments, mistakes and discovered lies by saying that he had been 'just kidding'.

Why had she not perceived these traits before marriage? Had she been blind? Probably not more or less than other young women.

She had been warned of course. He was an 'incomer' and her friends had been less than enthusiastic when she announced that she would marry the jaunty commercial salesman.

"Dorothy! Ye'll niver see him from wan year's end till the next!"

"An' hoo d'ye ken he's no' *goat* a wife somewhaur?"

"Shairly he's gey auld fur ye?"

"Ah niver think ye kin trust they salesmen!"

Dorothy put it down to the suspicion that always attaches to strangers in a small town. Suspicion and perhaps a touch of jealousy, for her fiance was a smart dresser and arrived in town in a small green car. Jerry travelled in toiletries and toys and though the elegance of the car was marred by the half open boxes and bulky, untidy packages in the back seat, it gave her great satisfaction to settle herself beside him in the front and give an understated wave to her mother as they drove off with a triumphant spurt of gravel.

Even her mother was unsure of Jerry, though she enjoyed having the car parked at the door, for only the doctor and the bank manager owned motors in Pittenweem.

Dorothy's mother, a fisherman's widow with memories of the continual struggle of that life, had made sure that her only daughter worked hard at school and acquired the qualifications for a job in the office of the Anstruther oilskin factory, a nice clean job with a steady wage and a pension. Dorothy wore a nice suit and high heels to go to work and her mother had secret dreams of the man she might marry. The grocer and the chemist both had marriageable sons of Dorothy's age and each shop was a good going business. Nevertheless she would not interfere and all she said to her daughter was,

"He's no' like the ither lauds ye've gaun oot wi', Dorothy. Ye're no' jist gettin' mairried because ye'll be twenty nine nixt year, ur ye? Ye're still a braw-lookin' lassie an' ye've goat a grand joab. Ye're a lang time mairried, remember."

Dorothy just tossed her head.

Shortly before the banns were called, Jerry explained that because of the expense of the car and its necessity for his job, it would be convenient for Dorothy to remain living with her mother in the meantime. She was astonished and furious, for Jerry in his wooing had often described the sophisticated shops and entertainments of the city and the nice little flat in Ibrox that could be rented so reasonably, but Dorothy's pride made it impossibly late to withdraw from her very public engagement.

Her mother silently accepted the situation and prepared the double room for them, but Annie, Dorothy's best friend, had certainly plenty to say.

Ten months later she was even more indignant,

"Ah've *niver* trusted thon fella. Why's he still lettin' ye stey oan wi' yer mither? He should be gettin' a hoose fur ye, noo the bairn's comin'. He's niver bocht ye furniture nor onythin' an' he's no' lookin' efter ye like a proaper husband."

But although she would not admit it to Annie, Dorothy was pleased to stay at home, for she dreaded the idea of leaving Pittenweem and becoming dependent on Jerry for her happiness. He was on the road most of the time and when at home, he was greedy, selfish, untidy and stupid. She had discovered aspects of Jerry that she would never have guessed in their courting days. He was mean and had a cruel streak, though always it was his stupidity which depressed her most.

Financially, she was dependent on him now that she had left her job, but perhaps she would return to it if her mother could help with the baby.

And what about the baby? Having no maternal experience, she felt depressingly sure she could never love a stupid baby.

Elizabeth lived across the road from Dorothy. She too was approaching thirty and apart from the bump under her apron had many of the attributes of an old maid. Her soft brown hair was dragged severely into a bun. Her clothes were simple and dark and invariably covered by a print 'pinny', uniform of the proud housewife. She had never worked away from home for she and her mother were constantly occupied in scrubbing, washing and polishing their small gleaming house. Even in an area like the East Neuk, where pristine cleanliness is a religion, the efforts of these two women were unique. Not a speck of dust marred the wally dugs or the prisms of the tingaleeries on the mantelpiece of the dim, front kitchen, for they were caressed several times each day with a gentle yellow duster. The few visitors declared that it was dangerous to sit on one of the darkly glittering wooden chairs, so highly polished that there was a strong possibility of slipping right off again. Their few windows were thoroughly washed inside and outside on a Friday, given a secondary 'wipe-down' on a Tuesday and buffed with a dry cloth most other days, especially if it rained.

Their three front steps however, were their buttress against the evil dirt of the world, their pride and joy, their *pièce de résistance*.

Every morning at seven o'clock, these steps were washed and a special ochre coloured paste applied to them in smooth perfection. This paste was made to a secret recipe but it obviously incorporated some of the strongly-stained mud of the Iron Burn, a stream which lies half way between Pittenweem and St Monance. As its name implies, this rivulet has a strong iron content, so strong that its water is coloured dark orange and the earth, rocks and sand surrounding its exit to the sea are dyed a deep rust. At that time, and perhaps still, there were many who attributed healing properties to the brightly tinged water and took a daily drink, though the flavour was as metallic and unappetising as the colour, but Elizabeth and her mother were alone in using it as a cosmetic for their front steps.

After the thorough morning application, the steps were gently wiped with a damp cloth at midday, then at six o'clock there was a repeat of the first or second regime. Those blemish-free steps commanded a lot of respect in the village. No one willingly stood on them, except the youngest and most ignorant of children, and they only did it once. The front door was always open but in order to tap at it or to reach the bell without sullying the steps with a footprint, it was necessary to support oneself strongly with one hand on the stonework while stretching dangerously across the intervening space to reach the door. Only the tallest found this a simple manoeuvre, but everyone did it, even the small and elderly. Most business was completed at the front door, at arm's length, but when invited to enter the house, those who could, took the three steps in one stride and those less able, apologetically struggled up two steps, then took a long leap across the third.

Was it disgust at such care lavished on an inanimate object that inspired the milkman's horse to urinate generously each morning exactly outside that spick and span house? And often leave an impressive pile which some keen-eyed rose-grower would rush out to collect on a shovel, almost before it had stopped steaming.

Elizabeth's parents were elderly country folk, staunch church-goers, old-fashioned and still almost disbelieving of the tragedy which had befallen their prim and exemplary daughter. The shame which hung over the family was never discussed and yet the perpetrator of their misery, the father of the baby, was not unknown to them. He arrived every Friday night, laden with gifts from his garden, a beautiful mixed bunch of flowers, an enormous crisp cabbage or a generous basket of strawberries. There was always a box of chocolates for Elizabeth, too. There was no doubt that Jim Caird, the fish auctioneer from Anstruther was madly in love with Elizabeth, but there was an insurmountable difficulty.

In his youth, Jim had, without too much difficulty, seduced an Anstruther girl who had demanded an engagement ring the following day. Jim, though realising that this was no great love affair, was overpowered by gratitude and guilt and invested in a minute diamond. Before the engagement could end in mutual unenthusiasm, the girl was diagnosed as having a life-threatening disease. No one seemed to know exactly what the doctor had called it, but it came to be accepted that poor Mary had 'the sleepy-sickness' and would quickly fade away from this life. That was twelve years ago and Mary certainly was a thin, delicate creature who slept most of the time and needed the unremitting care of her mother and aunt. It was a tragedy from which the honourable young man had never been able to extricate himself. Jim visited her daily and listened to her weak complaints and regrets that she would never be strong enough to make him a good wife, even assuring her, in spite of his conscience and desire, that she would soon be stronger and that one day the wedding would certainly take place.

Only on Fridays did he come to Pittenweem to spend time with his darling Elizabeth.

Did he secretly hope that the fragile girl in Anstruther might miraculously relinquish the slender thread of her life before Elizabeth's baby was born? No doubt Jim would willingly marry Elizabeth but Mary lingered on in her sad helpless state.

Did Elizabeth's religious parents pray for a similar fatal solving of their daughter's problem?

The fact of the baby and its future was never discussed by any of those involved and meanwhile the time drew inexorably nearer for Elizabeth when she must deal with more demanding tasks than housework.

Jennifer lived in a small house in Calman's Wynd. She was a plain girl, tall and overweight since childhood with a large nose, poor skin and straggling hair that curling tongs could not improve. Like Dorothy and Elizabeth, although for different reasons, she had always lived a life somewhat apart from the giggling groups of girls who wandered around Pittenweem in the evening, eating pokes of chips and teasing the young fishermen. Jennifer had never attended a dance nor as far as anyone knew had she ever had a boyfriend. She kept house for her father and two brothers who all worked for the town council. Sometimes she contributed to the household by picking up a few shillings' worth of casual work, baiting lines, mending nets or gutting when wives or daughters were disabled through childbirth or a slipped mussel knife. She also earned pocket money by knitting the heavy fishermen's socks whose lumpen quality echoed her own figure and personality. She was a silent, lonely girl with no real friends and dominated by the three men in her life. Because of her isolation and her shapeless figure she was well advanced in pregnancy before it was even noticed in the town. When her condition became obvious, there was much speculation as to who the father could be and none of it was kind.

"There's no' many wad be wantin' tae bed thon lassie, shairly."

"Weel, from the looks o' her belly, there must hae been *yin* at least."

"Aye, but wha cud it be? She's niver been up workin' tae auld Raymond, hiz she?"

This remark would be greeted by raucous and meaning laughter. Raymond was an ancient but reputedly lecherous bachelor who lived two miles out of Pittenweem who would occasionally employ a local girl to deal with his disreputable house. Whether true or untrue, it was almost mandatory for these girls to return with some shocking report of Raymond's improper advances. But Jennifer had never cleaned for anyone in or out of the town for her skills in that direction were suspect.

The next suggestion would be that mythical demon of remote villages,

"Whit aboot the black doactor? He's no' been here fur a while, hiz he?"

"Ah doot the black doactor widnae fancy fat Jenny, he likes the bonny lassies, him!"

Because of the dearth of other candidates, the gossipmongers were forced to consider the unthinkable, which they speedily did.

"D'ye ken whit Ah'm thinkin'?"

"Aye Ah ken. Ah wiz wun'erin' that masel."

"Shairly niver!"

"That's awfy!"

"Ah ken!"

"Wha else cud it be?"

"Aye, richt enough, wha else cud it be?"

And so it was accepted in Pittenweem that Jennifer's baby had been fathered by someone much too close to her, someone who should rightfully have been a grandfather or an uncle to the baby. Dire and gloomy whispered prophecies of mental and physical disabilities, of ugliness of both face and character, of extreme punishing birth pains, followed Jennifer about the streets as she shopped. Fortunately she was unaware of this gossip and the malicious suspicions were quite wrong. Jennifer's male relatives were entirely blameless.

A momentary madness on a day-trip to Arbroath was the secret that Jennifer would hold forever in her heart, and hold with some pride, for he had been a very handsome and charming soldier from Liverpool.

The fourth mother-to-be, Marion, was thirty two and the most powerful of the expectant women.

Her baby was no surprise to her and she had prepared for its future in a business-like manner. Marion's lover, Richard was an older married man. When it became apparent that he would always be unwilling to leave his wife and give up his comfortable respectability, Marion made him a proposition. After working in the Co-op drapery department for sixteen years, she considered that she could run a small business herself. If Richard would put up enough money for stock, Marion and her mother would take over the tiny house and shop in the High street which was available for rent just now. She would pay him back, without interest, as quickly as her profits allowed.

"Ma mither will be a grand help and keep it a' awfy clean. She cleans clean, ye ken. Then when it's a' runnin' smoothly an' Ah've goat a regular clientele, we can have a bairn!"

Richard was enthusiastic enough about the shop but less sure about the child.

"Noo, ye're aye sayin' ye love me an' this is jist a' Ah want. Ah'm ower thirty noo an' Ah'd niver tell wha the faither wiz."

"Ah expect it widnae be difficult fur onybuddy ' tae guess."

"But they wouldnae ken. Jist think, Richard, Ah micht hae a wee lauddie, ye'd like that, eh? Efter a' they lassies that she's hid ... "

Marion could never bring herself to pronounce his wife's name.

The idea of a son after five daughters appealed to Richard and soon Marion was signing the rental agreement and making out her first order for wool of all thicknesses and shades, print pinnies of various sizes, lisle and woollen stockings, celanese knickers, flannel liberty bodices and the less glamorous toilet paper, sanitary towels, needles, safety pins, tape, elastic which would keep the little bell on the till ringing regularly throughout each day.

After three months of reasonably successful trading, Marion found she was pregnant.

Was it earlier than she had expected?

Did her mother know that the birth was planned?

Probably yes to both questions for the forty seven pounds required to stock the shop would have to be explained in some way.

Marion was calm and happy. Her ambitions were fulfilled, she was pregnant to the man she loved, she had a nice little shop of her own where she could chat to her customers and make enough money to keep her mother, her baby and herself in security.

For all those years in the Co-op drapery, Marion had listened to maternal experiences, good and bad and she was knowledgeable about every aspect of motherhood from the first missed period to the wonderful day that the child left school and found a job.

Without realising her own importance, Marion became the hub and support of the other three pregnant women. Marion was their mentor, and the fact that she too was pregnant strengthened her position.

Dorothy dropped into the little shop regularly for advice and more baby wool. She would sometimes complain about Jerry's shortcomings, something she did to no one else. Then she would feel uncomfortable because Marion, just as pregnant as she was herself, had no husband. It was incredible that Marion seemed so strong and happy. Dorothy felt tremendously cheered by her joyful independence. Perhaps it was possible that she too would one day discard the disappointing father of her baby and, like Marion, gain control of her life, for she too could earn her living and had a willing mother.

Jennifer, too, was able to talk to Marion about her pregnancy and ask questions that her menfolk could not answer. For the first time in her life, Jennifer was attractive. She had bloomed, her skin was clear and her hair had thickened and she smiled more. Her figure had the strange grace of the very pregnant and she carried herself well and proudly. She found Marion so sympathetic and easy to talk to that one day, after exhorting promises of absolute confidentiality, she divulged the secret of her child's paternity. It was a relief to tell someone and the little shopkeeper was completely reliable for the story of the soldier in Arbroath was never revealed in Pittenweem. What Marion did do at every opportunity, and there were plenty of those in her gossipy shop, was to pour so much scorn on the idea of incest that the nasty rumour was eventually scotched completely. Jennifer would be the first of the four women to deliver her baby and had a quick, easy birth of a large, absolutely beautiful baby boy with thick dark hair, where the rest of the family was blonde.

Elizabeth, pale and thin, often slipped into Marion's shop though she never referred to her condition. She would ask to see various items, then regard them with her large eyes for several minutes before shaking her head sadly and assuring Marion she would return another day. Only once did she buy baby wool. Marion tried to help her but found herself unusually tongue-tied with the unhappy woman, though one day she asked Elizabeth outright when the baby was due. To her distress, Elizabeth's eyes filled with tears and she left the shop hurriedly. She returned the next day and after ten minutes of indecision bought a new pinny and two handkerchiefs, but the baby was never mentioned again by either of them.

In December it was particularly cold. A small paraffin heater burned in Marion's shop when Dorothy walked in, stamping her feet and brushing sleet from her coat.

"Pair Elizabeth! Have ye heard? The bairn wis born last nicht but it didnae live mair nor twa oors. Ah'm that vexed, Ah kin scarce stoape greetin', masel'."

Her eyes were red and the tears were very near.

"Och, Dorothy, Ah'm that sorry. Pair sowl. But then she wisnae wantin' it the wey we do."

"Ah cannae believe that."

"But they niver even spoke aboot it, nane o' thim even mentioned that she wiz expectin'! She wiz in here hersel' oaften an' oaften an' she niver said wan word aboot the bairn!"

"But she must hae wantit it a' the same. Ah lookit oot the windae last nicht an' her mither, the auld bitch, wiz talkin' tae someone at the door an' shakin' her heed ower they bloody orange stairs, niver steppin' oan them mind you, an' Ah could read her lips an' she wiz sayin' "Jist as weel, jist as weel" imagine that, jist as weel the pair wee sowl wis deed. It wis a wee lassie tae. Och it's awfy, awfy sad an' Ah'd like tae gan in tae see Elizabeth . . . but Ah dinnae ken whether . . . Och, Ah'm that vexed, Marion."

"Ye're fair wrocht up 'cos yer expectin' yer ain bairn an' a'. An' it brings it a' closer hame tae ye. Here sit doon by the heater an' Ah'll get Maw tae mak us a pot o' tea. Noo calm yersel' ma lassie, there, there. Dinna greet noo . . . sit ye doon, that's grand . . . ye'll be fine in a meenit."

In February Dorothy had a pretty little dark-haired girl of six and a half pounds, small but healthy, a daughter who would be a comfort to her in the difficult years that lay ahead.

In March, Marion produced a ten pound baby, a long, plump girl with a full head of yellow curls. If Richard were disappointed that it was not a son, Marion had no such regrets.

The Butcher

IT WAS A VERY SUCCESSFUL and long-established butcher's business, well-situated in the High Street, overlooking the market place but not of the market place. A broad pavement in front of the shop enabled those conversational groups to form both before and after buying their meat, those groups which are so typical of any small town where the exchange of local information forms an important part of daily life.

The shop, started by their father James Thomson in 1900, was now continued by Alice and her brother Robert Thomson. Their sister Mary ran the household and Robert drove the van around Fife for the remunerative country business. He was seldom to be seen but no doubt he was in the background dealing with the heavy lifting, sawing and hacking required of his trade, though Alice Thomson herself could wield a strong right arm when necessary.

Alice was the presiding goddess of the shop. A handsome woman with a commanding presence, she must have been around fifty at the start of the second world war when I first remember her. She was tall with a fine carriage and an impressive bust. Her hair was silver and curly, her skin pink and white with the cheeks becoming rosier with age, as is usual with that type of complexion, no doubt helped by an adequate intake of beef.

In her youth she had a fine singing voice and was an important item in the many local concerts of the first half of the century.

Although her blue eyes and charming smile gave me a sensation of prettiness, that is never a word I would have used to describe her. She was *imposing* and I thought she would have made an excellent matron of a hospital, with her undoubted air of authority. Whether behind the counter, carefully slicing sausage or wrestling successfully with a saw and overlarge joint of meat, or splendidly garbed in black silk for the kirk on Sunday, her slow correct voice, her perfect grammar and lack of local accent, set her apart as one of those notable characters of Pittenweem that will always be remembered by those who knew her.

When I was eleven, I made friends with Alice Thomson's niece, Alison, who was visiting from Dunfermline. Alison, daughter of another sister, Janet, was the same age as I was and we have remained close friends throughout our lives. It was through that friendship with Alison that I became closer to her Aunt Alice and learned to know her better.

In the summer, Alison and I would join the other teenagers in the marketplace each Tuesday and Thursday evening for the open-air dancing. Between seven and nine p.m. a little battered van with a loudspeaker mounted on its roof would play a variety of music, mostly Scottish country dance music but there were some more modern melodies. I remember "Sailing Down the River" was a favourite waltz and occasionally there was the uninhibited 'Hokey Cokey'. I admit that I held aloof from the latter. Generally only the younger folk danced, for the rough surface wreaked havoc on footwear, but crowds stood around watching and most of the windows which overlooked the marketplace had a couple of householders enjoying the scene. Alice and her sister Mary would always be there and we would wave to them when we remembered.

As we grew older, Alison and I graduated to the dances in Anstruther town hall and I think Alice enjoyed our girlish preparations and laughing conversations. She was kind and friendly and seemed to me a benevolent presence. I was grateful that she avoided the sin of handing out criticism, advice or dire warnings. Most older people were wont to do this, in my experience.

Of course not everyone was as fond of Alice as I was. My grandmother would quarrel with her at regular intervals and indignantly take her custom to the other butcher in town, but then my grandmother did quarrel with a lot of people. Generally, having had the winter to cool her ire, she returned her business to Alice the following summer, for she sold excellent butcher meat. During the war, it was necessary to register with one particular shop and my mother remained loyal to Thomson's during the years that we spent in Pittenweem. My mother was very different in temperament from her mother and was always friendly with Alice.

Alice had the habit of adding a couple of ounces to the amount of mince or stewing steak for which you had asked, then looking hopefully at you and saying in her slow way,

"That's just a little bit over the pound. Will that do?"

The customer would normally say,

"Yes, yes, that's fine, just leave it."

Thus a small increase was made on each sale. This may not seem a large sin, but it particularly enraged my grandmother, who always demanded that the product should be reduced to the exact weight that she had asked for.

"Just imagine how much more she manages to sell in the week with that way of working!" my grandmother would fume. "Pounds and pounds! She's *certainly* not going to *foist* extra meat on to me every time!"

And she managed to make the word 'foist' sound very unpleasant.

However in the days of rationing, when the slender meat portion was doled out by price, rather than by weight, this little quirk was a wonderful benefit which my mother fully appreciated.

One of the few food treats I remember having in wartime were the steak pies which, with beef from Thomson's, were baked at Adamson's the bakers. There was a small monetary deposit on the enamel pie-dish in which the pie was baked, which was reimbursed when the empty dish was returned to the shop. How different from the terrible waste of tinfoil and plastic nowadays in the ready cooked food industry.

It was a red letter day when we had a steak pie and it was usually eaten on a Saturday night. It was so delicious! I can imagine it now with rich tender beef underneath thick pastry, crisp and brown on top with strangely delectable soggy bits underneath where the gravy had soaked and softened it.

Another delicacy from the butcher's that we had during the war years were wood pigeons. My mother would stuff them, then pot roast them and although there was not a lot of eating on them, the flesh was strong and tasty, only marred occasionally by a scrap of lead shot, the significance of which I tried to ignore. The production of sausages and black puddings was also part of Alice's weekly tasks. One of her regular sayings was,

"Mother always said not to give away the secret of the black puddings!"

I wonder what that secret was?

My mother spoke of the time that she was horrified to see what seemed to be a terrible accident in the South Loan. The road was awash with blood! However she soon found out from Alice, who was lamenting the terrible loss. The butcher's boy on his bicycle had hit a stone, lost his balance and the whole pailful of blood, which had been slung on his handlebars was spilled across the tarmac.

"Annie, he was *awful* careless," Alice, with a sad shake of the head, reported in her slow correct voice, "and there will *be no black puddings, this week,* I'm afraid."

After the war Alice made meat paste which was delicious. That was before we had learned to call it pate. As the paste had no preservatives in it, a quick sale was necessary and often on a Saturday if I asked for a quarter, more than half a pound would be hurriedly tucked into my basket. She was also an excellent baker and would bring a delicious lemon cake for my mother when she came to visit us. I have never tasted another lemon cake quite like it.

Although Alice gave such an impression of superiority, she was certainly not above enjoying the gossip of the town. Indeed it would have been a poor shopkeeper who was ignorant of the latest scandal. Those loud vivacious groups in front of her shop would no doubt keep her informed as they shopped and Bob Moir, of whom I have written elsewhere, was her next door neighbour who visited her daily to share his fund of knowledge. He was still a young man and his interests ranged more widely than Pittenweem. Altogether Alice would have her finger on the Pittenweem pulse if anyone did.

Someone said to my grandmother,

"Aye, Alace Thamsin, she kens a' that's happnin' in the toon! She's that inquisitive, she'd ask the inside oot o' ye. She jist kens *awthin'* fur she's aye keekin' oot atween the rabbits' erses!"

The rabbits, still furry, hung in a long row across the butcher's window and provided a convenient curtain to peer through, while the watcher remained unobserved.

One last tale of her failings which happened in the thirties, before I can remember. Our family always had a roast on Sunday. The meat was bought on Saturday and, before the days of fridges was kept in a primitive pierced metal 'meat safe' in the cool shed, until required the following day. Before putting the roast into the oven, my mother's eye was caught by a slight movement on the surface of the large piece of sirloin. Looking more carefully, she saw something like mince where solid beef should be and realised that a multitude of maggots were feasting there on our Sunday lunch and had been for some time! Needless to say we had something more like scrambled eggs or macaroni that day and my mother marched to the butcher's on Monday with the offending roast.

"Just look carefully at that meat, Alice! We went without our dinner yesterday. Pipped at the post by a crowd of maggots. That's really disgusting."

Alice was not fazed and peered more closely and longer than necessary at the rejected roast as though unable to believe her eyes.

"And do you not like it that way, Annie?"

"NO! I most certainly do NOT like it that way."

"Well Annie, you know the gentry like their meat well-hung."

"The gentry can have what they want. I prefer my meat not to be pre-digested."

Will I give you another piece?"

"If you have a roast that is not second hand . . . "

"I'll get you a nice bit, Annie."

Alice was serene throughout the interview although I believe my mother had a difficult time containing her anger. Just as well it was not my explosive grandmother that returned that roast.

One of the family stories which my grandmother told so well, in spite of it being against herself, concerned old James Thomson, Alice's father. This happened while I was still a baby.

Agnes McGhie was ill for two years in the early thirties. She had become very thin and weak before pernicious anaemia was diagnosed and treated. She was fortunate because a treatment had only recently been discovered for this previously fatal ailment. She made a swift recovery once the problem was solved and quickly put on the weight which she had lost. Possibly a good few pounds more. Arriving in Pittenweem in the summer she felt strong and well. Perhaps the fabric of her summer dress was more tautly stretched than previously, but she was always a tall well-built lady.

On her first shopping expedition, Mr Thomson the butcher congratulated her on looking so well.

"Do you think so, Mr Thomson? Thank you. Yes I am certainly much better than I was last year. I had a bad time. I must have looked a sight."

Possibly she waited for further compliments, however his next remark was,

"Aye, but ye're fair pittin' oan the beef, Mrs McGhie. Whit'll ye wey, noo? Aboot thirteen stane Ah'm thinkin'."

"I am *certainly not* thirteen stone. I have put on some weight, but I had got so thin . . . "

"If ye let me lift ye, I could tell ye whit yer wecht is . . . "

"NO, I wouldn't dream of letting you lift me."

"Weel, judgin' by cattle beasts, ye're gey near thirteen stane, Mrs McGhie."

My grandmother left the shop in high dudgeon but lost no time in finding a weighing machine. To her horror she found herself only a few pounds less than he had judged and immediately started to cut down her intake of food.

It certainly made a good story and she told it with gusto. The phrase 'judgin' by cattle beasts' became a family catchword.

Alice was engaged for many years to Robert Hughes the jeweller, who had a shop on the other side of the High Street, but she never married. Perhaps the rigorous demands of the family business precluded a more domestic life.

One of her stories told of a walk with her fiance along the Dreel burn, when to their astonishment, they passed several large, *very* large piles of animal ordure.

"What do you think that can be, Bob?"

"I think there's nae doot aboot whit it is, but I dinnae know whit'n kind of animal could hiv . . . done it . . . !"

"It must have been a very big animal, Bob."

"Aye it must hiv been very, *very* big'."

They wandered on, puzzling and probably giggling slightly anxiously.

When they reached Anstruther, the problem was solved. The circus was in town and the elephants had been taken along the burn for exercise.

Alice appreciated the best of everything. She had a good eye for paintings and had acquired several works from the artists who frequented Pittenweem at the beginning of the century. She also had some excellent antique furniture and china. Her clothes were always of the best quality, usually dark, tailored suits worn with a cream silk blouse, clasped by an old gold brooch. Of course I saw her mainly in her traditional working gear and that is how I visualise her now.

I always felt that Alice and I had a special sympathy with each other and she and my mother got on very well, but I was never quite sure of what she and my grandmother might say to each other.

She came to my wedding, looking like a Duchess in a beautiful rose-trimmed hat and navy suit. She would be seventy then and I have a film of her that day, rosy-cheeked, composed, benevolent. There is another film clip of her in her butcher's stripes. She and I are strolling across the pavement outside her shop. We are arm in arm and my slender, youthful figure, alas long gone, contrasts with her tall, stately, full- bosomed maturity. Her comment when she viewed herself on screen, was,

"My, but I'm a hefty piece, am I not."

But to me, she was just the perfect shape for a lady butcher.

Headland wind

On a headland high above the ocean, past scenes and sounds evoke
   emotion.
A strong and constant stream of air envelopes me as I stand there.
Pouring relentlessly, yet not cold, that wind brings memories of old.
Questions unanswered! From whence does it flow?
Even more puzzling, where does it go?
For twenty paces from the brink, it disappears! And you would
   think
The day was calm without a breeze. Not one leaf stirs amongst the
   trees.
A torrent of memory seems closely akin to the displaced air which
   caresses my skin.
That airy cliff overlooks a scene, were once a swimming pool has
   been.
Where rocks and sea were utilised to form a place which many
   prized.
I stand and gaze down at that pool. Deserted now! But once so full,
Of shivering laughter, shouts and cries.
Of happy swimmers of every size
A mirror, a mangle, the icy sea was paid for by a modest fee
Plus a changing box, which was all they required, though
   sometimes a deckchair might be hired.
Some came to paddle, some to crawl, back-stroke, breast-stroke.
   You saw them all.
Picnics were eaten, sand pies were made. They dived from the dail
   who were not afraid.
Holes were worn in each bathing suit of those who delighted to
   slide down the chute.
Lipsticked beauties sat in a pose with generous costumes and
   pointed toes,

While headlong, strutting youths dived in, some of them pale and
　　very thin.
The feet of poor babies were dipped in the chill, most of whom took
　　it very ill,
Filling the air with infantine wail, whilst their siblings collected
　　crabs in a pail,
Or sailed their boats in the smaller ponds or burst the bladders on
　　seaweed fronds.
Romances blossomed, friendships grew, probably quarrels were
　　quite a few.
Pushings and splashings were the rule on the raft,
With shouts of "Watch oot, noo!" and "Dinnae be daft!"
Those distantly echoing calls and shrieks were continuous
　　throughout the summer weeks
And it does not seem so very long since I stood here before and
　　watched that throng.

First Kiss

AS FAR AS THE EYE can see on this stretch of the Fife coast, parallel and evenly-spaced promontories of rock jut into the ocean like the teeth of a giant comb. These 'teeth' occur at twenty or thirty yard intervals and are about one hundred yards long and never more than six or seven feet higher than the sandy bottom. The result of some ancient cataclysm, these dark seaweed-clad spits of rock shooting out into the rough waves of the Firth of Forth with an almost mathematical regularity create an unusual and unforgettable coastline. On the shore a series of sloping sandy beaches has formed between each of the 'teeth'. Behind every beach rises a small sheltering cliff which varies in size, sometimes only a few feet high, but sometimes rising to twenty five or thirty feet giving a feeling of seclusion and privacy to the bay. A pathway surmounts this cliff and meanders pleasantly along the coast from one small fishing village to the next. Beyond the path the land again rises, though not so steeply, for another twenty feet to the rich rolling farmland of that area. On the brow of the hill, another straighter, more determined path, 'the high road', skirts the fields of grain and root crops, providing a breezy and invigorating walk on a typical Scottish summer day and giving a wide view of the varied and interesting marine traffic of the Forth estuary. The whole area of beaches and paths is referred to as 'the braes' and if a local says that he is "going along the braes", he will be perfectly understood.

In the early part of this century, when sea-bathing was entering one of its periodic bouts of popularity, Pittenweem Town Council, like other councils of that attractive coast, decided to build a swimming pool, with the object of attracting summer visitors from the cities. The Pittenweem pool was simply and cheaply made by using the natural rock formation which I have described. At the edge of the town two of these rocky outcrops which were about twenty five yards apart were chosen. Some seventy yards from shore, a seven foot high concrete barrier, called the 'bar', was built between them. The water from the receding tide was thus retained and a very adequate swimming tank was created. Concrete pathways were built on either side of the pool. As a the result of the natural slope of the sand, the water at the seaward end of the pool was seven feet deep and concrete steps led down enticingly into the clear water. With a diving dail and two ad hoc springboards at the deep end and the water at the shallow end lapping on the beach in the manner of all proper seasides, the capability and requirements of every type of swimmer were catered for. The pool had the further benefit of needing practically no hygienic maintenance, as the action of each tide pouring relentlessly back and forth over the barrier kept the water in the pool as fresh as the open sea, and as cold. At low tide the construction of the pool was obvious with the outer wall of the bar visible, dropping down seven feet to the sandy bottom beyond the pool but at high tide the bar would be submerged in two feet of water and the pool and sea were reunited as one entity.

Unlike the splendid strands of Elie and St Andrews, the sand on this part of the Fife coastline is coarse and not plentiful and the beach was hardly adequate for such a splendid pool, in fact at high tide it was completely inundated. However the grassy hillside behind the beach formed a natural amphitheatre and holidaymakers could escape to higher ground with their picnics, belongings and small children as the waves advanced. This was an added excitement and was usually accomplished at the last possible minute, amidst laughter and shrieks and dampness for those who procrastinated.

Before the First World War, the changing facilities were primitive, with only a small communal changing hut for ladies, but by the thirties, individual bathing-boxes were constructed for each sex on the hillside above the pool, twelve for women on one side and fourteen for men on the other. At the time of this story, a few years after the end of the Second World War, these boxes had been regularly vandalised each winter and as regularly repaired and given yet another coat of thick cream paint each summer for twenty years, just as the concrete paths had cracked and been patched and re-patched. With a chute, a cork raft and the possibility of hired deck chairs, the swimming pool became the centre of social life for young and old, for locals and for visitors each summer.

Over it, in the thirties, presided a retired seaman with the inexplicable name of Jocky Daddy. With a halo of long wild hair and a violently bright red nose, he bore more resemblance to a clown than a seafarer. He had a friendly manner and would sit through the long summer days in the doorway of one of the boxes and for a few pennies dispense deck chairs, rusty keys for the boxes and small unwrapped slabs of homemade tablet, that most Scottish of sweetmeats. His disreputable dog lay at his feet, showing an un-canine world-weariness. A lifebelt hanging on the wall, a toilet which it is best not to describe, a wringer mounted in concrete for removing surplus water from the heavy woollen costumes fashionable at that time. A large chipped mirror for after-swim preening completed the facilities in the 1940s, and to visitors and locals, the Pittenweem swimming pool seemed a perfectly satisfactory and well-appointed leisure centre.

By 1947, Jocky Daddy had retired and friendly Mr Black was in charge of the pool.

John Smith avoided the old fisherman and walked along the edge of the swimming pool towards the deep end, leaping over the puddles and cracks in the concrete path. Apart from the cries of a seagull, the slapping of distant waves and the intermittent gusts of a brisk east coast wind, it seemed silent and still. It was ten-thirty in the morning and, apart from the attendant, only one other person was in sight, some crackpot girl doing all sorts of fancy dives by herself at the deep end.

John felt relaxed in the lonely serenity. By noon the scene would have changed completely. John had watched this daily trans-formation for a fortnight. In the afternoon the small beach would be packed with untidy rows of deckchairs, tartan rugs and holiday-makers of all ages. Mingled with the laughter and the noisy conversation would be bitter scoldings and infantine wailings and behind it always a cosy murmur of the unwrapping of paper bags and the explosive unscrewings of warm ginger beer bottles. In all parts of the pool there would be shrieks and splashings. At the shallow end, mothers would be swinging and dipping their unenthusiastic babies. Weeping, wet toddlers would be rescued by grumpy fathers with a slap, eliciting even louder cries. Halfway up the pond, large-breasted elderly ladies would swim decorously from one side to the other, avoiding the seething raft, where older children 'kept the pot boiling' by climbing aboard and pushing others off with as much violence as possible, before they in turn were toppled back into the churning water. At times, by clever manipulation, the raft was capsized and nine or ten struggling children were noisily deposited in the waves at one time. On the distant diving boards, with loud remarks and bawdy laughter, young and not so young men would plunge and somersault with vigour if not with grace. Their audience of young women in swimsuits, some of them daring two-piece creations showing at least three inches of midriff, would be seated on the rocks and on the 'piano'. This last was a crumbling concrete structure of unknown origin, so-called because of its resemblance to an upright piano. In earlier, less sophisticated days, local men had undressed behind the piano. Then, with cupped hands tactfully placed to preserve their modesty, had hurled themselves naked into the water. Nowadays, though decrepit and uncomfortable, the piano made a dramatic seat for the girls in their studiously posed attitudes, those attitudes gleaned from films and movie magazines and as rigorously stylised as the movements of a geisha. An unlikely blonde might have legs elegantly crossed with a strenuously pointed toe continuously bobbing, while a brunette, a Hedy Lamarr doppelganger, might stretch an arm languorously along the back of the piano while the other hand, with raised wrist, painted nails and extended fingers, rested unnaturally on knees tightly pressed together above ankles in the same forced condition. Two character-istics they all had in common: bright red lipstick adorned every mouth and not one girl had any intention of entering the water.

John was familiar with both the morning and the afternoon scene and being sixteen and shy and lonely did not enjoy either very much. Probably this solitary morning view was more comfortable for him and perhaps, just perhaps, he *might* meet someone. It had never occurred to him that he might enjoy a swim himself.

John admitted to himself that he should have followed Aunt Bessie's advice that morning and worn his pullover, but he had worn it every day of that chilly fortnight. Today was the last one of his holiday and he had hoped, without any basis for that hope, that it would be a scorcher.

Apart from Aunt Bessie and Uncle Tom and his two young cousins, he had hardly spoken to anyone for two weeks in this small fishing town. The man in the newsagent where he had bought ten Woodbine had seemed friendly, but with the strong Fife accent, he might as well have been speaking Spanish or German for all John understood. John had sidled out of the shop with a silly smile and a nod and bought his next packet in the grocers, where they were too busy to start a conversation with a sixteen-year-old 'Glesca keelie'. John was aware that amongst the locals there was some dislike, probably distrust, of the visitors who came for the Glasgow Fair holiday. He could not fully appreciate how alien the city folk appeared to the insular villagers, much more alien and with more unfamiliar accents than the dancing Fred Astaire or the sinister gun-slinging Cagney, old friends for years in the local cinemas. However strange and foreign the visitors seemed, they were financially important to the town. The population doubled when the brightly-clad, free-spending Glaswegians arrived in July. The fisherfolk moved into their garrets and rented their modest, scrupulously clean homes to the city folk for comparatively large sums. But although the cash registers in the town rang merrily and everyone agreed that the "Glesca fowk were awfy guid-natured and awfy grand spenders", yet the epithet of the 'Glesca keelie' was always there and suspicion of the unknown vices and violence of the city, with its terrors of gang-warfare, knives and razors, hovered always at the back of the local collective mind. John, knowing himself to be a law-abiding and rather timid lad, was hurt by this atmosphere and in spite of the crowds thronging the little town, he had had little conversation with anyone throughout the fortnight.

If he could have danced, he might have joined the open air dancers in the market place on Tuesday and Thursday evenings, when a small battered van with a loudspeaker mounted on its roof, blared out Scottish country dance music between seven and nine o'clock. But he could not dance. Everyone gathered in the High Street as soon as the first strains of music struck the evening air, but it was mainly young women and children who danced the military two-step, the Pride of Erin waltz and the occasional frenzied Hokey-Cokey. It seemed simplest for John to become part of the crowd that stood and watched with smiling nodding heads. The previous Thursday, six members of the Harthill Boys Brigade, who were camping locally, arrived and stimulated the proceedings with a fast and exciting Strip-the-Willow. One of them had grabbed John's arm and said,

"Come oan, jine in wi' us! Wur needin' mair blokes here."

But John, in spite of having worked for two years since leaving school, was a bashful youth and had no confidence in his abilities to whirl the girls at the required break-neck speed. Shaking his head, he moved further back in the crowd and soon afterwards left the marketplace and was, for a change, first in the queue for chips. For when the van stopped playing at nine o'clock, the dancers and the audience, to a man, would surge along the High Street to their favourite fish and chip shop. There were two of these in the town, each serving delectable fish such as never was tasted in Glasgow and on the nights that there was dancing in the market place, business was even brisker for these establishments than it was on the other evenings of the 'Fair'.

"The fish suppers are jist deelicious an' they'll build you up, so they wull," his aunt Bessie had assured him in May when she had first insisted that he come with her and her family to the east coast resort where they holidayed each year.

"It's real bracin' air ye get there an' that's jist whit yer needin', hen. Thon fresh air fair gies ye an appytite an' ye're still peely-wally an' peakit since yer accident. They've goat lovely fresh rolls an' vegetables an' creamy milk there an' ye should be stuffin' yersel wi' a' they good things. Ye're richt *shilpit,* so ye are, John."

John's mother had not been too pleased with this last remark but she saw the sense of the suggestion and, from an unknown source, miraculously produced ten pounds 'towards expenses'.

The holiday had undoubtedly been good for John's health, but his aunt and uncle were too old and his cousins too young to provide companionship and it had been a lonely fortnight for him. He had walked many miles each day, back and forth along the coast to the neighbouring villages. He had not seen the sea since he had been a toddler and it astonished him. He had thought that it would always be much the same but he was constantly surprised by its changing colour and moods. Neither had he ever been so aware of the sky. There seemed to be much more of it than there was in Glasgow and it, too, was always changing, with days of small high clouds scudding across a blue sky and other days of large dark lowering clouds which threatened rain but, again very unlike Glasgow, none ever seemed to fall. The sunsets were full of brilliant colour which stained the sky for much longer than John had realised was possible. As well as the coast, he had explored the mysterious country paths which led inland to the aristocratic estates, which in 1947 still retained remnants of their former grandeur. John was to remember for the rest of his life an exotic glimpse through the window of a hot-house, where a leafy vine was laden with immense bunches of tightly-packed dark, dusty grapes. Grapes were a luxury that John had never tasted. On another estate, he watched a gamekeeper feed a family of stoats and the constant smooth motion of their bodies as they poured over, under and around each other in their cage, was just like water. It was more wild and fascinating than anything John had ever seen. The gamekeeper spoke to him in a friendly tone but again the accent was so broad and incomprehensible that John just smiled nervously and moved away from the cage in such an indecisive and crablike way that the gamekeeper's suspicions were aroused and he frowned and watched the boy until he had disappeared down the avenue of tall beech trees.

John was still thin though not so pale. The holiday had certainly done him good and he felt strong and ready for . . . what? Adventure? Going back to work? Not exactly but there was no choice really, was there?

In the silence of the sharp fresh morning, he felt a determination to make *something* happen on this last day of his holiday. He yearned for an adventure that he could always remember. He could not foresee that throughout his life, the cool, gusty weather, the vast bright sky and the ever-changing sea allied to the freedom and innocence of that fortnight would recur to him again and again in perfect clarity.

As he approached the deep end of the swimming pool, the girl suddenly set off towards the beach as fast as she could swim with an unusual stroke for a woman. John thought it was called the 'crawl' and was impressed but he watched with dismay as she headed purposefully for the shallow end. As they were the only people in sight he really had thought that he would have been able to speak to her but she must have wanted to avoid an encounter.

Stupid, he'd been stupid. He'd never have found the guts to talk to her anyway. Stupid and useless, that's what he was. He kicked some stranded whelks off the path and back into the water. He was as useless as a whelk. At the start of the holiday his wee cousins had collected a pailful of whelks and had brought them home shouting,

"Wulks, Wulks. We've brung wulks fur the tea, Maw!"

Auntie Bessie had boiled them up and then the whole family, except John, had eaten them with relish giggling as they picked out each small morsel with a pin. It had seemed a bizarre and barbaric practice to John, like something that cavemen would do and he had munched bread and jam and gazed disapprovingly out of the window.

That girl would be getting out when she reached the shallow end and dressing and going home on a chilly day like this. He tried to imagine what sort of girl would go swimming all by herself in the lonely pool. What sort of job did she do and what sort of house did she live in? Was she a visitor like himself? or a local? She must be awful different from any of the girls that he knew. *Just fancy going swimming on a cold day like this ... mad ...* and he strolled disconsolately back towards the beach, kicking whelks and gazing into murky rock pools. He slipped on a piece of green seaweed and only just avoided falling. He walked more carefully after that. A quick look told him that the girl still had her head submerged and he was relieved that she had not seen him stumble. To his intense pleasure he saw her turn and start again for the deep end with a complicated stroke which involved a turn of the body. She seemed to be enjoying herself anyway. John quickly retraced his steps to the deep end. This time he really would speak to her.

It was an hour or so after high tide and the sea had ebbed to the stage where the bar was no longer submerged and the water was exactly the same depths on either side of it. The girl pulled herself out of the water and on to the side quickly and easily, using the strength of her arms and shoulders, as a boy would have done, John thought. She wore a bright blue costume and a red bathing cap without a chin-strap and she was taller than he had expected. She paused for a moment looking out to sea and then dived back into the water on the outside of the bar. While the surface of the pool was only slightly ruffled by the breeze, the water in the open sea beyond the bar was choppy and small waves were beating against the rocks. Those waves looked menacing to John and he felt a thrill of danger as he watched her disappear momentarily. He supposed that she knew what she was doing in that rough water and she seemed like a very strong swimmer, but what if something happened? He walked more quickly towards her and clambered over the rocks which projected beyond the concrete path without knowing exactly what he could do. He was no swimmer, he could only just do a doggy-paddle and those wild waves made him shudder. He need not have worried though, as she was again bobbing and playing in the water in a very relaxed way.

She seemed entirely self-absorbed but after a few minutes, she looked up at him over her shoulder and smiled and John felt himself shudder with surprise and pleasure.

She was good-looking rather than pretty. Her teeth were

spectacularly white in her tanned face and though she wore no make-up, the drops of sea-water gave a magical brilliance and sparkle to her skin. To John she looked very like a film-star.

He stood there not smiling nor able to find a word to say. After a moment John turned ice-cold as she disappeared beneath the surface.

Elizabeth did a surface dive and swam underwater for as long as she could hold her breath in order to hide her embarrassment. She had smiled in a moment of impulsive courage but it was *awful* that he had not responded. Then she decided that swimming underwater might look like showing-off, so surfacing again, she swam away from the boy and out to sea for twenty yards, though as she swam she realised that it was not a friendly nor an encouraging thing to do and she wanted to encourage him. Elizabeth, at fifteen, was also experiencing a lonely holiday on the east coast. She had watched John wander up and down the pool side from the moment that he had arrived that morning. She had seen him before, sauntering around the harbour or standing on the outskirts of the crowd in the marketplace on dancing nights. She had thought he looked an interesting fellow, though so terribly skinny.

Elizabeth was an only child and attended a girls' school. She knew no boys and despaired of ever meeting any. The school dance last winter had been a disaster. Elizabeth had worn a pretty dress and looked reasonable enough, she supposed, but when the pupils from the Boys' High School had arrived in their hairy Harris tweed jackets and grey flannels she might as well have been invisible for *nobody had asked her to dance.*

Fortunately she had gone with few expectations because she sat there 'like a turnip' during the entire evening.

But perhaps she would not have been able to follow their steps anyway and in her imagination Elizabeth had conjured up such a fiasco of entangled legs and eventual ignominious crashing to the floor that, in a funny way, she had been quite relieved that not one soul had approached her. But when she had gone home and humorously recounted her failure, her mother could not believe it and was much more upset than Elizabeth herself.

"I just sat there all night like a turnip," she laughingly told her dismayed mother.

"What on earth was the reason?" Her mother asked, with anguish in her voice. "Were those boys blind? You looked as pretty as a picture. Could it be your hair, darling?"

Elizabeth wore her two long plaits in a crown which was severe and vaguely Germanic and very different from the short bubbly perms of the other girls but she was a girl more likely to flout fashion than to follow it.

"D'you think your hair put the boys off? Was it too unusual, I wonder? Perhaps you should have had a touch of lipstick too. I'm sure your dress couldn't have been nicer. Would you like to have your hair cut and permed? I could give you that for your birthday present."

Her mother was really grieved and fretted and questioned herself and Elizabeth for days, urging various adaptions and possible improvements to the girl's appearance but Elizabeth was philosophical. She did not intend to change herself. She expected that she would meet someone quite soon, someone that would appreciate her just as she was. She did feel strongly that it was *time* that she was kissed. She had never been kissed and it was humiliating to admit to this fact. Every one of her friends had been kissed. Some of them by several different boys! It did not even need to be a big romance, just a kiss on the lips from a boy. That was all that was required to make her feel properly grown-up.

Last year there had been two men that she had yearned to kiss. Strictly speaking, a man and a boy. One had been Jack, the son of her mother's old school-friend Isobel, who had been on holiday on the east coast too. The idea of a summer romance was very attractive to Elizabeth and Jack was fifteen, tall, blonde and raw-boned, clever at school and a wonderful classical and jazz-pianist. Not perfect of course, because although he was obviously less at home in the water than she was, he constantly criticised her swimming style. He also had a pronounced squint and tendency to grab the last cake or finish the last of the ginger beer. And yet she adored him. The most serious drawback was that he saw her only as 'one of the gang' and not as a kissable girl. She thought about him for several months after the holiday finished but then, as he lived in another city, his image faded.

Back in Glasgow, a young student called John Hennington had come from London to lodge with the two old ladies who lived in the flat upstairs and immediately Elizabeth discarded all memories of Jack. John Hennington was a medical student, very tall and magnificently dark and handsome with an intimidating BBC accent. He was friendly and spoke to her at the bus stop but Elizabeth was a realist and always knew that, for a fourteen year-old girl, a medical student of twenty was unattainable for any kissing experience. Nevertheless the winter was passed in romantic and delightful dreams.

Now it was summer once more and she was fifteen and still she had not been kissed.

Elizabeth turned and swam towards the boy who was precariously balanced on the seaweedy rocks. His eyes seemed enormous in his thin white face.

"Are ye a' right in thae big waves?" he shouted loudly.

"Fine" she laughed, adding "Thank you."

After a few more minutes she swam close to where he stood, intending to climb out of the water but because of the strength of the beating waves and the fact that the sea was receding it was more difficult than she had expected. Several time she was knocked off-balance before she could find a foothold in the rough rocks. John steadied himself above her and extended a helping hand which she ignored at first. Eventually it became the sensible thing to accept his offer and he hauled her up with a determined strength.

"Aw, yer knee's bleedin'. Ye've scraped it oan the rocks."

Elizabeth was a proud and independent girl and not best pleased that after demonstrating her skills in the water she should emerge with a bleeding knee, but the words were so simple and so full of sympathy that she forgave him. In fact she was charmed that he should notice and seem to care.

"It'll be fine," she mumbled, splashing some water on it and giving it a rub. "It's nothing."

"Is that wa'er no' freezin'?" he asked.

"Once you get in and swim about a bit you don't feel it much. It's rather a shock to begin with. You have to go fast to get warmed up."

She scrubbed at her knee as it seemed to be bleeding more than ever. It was a mess.

"Don't you swim yourself?"

John shook his head. He now realised that the girl spoke very differently from himself. She used the clipped and exact enunciation of the educated Scot. Just like a teacher, he thought and he tried to retrieve some of his own lost consonants.

"Not very much. Not reelly," but his voice sounded false and horrible in his ears, like a child mimicking a 'posh' person.

" I think I've seen you in the crowd at the market place, haven't I? At the open-air dancing?"

"Aye. Ah wiz therr wance or twicet." Now he heard himself sound like a complete 'ned', but she seemed not to notice.

"Did you not feel like joining in? There's never enough men."

John gurgled in his throat. It was astonishing that she had said 'men' instead of 'boys'. Although he was delighted, his voice now deserted him. He had never reckoned that she would speak like a teacher and look like a film star and call him a man. He felt paralysed by embarrassment and awkwardness. The situation was beyond him, and he wished he could be back in the village or even in the next village a mile along the coast.

"I think I'll go and get dressed now. It's cold when you come out." And she smiled before running back along the concrete pathway towards the girl's changing boxes beside the beach.

His panic subsided and he watched her go with a feeling of desolation, as though she were running right out of his life. She had very nice long strong brown legs, almost boyish-looking. In fact he realised that she was quite boyish in lots of ways, in the way that she had climbed out and then ventured into the open sea and in the way that she didn't want him to help her. And most girls would have fussed and whimpered about a grazed knee but it was almost as though she wanted to forget about it. Thinking about her swimming in the waves, he started to exaggerate the dangers that she had faced. What a marvellous girl! What bravery! What a heroine! She'd never waste any more time speaking to a bloke like him. Probably she would just climb up the hill when she was dressed and not look back and he would never see her again. He looked at the sea which was turning greyer and wilder every minute and sighed.

In the small, damp, sandy, smelly changing box Elizabeth scrubbed her face hard with the rough towel and smiled broadly. Was this the one? He had seemed very kind, very thoughtful. She appreciated that. Was this nice caring young man going to be the first one to kiss her? Her knee was stinging like the devil, silly ass that she was. Fancy scraping her knee just when she wanted to be alluring and mysterious. Truthfully she might not have scraped it if he had not pulled her out of the water so enthusiastically. But then she might not have managed to climb out at all without his help. It was her own fault. Showing-off. She knew that she had been showing-off. Perhaps it was not such a sin if one were aware that one was showing off? The problem was that no one here was much of a swimmer and *anything* that she did seemed like showing-off. Would he still be outside when she was dressed? Would he speak to her? Must she speak to him first? Perhaps he had gone home. Could he be the one? Above all she wished that her knee would stop bleeding so much, the towel was a mess now.

Warm summer evenings seemed to hold the best opportunities for kissing and as she spent the two summer months here at her grandmother's house every year, her dreams had taken it for granted that the kissing would have to take place here. The choice of kisser therefore lay between the local lads and the working-class visitors and they all struck Elizabeth as fairly uncouth but this polite and sympathetic boy looked sensitive and seemed more attractive and, despite his accent, much more of a possibility. John would have been surprised at the good impression that his awkward shyness had made on Elizabeth for he certainly seemed to her to be the most likely candidate so far. Elizabeth giggled, the *only* candidate so far she had to admit.

She shoved her sandy feet into her sandals and struggled with the rusty key with the usual panic that it might not work this time and she would be imprisoned for hours, knocking and shrieking in the noisome little chamber. However, as always, the door did eventually open and Elizabeth stepped out with relief into the fresh brightness. The young man was standing just where she had last seen him, looking at the horizon.

She felt very shy. What could she say to him now? How much easier to pretend she did not see him and just go home. Her knee was still bleeding slightly, too. What a guy she must look. She hated this yellow dress that she was wearing. It was last year's and she had grown since then, in every direction. The light padding accentuated her swimmer's shoulders and the skimpy skirt showed too much of her muscular legs. It felt tight across the back and had a tiny rip near the hem, torn when she had been climbing on rocks last year. However this was her chance and she had better take it.

She marched up the long pathway to where John stood. He watched, unsmiling, as she approached, not believing his good luck. It did not occur to him to walk to meet her and although he gazed at her as she made her way towards him, John was in a sort of dream and he actually jumped when she spoke to him. He felt terribly pleased though. She was giving him another chance to make friends and he determined that he would not be such a sap this time. After all she was obviously younger than him and she must want to be friends when she had walked all the way along the path to continue the conversation.

"My name is Elizabeth and I'm here on holiday. I suppose you're on holiday too. Are you enjoying yourself?"

Shyness gave an aggressive edge to her voice.

"Aye, Ah'm here wi' . . . with ma Auntie Bessie an' her faimly, but we're gaun back the morra. Ma name's John Smith."

He was not prepared for her laughter. It was partly the fact that a third John had entered her life, she seemed haunted by that name but also John Smith was a name of such extreme ordinariness . . . it was Mr Everyman. What parents called Smith would choose John for their baby. What John Smith could ever become famous? She could not say that to him of course but her laughter needed some explanation. Always a quick thinker, she said,

"That sounds like an alias. Are you sure you are not a secret agent with a name like that?"

"Naw, Ah'm an apprentice jiner."

He looked a bit put out and Elizabeth realised that perhaps jokes with people's names were in bad taste. She suspected that he had not quite got the joke anyway and felt contrite. She changed the subject as best she could.

"Oh, you work, do you! I'm still at school. I've got another two years to go before I leave." Instinctively she stopped herself reeling off the further four or five years of study she expected to complete before she started to work.

"Aw, poor soul you. Ah left school two years ago. It wis jist great tae leave. Great tae get away."

He shook his head slowly from side to side, grinning widely.

"Is working really so much better than school? Is it more fun? I've often wondered. Your hours are longer surely and the holidays are short?" Elizabeth was really interested, but John had always accepted that leaving school was a terrific step towards happiness and he was very positive as he replied.

"Aye, s'really, really great."

They walked side by side towards the village, each noticing small things about the other. With a shock, he noticed how sandy her bare feet were in the well-worn leather sandals and that one of her front teeth was slightly chipped. Her nails were very short and not very clean. In spite of the bathing cap, her hair was soaking wet and dripped down her neck making a damp patch on the back of her dress. Her hair looked very dark and must be long for it was twisted round her head in a strange way. She looked much less like a film star now, quite pretty but not spectacular and really untidy. It made him feel easier. But she was still very different from the girls he knew in Glasgow. More straightforward and not so feminine. Fancy her still being at school at fifteen and another two years to go!

Elizabeth in turn was noticing how thin and pale he was, how poor was the quality of his tweed jacket and that his well-washed white shirt was frayed at the cuffs. She turned her eyes quickly away from his black sand-shoes. She had always felt that only the lowliest of the low wore that type of footwear outside the gymnasium. Almost immediately and not for the first time she chided herself for being such a snob.

In spite of his accent, he had a nice deep voice and he was quite funny and he listened carefully to what she had to say as though he were really interested. She was surprised when he produced cigarettes and offered her one and she experienced a momentary qualm about the flavour of that possible kiss. However she enjoyed watching his confident and deft lighting of the cigarette in the breezy day.

They had reached her house.

"I'll have to go in now and start the dinner."

"Ye'll hiv tae stert the denner!"

His astonishment made him forget to speak carefully. No girl that he had ever met did more than wash a few dishes. A big fat Mammy presided in every kitchen that he knew.

"Oh yes, I do all the cooking, well you see my grandparents are elderly. Grandad is getting a bit forgetful now and he's quite a handful for Grandma and Mummy is in a wheel-chair, though she helps a lot, peeling potatoes and anything like that.

John was trying to readjust his perception of this girl. The spoilt la-de-da girl that he had supposed her to be when he first heard her speak seemed to be quite the wrong idea altogether, although the word "Mummy" made him cringe a bit.

"It's no' much o' a holiday for you."

"Oh yes, I have a lovely time," she laughed and he could see that she meant what she said. "I'm here for two months and I go swimming a lot. Twice a day sometimes and dancing in the marketplace and I read a lot. Anyway I like cooking and baking and stuff and I write long letters to friends. It's a change from school."

"D'ye no' do cookin' in school?"

"No, our school is purely academic."

John was not quite sure what that meant. After a silence he asked, "D'ye have a boyfriend?"

"Here, d'you mean? Or in Glasgow?"

"Well . . . anywhere?"

"No I don't. Actually I go to an all-girls school and it's quite difficult to meet . . . " her voice trailed away as she wished that she had not entered into any explanation.

"Nae boys at a'?"

"None at all."

"Fancy! Ah've niver heard o' a skill like that! Is it no' a bit strange?"

"You get used to it."

"Wid ye like tae go a walk this efternin?"

"Yes that would be nice."

"Honestly, Ah've nae cash or we could go tae the cafe."

"Never mind, neither have I. I'd like to go for a walk, really I would."

"Well, Ah'll see ye up above the swimmin' pool at two-thirty, OK?"

"I'll see you at two-thirty, John," and she flashed her brilliant smile at him as she put her shoulder purposefully to what was obviously a very stiff front door.

Elizabeth was still smiling as she poured the boiling water on the potatoes.

Really John was a very nice name when you thought about it, simple and old-fashioned.

John ran all the way home leaping over every drain and manhole, restraining himself with difficulty from bounding over a sleeping tabby cat.

He was starving.

They arrived on the cliff-top at exactly the same time. The weather had changed completely. The sharp east wind that had blown throughout John's holiday had died away and a gentle west wind caressed the holiday-makers. A searing sun was beating down on a sea that was as calm and as blue as the Mediterranean and a mirage of heat shimmered over the fields. Below them, the swimming-pool and the beach were even more crowded than usual and it seemed to John that when they had met that morning it must have been in some other country. This most perfect day was by far the best day of John's holiday. He had not realised that this sort of weather ever existed in Fife.

John had shaved, perhaps unnecessarily. He wore a tie and his straight hair had a harsh side parting and was severely sleeked to his head with Brylcreem. Elizabeth's hair was surprisingly blonde now that it had dried and she looked different although she wore the same dress and sandals as in the morning. John felt a pang of disappointment. In his experience girls dolled themselves up a bit to go on a date, lipstick and high heels at least, perhaps nail varnish too. He liked nail varnish.

In unspoken agreement they started to walk along the cliff-top path westwards towards St Monance It was almost unbearably hot and the weeds and grass growing beside the upper path smelled rank and earthy. On their left the sea seemed immense and unmoving. John found this change in the weather incredible but Elizabeth was used to the vagaries of the unpredictable North Sea climate. On their right grew fields of nearly ripened wheat and barley with the vivid splash of scarlet poppies at the margin. The dark red reminded Elizabeth of the raw patch on her knee, hardly an attribute in any romantic scenario, she feared. A sore knee, as well as being unaesthetic seemed to drag her back to childhood.

For John also, the poppies conjured up the image of blood with memories of his accident in February. The speed and violence of the gushing blood and the sound of the ambulance bell ringing as he was rushed to the Royal Infirmary ... the feeling of weakness and of fading away that had been almost pleasant ... he shook his head violently to banish the memories. At least he did not start awake in bed now with the sweat on his brow, or only very seldom. Fortunately Elizabeth had not noticed his contorted face as she was trudging on ahead of him on the narrow path as though intent on reaching the next village as quickly as possible.

"Ye're racin' away in a terrible hurry, therr. Will we no' hiv a wee seat soon? It's awfy hoat!"

He had to shout as he felt embarrassed to use her name. What if he had heard her wrongly and called her the wrong name! Elizabeth turned and looked at him a little stupidly. Perhaps because she always liked to have a goal, she had been marching purposefully towards St Monance. It was in her mind that this afternoon might be the time for the first kiss but somehow she had not thought that this exposed pathway would be suitable. It was hardly private and many people walked here throughout the afternoon and also they would be in full view of anyone walking on the lower path. In fact it was probably about the most public place that she could think of! But then she was such a novice about the whole business. Perhaps one should wait until darkness fell.

"Come on doon the hill a wee bit and Ah'll lay out ma jaikit tae sit oan."

They stepped off the pathway and into the long dry herbage and carefully descended the steep incline for a few yards. The sharp leaves scratched Elizabeth's bare legs and suddenly she felt a terrible shyness and unwillingness to proceed. What had she got herself into? Why could they not just walk all afternoon and have a nice friendly conversation? What exactly would be expected of her? What sort of young man was this that she was hiding with on a hillside? Because now she saw that they were completely hidden in the verdure and no one on the upper or lower pathway could glimpse them. It was like a little nest and Elizabeth could gaze over the sea and hear the distant shouts of the swimming pool and yet no one would know that they were there. It was clever of John to realise the privacy of the hillside and yet it was almost too suave. Elizabeth felt a moment of panic. Had he brought lots of other girls here? However as John spread out the jacket with a great deal of arranging and rearranging, Elizabeth realised that he was just as nervous and awkward as she was. Besides, he was such a slight chap and she looked down complacently at her muscular tennis-playing arms. If it came to a tussle she had no worries about winning, she would just throw him down the hillside! The vision of his disappearing into the ferns and thistles made her smile.

"Whit ur ye smilin' at?"

"Oh, I was just thinking what a nice secret place we have found, well you found it."

Just then an unseen couple walked past on the upper path. They were arguing and every word was clear.

"Aye ye're richt, Ah'm *bloody* mad! Whit the hell did ye spend fifteen shullins oan twa-three skittery curls fur?"

"Ah wis *needin'* a bloody perm, ye mean bugger, an' ye ken, ye niver . . . "

But the voices faded as the couple walked out of earshot, no doubt speeded by their mutual anger.

John grinned but he felt embarrassed by the swearing. He wondered if Elizabeth was shocked.

They both sat and gazed at the sea for fully five minutes, their eyes following the flight of seagulls and occasionally glancing sideways at each other and smiling dumbly.

"Ah'm gaun hame the morra," John finally said in desperation. He had not realised how paralysed his tongue would become once they were so undoubtedly alone.

"Yes you said that this morning. I'm sorry. It seems a shame when we have just met each other. I don't go home until September. Where do you stay in Glasgow?"

"Blackhill."

"I'm afraid I don't know where that is."

"It's near a place ye'll know fine. It's aye in the papers, the Garngad."

He said the name with a wry expression unwilling to acknowledge it and yet basking slightly in its notoriety.

"No I don't know that either, the Garngad, did you say?"

"Aw ye *must*. It's where a' the gangs ur."

He looked at her in astonishment as she still shook her head.

"An' where dae you stay?"

"I live in Hyndland, near Byres Road, near the University."

But John was as ignorant of the West End as Elizabeth was of the East End.

Again they gazed out to sea for a long silent interval. Elizabeth glanced down at her knee and was dismayed to see that it had again started to bleed. As she had no handkerchief, there was nothing that she could do about it and she hoped that John would not notice

At last John again broke the silence. The one adventure of his life, the moment last February when he had almost left the world became too important to hide from this girl. Without any thought of impressing her or of gaining her sympathy he told her the story of his accident. He wanted to share something with her and there seemed so little that they might share. First of all he turned his sleeve back and showed her the inside of his wrist where a nasty jagged scar burned red in the sunlight. After her exclamation of horror and sympathy he proceeded to give a short and succinct description of the accident, a resume which would have delighted and astonished his old English teacher. John avoided mentioning the cause of the accident, the carelessness of the other apprentice and the subsequent fury which he felt towards the man. Nor did he speak of the vast amounts of blood which he had lost or the terror he had felt, but he made it clear that he could have died and he described the blood as 'spurting' and Elizabeth's face mirrored the dread of those thoughts. She had never met anyone who had nearly died before. She was able to understand much more than he told her by the tone of his voice and the expression in his eyes. It was a brief story as John related it, but after hearing it Elizabeth felt that she had known him for ever.

As John was speaking, it suddenly seemed to him that the frightful violence had happened long ago and to someone else. He felt almost bored by it all.

It was after the story was told that they turned towards each other and John put his arm across her shoulders and kissed her, though not quite on the mouth. Who is to say who was at fault? Neither of them was practised. The second kiss was better placed and lasted longer. This was an era when a kiss was accomplished with tightly closed lips and was judged for its degree of passion by its strength and length. The second kiss lasted much longer than Elizabeth found comfortable for breathing and the pressure on her front teeth seemed dangerous. There were several more kisses and she became used to the bony arm leaning heavily on her shoulders and the breathless intervals. It was like swimming under water for just that little bit longer than you thought possible. Kissing was evidently a sort of endurance test and not exactly what she would have called enjoyable, but she knew that she was grown-up at last.

Ice Cream and Sweeties

IN THE FIRST TEN YEARS of the last century, when my mother, Annie McGhie, was a small girl in Pittenweem, there was a thriving cottage industry in home-made toffee and tablet. These products could be made in any kitchen and sold at the front door or perhaps to a shop that was happy to have a tray of home-made sweets for summer visitors. Toffee could be chopped into small chewy pieces, 'teuch jeans', which were a danger to anyone with fillings or false teeth. The same rich brown toffee could be 'pulled' until it was a creamy colour, then twisted artistically with a strand of the dark stuff. Tablet, that uniquely Scottish sweetmeat, had its simple variations too, flavoured with peppermint, delicately coloured pink with cochineal or mixed with desiccated coconut.

My mother told me of a very little shop near the harbour that she and her brother liked to visit. The old lady behind the counter made Boston Cream Soda, which was a fizzy drink. It was mixed as they waited and watched. Probably the watching was a big part of the pleasure, a sort of ritual as the different ingredients were carefully measured out, spooned into the glass and blended before their very eyes. Then as the foam rushed upwards towards the brim of the glass, the children were strongly urged to,

"Drink it up quick, noo. Hurry, hurry! Quick, afore the bubbles gang awa!"

In my childhood, the nearest thing to Boston Cream was Creamola Foam. It was a powder which came in a round tin and fizzed up excitingly when a spoonful was added to water and stirred. It may still be available for all I know. I liked it very much, but I felt it lacked the drama of my mother's experience.

As a child, I spent all my summer holidays in Pittenweem. There was a wonderful sweetshop in the High Street. I suppose there is always a remembered magic about the sweetshops of youth, but that shop sold items which I never saw in Glasgow. There were all the usual bars of chocolate and the familiar boiled sweets in large glass jars, pan drops for my grandfather, while my grandmother liked a sweet of the same size and type but orange in colour and with a hard toffee centre. My mother enjoyed black and white striped balls and I preferred satinettes. The latter looked like tiny, shiny, striped cushions and were filled with chocolate which melted and spilled into your mouth delightfully after the hard outer covering had been sucked for a few minutes. The final crunching was highly satisfactory. My mother had described soda biscuits to me from her childhood and how they melted in the mouth in a heavenly way. They were still available in my time but had a scarcity value as only three or four at a time were included in a package of other things, one of which was a bar wrapped in a rough reproduction of a miniature newspaper. I think it was called the Daily News but it has faded from my mind. My favourite purchase was the small, round, split wood box of delicious sherbet. Inside each box was a miniature tin spoon with which to enjoy the fizzy powder. Also enclosed was a ring which might have a sparkling green, clear yellow or milky pink stone and was very exciting. Although the ring was always rather loose on my small finger, I thought it the greatest treasure trove. Occasionally, I was allowed a packet of brilliantly coloured Tooty Frooty chewing gum, a new and daring product. My grandmother's greatest fear was that I would swallow it in a moment of forgetfulness and perhaps suffer unknown agonies.

"Have you finished with that chewing gum yet, my pet? Now, my jewel, you will remember to spit that out when you don't want it any more. Will you remember that? It would be very bad for your tummy if you swallowed it."

As far as I remember, I never did swallow it to find out if there were grave consequences. It tasted delicious only for the first few moments, I am afraid, and then became just as tasteless as ordinary chewing gum.

My grandmother's worries about my safety extended to the silver paper in which chocolate bars were wrapped. She was convinced that the ingestion of the smallest piece of silver paper was almost certainly fatal. Quite often a piece of chocolate would be snatched from my hand just as I was about to bite it:

"I thought I saw a piece of silver paper there, darling, but it's fine now."

The ice cream in this shop was very good and had generous additions of 'raspberry' dashed over it

Just as important to me as the confectionery was the fact that behind the counter was a *very handsome young man.*

Willie Watt was dark and like a film star in my six-year-old opinion. It is possible that he bore a similarity to Richard Greene, a real film star that I much admired. I certainly thought so and in my daydreams, could hardly distinguish between them.

Although it must have been a rather small shop, there were two or three little tables for those who wished to sit and eat their ice with a spoon or perhaps have an ice cream drink, when a scoop of ice cream was added to a large tumbler of ginger beer or other fizzy drink, then stirred with a long spoon but never stirred too much, or all the ice cream would disappear. That was a favourite 'special treat'.

Just recently I saw an old photograph of this shop and was surprised to see a striped pole above the front door, advertising that barbering facilities were available inside. That must have taken place in some tiny inner sanctuary and I was never aware of this service as a child, but perhaps I was too intent on my sherbet to notice.

The photo also showed that the shop was a mere appendage of the ancient and elegant Kelly Lodging, which we always called the 'castle'. Built, like a wen, in the front courtyard of this historic building, the tiny premises must certainly have been a very cramped environment for such a varied business.

Across the road at the top of the Water Wynd, was another ice-cream shop, the Italian owner was known as Dom. This shop also offered snooker tables to those who searched for more sophistication than ice cream provided. Then Brattesani's cafe in Anstruther was another popular meeting place. Of course neither could compare with Jannetta's splendid South Street establishment in St Andrews, which had a proper ice cream parlour, a fish and chip shop next door, three snooker tables, card-playing and illicit gambling in the back premises, with possibly a few bottles of wine enjoyed. Sadly, at the start of the second world war, these men of Italian extraction were rounded up and interned, in spite of the fact that many of them had been born here and their fathers before them. In some instances the wives kept the shops open throughout the war, selling sweets and cigarettes, for ice cream was one of the luxuries which disappeared for the duration. The Water Wynd sweet shop became the canteen for the Polish soldiers who were billeted in Pittenweem during the war years.

Anstruther had a tiny sweet shop and cafe opposite the Regal cinema. Occasionally my grandmother would have a cup of tea and conversation there while I had an ice. Perhaps she was friendly with the lady who owned the shop but she probably chatted with everyone. There was a minute courtyard at the back and I think we sat out there, perhaps not, but I was certainly outside and stood entranced, listening to the sound of what seemed like hundreds of birds chirping. I could not help smiling because they sounded so happy. I was listening to the sound of the aviary belonging to Dr Armour, who lived next door and bred budgerigars. I can always bring to mind the stillness of a hot day and the unexpected clamour of the birds. It is one of my most special memories. The doctor was an interesting man who had been involved in the very early days of human flight. Forty years later I would become friendly with old Mr Band, who kept the garage in Anstruther. He talked of the flying adventures he had shared with the doctor and also the wonderful aviary.

After the war, ice cream made a welcome come-back.

Grocers and newsagents were selling Lyons and Walls ice-cream in large and small blocks, but I disliked it intensely, to me it tasted too rich and ersatz. There were rumours that it contained whale oil! Nothing can compare with an old-fashioned cone or slider, eaten as one walks along the street on a summers day.

John Paterson started a small ice cream factory at the west end of the High Street and did very well indeed with two outlets, one at the factory and the other in the Water Wynd shop. He also supplied several Fife shops and his ice cream cart was parked above the busy swimming pool throughout the summer. How delicious his cones were after the years of deprivation.

I expect that the hotels offered lunch in the East Neuk before the war, but it was only when we went to St Andrews for the day that we ate out in Fife. It was generally the Tudor cafe that we chose and I liked that because it seemed rather English, almost foreign! It had a cuckoo clock, the only one that I had ever seen. Sometimes we chose the more formal Victoria cafe where Brown Windsor soup was always the first course.

In Pittenweem, the two High Street bakers, Adamson and Watt had modest tearooms I believe, though I was never in them. They both sold very delicious cakes, but we bought in the shop and ate them in our own garden.

The fish and chip shop that I remember in my early childhood seemed terribly tiny, even to a small child. The counter bent around a corner, which seemed strange and I liked the pile of twisted paper pokes that were made up and ready to be filled with chips. I enjoyed watching the whole process, with the sliding metal doors to keep the chips hot and the opening doors above the hot fat where the chips were chucked in. The opening and shutting of these doors seemed a mysterious and fascinating occupation, one which I might like to pursue when I was an adult.

There were two fish and chip shops in the High Street in the forties and fifties. The shop nearest the town clock had a very primitive seating area, with plain scrubbed wooden tables and benches. Nevertheless it was a little more special to sit down and very handy for visitors if it were raining. By the fifties, the other shop, which belonged to Mrs Taylor, had turned the adjoining shop into a sweet shop and cafe. It was called the Arbour Cafe and had a primitive mural of Pittenweem harbour inside. I was never sure if the picture and the name indicated a play on words, but probably not. It was a very nice place to be taken for a cup of coffee. I am not sure whether there was food other than fish and chips available. The fish suppers were excellent at either shop so one tended to choose the least busy to make a purchase. In the days of the influx of the big city holiday-makers, both shops would be very busy throughout the summer, especially after dancing in the market place finished or after the early show at the cinema.

Mrs Taylor must have had a wonderful garden because on my first visit to her shop each summer of the fifties, she would present me with a beautiful bunch of mixed flowers for my mother to paint. No matter how many were waiting for their suppers, she would leave the shop and return with a newly plucked bouquet for me.

In the seventies and eighties only one shop remained but it had a reputation for gourmet fish suppers.

As well as using fresh fish and local potatoes, the owner, Peter, took infinite care in preparation. He was an artist and it was educational to watch the way that he delicately dipped each fillet, coating it with the exact amount of batter. When the fish was cooked, it was placed on end to drain off fat, with an almost maternal care. All his dedication was worth it because the suppers were absolutely perfect and customers came from all over Fife to buy. The work was slow, because perfection cannot be achieved in a hurry and the queues were long. Sometimes one might wait forty five minutes to be served. However his reputation was international, for I have met people in London and Toronto who knew of Peter's fine Pittenweem fish and chips.

Today you can still buy the very best of fish suppers at the end of Pittenweem High Street and nowadays the service is prompt.

In the sixties, with the more affluent times, it became apparent that something more sophisticated than fish suppers was required.

In Anstruther, Mr Clark had a licensed grocer's shop, seven daughters and a clear view of the East Neuk's changing economic situation. He bought the old manse and turned it into a thriving restaurant with function rooms, just at the time that the fishing industry was booming. "The Craw's Nest" was the brilliant name chosen for his project and there was a French chef, dinner dances, cocktails, a perfect venue for weddings, especially silver and gold weddings which were celebrated in style, committee meetings, then dances and office outings. It was a marvellous addition to the social life of the area.

It was just what the East Neuk had been waiting for!

Mr Clark joked that he had only started the business in order to save himself money, as the seven weddings that were bound to happen in the family would bankrupt him otherwise. He lived to see his seven daughters marry and at the last wedding, all the girls walked down the stairs in their wedding gowns. What a marvellous sight it must have been.

Also, very unusually, the Queen graced the Craw's Nest with her presence for a meal.

We took my grandmother along for dinner several times and the food was very delicious though always rather too much for her, as she was by then a very old lady. She enjoyed the experience I think. Mr Clark would always come to speak to her and assure her that he would send a meal along to Pittenweem any time she liked to phone up. I think that she must have known him in her golfing days.

In my daughters' childhood the High Street sweet shop was kept by Mr and Mrs Imrie, who seemed to me to have the patience of saints as they waited for slow youthful decisions to be made. As well as boxes of fine chocolates for adult tastes, their shop had an excellent range of low price items and the Saturday allowance could be stretched to buy a wide selection.

Mr Imrie was also a photographer and took my first passport photograph.

Nowadays, supermarkets thrive, every merchant sells sweets, gift shops serve exotic soup and toasted sandwiches, pubs and hotels provide 'two for the price of one' tasty meals, Chinese and Indian restaurants are scattered all over Fife and those unique shops of long ago, slightly amateurish and possibly somewhat unhygienic, but so very friendly, have nearly all disappeared.

Luckily, in Pittenweem we still have a very charming, old-fashioned sweetie shop at the harbour which I visit with my grandchildren. It sells Jannetta's delicious ice cream in various flavours and the shelves are filled with nostalgic glass jars of boilings, while at a suitably low level, liquorice straps, sherbert dabs, gob stoppers, fruit chews and all sorts of forgotten delicacies are temptingly laid out.

While the children decide which flavour of ice-cream they want, I look around the little shop with a comfortable feeling that life has not changed so very much after all.

The Grocer's Flitting

I WAS NINETEEN AND on holiday in the East Neuk of Fife, that summer of nearly fifty years ago. My grandmother, after my grandfather's death, had moved to the holiday house, transferring her infinite grumbles and aggressions, together with her undoubted fascinations, from one side of Scotland to the other. A difficult and complex woman, my grandmother, and although her strong personality no doubt had a kindly, tender and generous side, this aspect was most likely to manifest itself outwith the family circle.

Now, as a permanent inhabitant of the town, she had become more involved socially than she had been as a summer visitor and she took especial pleasure in winkling out the weaknesses and small failings of the village community and turning them into a good story.

An inveterate talker, she was prepared to hold the floor until late into the night and my mother and I became her captive audience as soon as we arrived in Fife. As well as being charming and amusing, she was sarcastic, superior, malicious and quick to take offence. Many anecdotes concerned disagreements and quarrels and one evening, my mother laughed gently, as her mother detailed yet another quarrel that she had had with a shopkeeper.

"What are you laughing at?

My grandmother glared her gorgon glare. This was a story to demand our sympathy for the iniquities she had suffered and my mother should not have laughed. She did not improve matters by explaining,

"Och, well, I was just wondering if there was anyone left in town that you *were* still speaking to."

My grandmother's face changed to the stony stare which I dreaded. She turned her head slowly towards the fire, took a deep breath, exhaled with slow significance and said no more. Her right foot tapped an ominous 4/4 beat and in silence we escaped to bed, for it was after 2 a.m.

There were friends that my grandmother made and kept, of course. Rather unlikely friends they often seemed to me in my snobbish young days. It did not occur to me then that their very shortcomings were what attracted my grandmother and brought grist to her conversational mill. My mind was not a complex one but she revelled in the unconventional and outrageous.

One such friend was Mrs Dobson, a diminutive lady from the Borders who had arrived in the town two years previously to take over the grocer's shop.

The previous owners of the old-fashioned Italian warehouse, Mr and Mrs Gordon, had been good friends and interesting people. There was a sophisticated Miss Gordon, who painted her toenails and went abroad to teach. When life was simple and innocent, the very word 'abroad' made me shiver with excitement and her scarlet toes in leather thong sandals seemed as exotic as a Hollywood musical.

After the Gordons moved away, my grandmother continued to be friendly with the new grocers, whether from convenience or inertia, I am not sure.

Though under five feet tall, Mrs Dobson was a dominating matriarch who issued orders that expected and claimed obedience. She had a son who 'travelled', and two daughters, one with a husband who worked mainly out of town. They all spoke with a strong unfamiliar accent, of which I understood less than half and at different times, they all helped in the shop. In the brilliance of their small mother's personality, they seemed a shadowy bunch.

There was a Mr Dobson, a silent and faded man who seldom appeared.

In fact at this distance of time, I almost wonder if I imagined him.

When Mrs Dobson spoke, she cocked her head to the side coquettishly and the strange vowels seemed forced from her little pursed mouth. She would engage customers in conversation, while one of her family served them. She knew where every article was and what it cost and would deal with the local gossip, while simultaneously delivering a continuous stream of directions as to cutting, weighing, wrapping the goods. If something were not available, she knew when it would be in. She certainly made a business-like impression.

Mrs Dobson was in our house regularly that first summer and we visited them in return, several times. They were boring visits for a teenager and no teenager would contemplate it nowadays, but I was expected to attend and dutifully I did.

I remember the contrast of Mrs Dobson's tiny plump figure with my tall stately, deep-bosomed grandmother, as they walked around our garden. Mrs Dobson was very interested in gardens and indeed in all sorts of skills and crafts. As they spoke the small woman was forced to look upwards and she did it with a charming eagerness, like a bright three-year-old anxious to be considered a good girl, while my grandmother inclined her head graciously to catch those unfamiliar accents.

Later, my grandmother described their conversation.

"Mrs McGhie, div ye smoke?"

As my grandmother had a Gold Flake poised in her elegant hand at the time, she was at a loss.

"Smoke, ye ken. Smokin' on yokes, like. Smokin' on wee babies' dresses . . . "

At last my grandmother understood.

"Oh smocking! No, I've never tried smocking. Have you?"

"Naw, but I'd like tae. Ah thought ye micht teach me."

"No I'm sorry . . . I have never . . . "

"Tattin'? Kin ye dae tattin' thin?"

A glottal stop deprived the word of all but the first T and it sounded completely foreign to my grandmother.

"I beg your pardon?"

"Tattin'. D'ye ken hoo tae tat?"

"No I'm sorry. That's a mystery to me."

"Ah'll teach ye then."

And Mrs Dobson set herself to teach the ancient art of tatting to three generations.

I was an unwilling pupil and I do not think my mother was much keener, but there was no gainsaying our determined teacher. She came daily for a week and insisted on our practising. I should explain that tatting is a type of fine knotting, rather like macramé on a minuscule scale. We used thin crochet thread and a little shuttle less than two inches long.

It must have been unrewarding for Mrs Dobson, because, although we were all competent knitters and crochet experts, this unexciting and fiddly skill completely eluded us. The fact that not one of us had any motivation to learn must have been a grave handicap. There is a necessity to keep the work sliding on the main thread but none of us could do this. We produced knotted little bundles of thread and seemed unable to understand where we had gone wrong. We tried but we were *dunderheads* at tatting. Mrs Dobson's rhythmic shuttle movements looked simple and elegant and very quickly she produced several inches of lacy edging, though what one was to do with it puzzled me. It seemed unattractive as well as difficult. But how did she do it? We would all start again and once more produce pitiful bunches only fit for the cat to chase.

Like any good teacher, she was infinitely supportive.

"Aye. Ye're getting' it noo. Ah kin jist see the pawtrin there!"

I do not know how often she made this optimistic remark, but at the end of the week the three of us suddenly all broke into helpless laughter. It was so patently untrue. Mrs Dobson urged that we only needed practice, but our family was never going to learn how to tat and the lessons stopped.

At that time my mother would amuse her friends by telling their fortune, either with cards or tea leaves. She herself had no belief in the supernatural, but she could imagine a good dramatic story and people enjoyed it as a party trick. When Mrs Dobson heard that my mother could 'read the tea-cups' she was insistent that Annie would read her fortune immediately.

"Now you're not to take this seriously, Mrs Dobson, it's just a bit of fun. I don't have any occult powers or anything like that. I don't believe in that sort of thing. Are you really sure, now? Oh very well. Turn your cup upside down in your saucer, then twist it round three times clockwise and make a wish."

I watched my mother gaze into the cup and bite her lip as though thinking deeply. She certainly gave the impression of tapping into secret knowledge. The silent room was heavy with expectancy and I hardly breathed. When she spoke, her speech was more deliberate than usual and she laid an emphasis on some words. The effect was excellent.

"There is *someone* coming to visit you. Quite soon, I think. He'll bring a present . . . *and* . . . a bit of *unexpected news* . . . quite *nice* news, I would say."

I knew this was all balderdash but Mrs Dobson nodded her head seriously.

"Ah winder wha' tha'll be?" she whispered.

"Then . . . you are going a trip yourself soon. And you're a bit *worried* about that. There's some *problem* . . . someone wants you to *do* something that *you* don't want to do. But you should listen to their advice. *It's good advice.* And I'm pretty sure your wish will come true . . . or *part* of it will, at any rate"

I could not but admire the confidence with which my mother delivered this rigmarole and it was very obvious that her listener was completely carried away.

The cup and saucer were removed and the atmosphere of the room had returned to normal when Mrs Dobson spoke,

"Ah'm gan tae Jersey next month tae see ma suster." After a long pause she continued, "An' thur a' at me tae ging in an aeryplane but A'm feart . . . but seein' as whit the tea leaves ur sayin' like Ah shud tak ma freend's advice, Ah'll mebbe jist flee doon efter a'. But Ah'm still wunnerin' wha thet veesitor is?"

After she had left my mother reproached herself.

" Poor wee soul. What if she goes in a plane and it crashes? It'll be my fault!"

"Nonsense! But did you really see all that in her cup?" I asked.

"Of course not! There were hardly any tea leaves left to see. It was mostly sugar. I just made it up as I went along."

Within a week, a cousin unexpectedly arrived to visit Mrs Dobson and brought her a green glass vase as well as news of his engagement. Also a large honeysuckle bush in her garden, which had looked quite dead, suddenly started to bloom and that was her private wish fulfilled.

"I'm reading no more cups," vowed my mother, but such a successful spaewife was not allowed to retire and she read teacups and laid out the cards for Mrs Dobson many times that summer, though never again with such success.

That same summer, we had a meal with the Dobsons in the large house above the grocer's shop. 'High tea' it was designated and it was certainly a high point in my experience. At that time there was still rationing and food shortages and as a lanky, energetic fourteen-year-old, I almost never felt that I had quite enough to eat, but high tea at the Dobson's was a feast to remember.

The scrambled eggs were served on toast and tasted as no scrambled eggs had tasted to me before. Ambrosia! Afterwards there were home baked scones and pancakes with unlimited butter and jam to put on them. A noble piece of cheese sat there too. An iced sponge, biscuits and a rich fruit cake completed the table. I had never seen anything like it and no doubt did it complete justice.

When we got home I asked why the scrambled eggs were so particularly delicious, but I was ignored.

"Have you ever seen the like? Astonishing! Absolutely astonishing!"

My mother's large eyes were certainly wide in astonishment but her mother was more matter-of-fact.

"Such extravagance! That meal never came out of their own rations! *They* won't last long, I'm afraid. They've never had a business before and they've *no idea* how to run it."

My grandmother's voice held the echo of doom and she shook her head sadly, but she also had an indefinable air of satisfaction.

My mother shook her head too and laughed her gentle ironic laugh.

"How do they manage? And they've got that big family. Do they eat like that all the time?"

"It's a wonder there's any rations left for the customers."

Once more I asked my question about the scrambled eggs. Why were they so good?

"Oh, butter! Just loads of butter. The toast was *drenched* in butter. And plenty of eggs too of course, cooked in tons of butter. Nothing skimped. Mind you, it was like old times," my mother paused nostalgically, "but I don't know if I could deal with such rich stuff now. My stomach feels overloaded."

"Mine too."

And my grandmother belched loudly and smiled broadly. Her bodily functions gave her great pleasure.

Within a week, Dobson's was unable to supply the rightful rations to their customers. They had run short of the basics!

It had never happened before. The Gordons had faithfully kept their customers' trust throughout all those hard years of the war and now these newcomers could not fulfil their obligations! The village was agog. Some maintained that they "had seen it coming". Many expressed their belief that the Dobsons would 'do a bunk'.

At that time, the weekly allowance of butter, bacon, cheese and sugar was so modest that even the canniest housewife had no store to fall back on and, with the necessity of registering at one particular shop, there was no possibility of buying these commodities elsewhere.

It was a scandal and a disaster!

Hungry fishermen, starving farmworkers and their vociferous

wives were incensed and those loud voices, trained to rise above shrieking east coast gales, were heard complaining in the High Street. Dobson's drew down its blinds and closed its big wooden storm doors and no member of the family was seen. Only the owners of the two fish and chip shops, who did a roaring trade for a week, were happy.

At first, application was made to the Food Office in Anstruther, then expensive and difficult phone calls were made to the Food Ministry in London.

A week went past, then, after a big black car had been parked outside the grocer's for three hours, a van delivered supplies. Next day, Dobson's opened its doors to the public and resumed trading. Whether they were fined or only warned, we never found out, because it was never mentioned, although Mrs Dobson popped along to see us that night as cheerful and talkative as usual, her tantalising little shuttle effortlessly producing yards of coarse narrow lace.

The following winter, there was a terrible rumour in the town that Mrs Dobson's daughter had been accused of embezzlement in Leven, but Mrs Dobson explained that it was a misunderstanding. I could visualise my grandmother's sceptical face as she listened to *that* explanation.

Three years passed and in spite of my grandmother's dire warnings, the grocer's shop apparently flourished in the High Street.

Now we come to the year that I was eighteen. How remote it seems. My boyfriend Murdo was to visit us. He was twenty two and a university student and I was very proud of him. I had planned all the things that we would do from the moment that his train arrived on Friday night. First, we would eat fish suppers as we wandered around the romantic harbour where soft gas lights reflected in the water and imperceptibly moving boats creaked gently.

On Saturday morning we would swim in the icy open-air pool. That would certainly be a testing of his love for me! In the afternoon we might perhaps drive to St Andrews in my ancient Vauxhall and buy cakes to bring home for tea. At night we would leave the car at home and go dancing in Anstruther town hall, then walk home along the seashore, pausing at intervals for sweet and innocent kisses.

"When your young man is here tomorrow afternoon, I've got a job for him!"

As always, my grandmother's voice was full of confidence.

"You know wee Mrs Dobson's bought a house down School Wynd? She's hoping to rent it out and she wants some furniture taken down, so I said you and Murdo would be pleased to do that for her. It'll just be a few light things, I expect. Cups and saucers maybe, pots and pans. Just to make it habitable. I said you'd be along at the shop about two thirty."

I was speechless and not very pleased but no one ever argued with my grandmother. Besides I felt under an obligation, for it was a great and unusual favour to have a friend to stay. It had never happened before.

On Friday night, delicious fish suppers and the romantic, though cool, harbour strengthened Murdo for two hours of my grandmother's anecdotes before bedtime. Next day we swam in the pool, Murdo blue but determined to survive. At two thirty we reported for duty at the grocer's.

We were astonished at what we were expected to take down! Certainly the really large stuff like beds and armchairs had been moved already, but we were faced with occasional tables, a bookcase with all its books, a corner cupboard, two small display cabinets, several rugs and mounds of blankets and quilts. There were cutlery boxes and a jam pan full of towels and at least ten small boxes with ornaments carefully wrapped in newspaper. Four pretty little wooden chairs and two footstools, a vacuum cleaner, carpet sweeper and other household necessities were ranged beside the pile.

"Sorry about this. It must be quite a big house she has bought. I thought it was just a wee place," I mumbled.

The new house was half way down the wynd and at no great distance from the shop in the High Street. The car was of no use and we would just walk. There were many journeys and all made in full view of the Saturday shoppers. I felt cross and humiliated as we struggled with boxes and unwieldy bundles. It was not the sophisticated day that I had imagined.

When all the furniture was shifted and the numbness which Murdo had suffered after his bathe was replaced by the glow of honest toil, I felt tired, an unusual sensation for me in those days. Every corner of the small house was absolutely packed. It was difficult to see how anyone could live in the house. Perhaps there was an attic for some of the objects?

Returning home, we appreciated my grandmother's home-made pancakes and raspberry jam. She was a wonderful baker. She enquired what sort of things we had been shifting and expressed some curiosity.

"I wonder why she's putting so many ornaments in a rented house?" she murmured with a thoughtful expression, and she hummed softly to herself.

Then she suggested that Murdo might as well cut the grass, which he did with every evidence of delight. He was a wonderful fellow.

That night, Anstruther town hall echoed to the ever popular, though melancholy strains of 'Blue Moon' played on an electric guitar while Murdo and I danced dreamily cheek to cheek. At the interval we enjoyed a doughnut with a cup of tea, while other hungrier dancers indulged in pies and brown sauce. A delightful walk home with the faint glitter of a new moon on the sea and the various small sounds of seabirds at night, was every bit as romantic as the French films that were shown at the Cosmo in Glasgow, a favourite haunt of students.

We took an hour to walk the mile home and arrived in the High Street around midnight.

Normally the town would have been dark and silent, as street lights in Fife were economically extinguished at eleven, but to our surprise the whole town was aglow. Every window was brightly lit and groups of people, some in dressing gowns, stood talking excitedly in the High Street beside two large fire engines with blazing searchlights and attendant firemen. There was a strong smell of burning and thin streams of smoke leaked from the whole façade of the grocer's building!

We looked at each other in horror and without stopping to gaze, hurried past the exciting scene as unobtrusively as possible. Our very disinterest might have suggested a guilty conscience if anyone had noticed.

The same terrible thought was in both our minds.

The removal of the valuables that day had been a prudent foresight, for this fire had been planned and *we had been the unwitting accessories to arson!* There was no denying it! The whole town had watched us shift the best pieces of furniture and the most precious ornaments and rugs throughout the afternoon.

Would a heavy hand drop on our shoulders at any moment?

We arrived home safely and my grandmother listened to our breathless tale with a gentle laugh and little surprise.

"Oh, *I knew* that business would never last and when I heard about the ornaments going down the wynd . . . well she never meant to rent that house . . . I *was pretty sure about that* . . . "

For a few moments, my grandmother gazed into the glowing heart of the fire with a faint smile on her face and an almost imperceptible shaking of her head. The smoke curled gently from the cigarette which she held gracefully in her right hand, her left elbow leaning on the arm of her chair with her chin resting lightly on the back of her outstretched fingers, a fashionable pose at the beginning of the twentieth century and a favourite one of hers.

She spoke once more,

"I *always* thought there was something peculiar about that whole family. I could see something like this would happen *sooner* or later."

Then with a last deep inhalation and exhalation of her cigarette, she threw it deftly into the fire with a dramatic finality.

Youthful pursuits

IT IS INTERESTING TO compare how five generations of my family spent their leisure time in those east coast summers as they grew up.

My grandmother was only nineteen when she came to Fife. Their first house was in Kilconquhar and within a year she was a mother. As well as the demanding domestic responsibilities of those primitive days, she often modelled for her husband. There is a lovely painting of her sitting under a corn stook, feeding her new baby, Annie, my mother.Iin the picture is a teenage girl is who might have been my grandmother's sister and also an older lady, who is no relative.

In the previous ten years, bicycles had become 'all the rage' and the young couple loved their bicycles. They had taken a bicycling honeymoon. Of course they also walked a lot, as everyone did at that time. After a visit to friends in Pittenweem, they walked the four miles home. The baby Annie was a few weeks old at the time and Agnes carried her wrapped and supported in a shawl, in the old-fashioned way. Though my grandfather offered several times to carry what I believe was a very weighty infant, Agnes refused to part with her. She must have been a strong young woman. I suspect that those first years were hard work with little opportunity for playing. However I know that by the time she was thirty, Agnes enjoyed swimming and golfing. Perhaps she attended whist drives and I know that she and John played bridge. From 1911 onwards, there was a great deal of entertaining. It was partly social, with many friends coming to stay, but also business associates, with prospective buyers dropping in to see the McGhie's 'country residence'.

Agnes's mother came to visit regularly and each day would walk along towards St Monance and take a long drink at the Iron Burn, having great belief in its healing properties. She also liked to dip her feet in the sea. Sadly that is practically all that I know about my great grandmother.

Although I remember no mention of her visiting, there is a photo of John's older sister Martha in Pittenweem. It must have been about 1917, as the photo shows my mother as a well-grown girl of fourteen or fifteen, with the sullen look often associated with that age and her ten year-old brother Willie, rather quizzical. Agnes, in her mid thirties, is still a young and very attractive woman, with her mass of brown hair flowing over her shoulders to dry, as they have obviously been swimming. In contrast, Martha McGhie in a formal, almost Victorian black outfit, might be from another era. She would be about fifty at that time and had never married but kept house for her father and brought up her brother John after their mother died. Martha probably found it difficult to accept the young, flamboyant wife that John had chosen.

The next generation added tennis and dancing to the family pursuits. There is a photo of tall slim young people, very elegant in white, the boys in open-necked shirts and the girls in long dresses with Suzanne Lenglen headbands. They look sun-burned and slightly jaded, like young aristocrats in an Evelyn Waugh novel.

There was a memorable dance on the tennis courts one year with Chinese lanterns adding a romantic touch. I am not sure if the music was live or from a wind-up gramophone, but according to my mother it was a marvellous night, though it probably did not improve the surface of the courts. They wore wonderfully comfortable tennis shoes to dance in, with soles made of an ersatz rubber invented by a Glasgow man, Dick Balata. Evidently those shoes just never wore out! When this dangerous fact became apparent to the manufacturers of rubber, the Balata firm was immediately bought over by one of the big companies.

Some of those tennis players would be visitors and some local. One might have been Gertrude Murray, whose family had a large haberdashery and furnishing business in the High Street, for she was a leading light at the tennis club. My mother remembered her as 'rather a bossy besom'. My mother was particularly friendly with two girls, Ellen Don from Elie and Florence Peebles, whom I would meet in later years as severe belt-wielding teachers, when I attended Pittenweem primary school during the war. I found my mother's description of them in their youth very hard to believe. Miss Don had been a speed fiend on a bicycle, with her red hair flying in the wind, and Miss Peebles an uninhibited dancer of the Charleston and the

Black Bottom.

All her life, my grandmother was a collector of curios and anything unusual or beautiful that she could pick up for a bargain price. When visitors arrived there were clothes for fancy dress parties and charades and no doubt the evening ended in dancing to the gramophone in the small sitting room.

It should not be forgotten that the summer months were not a holiday for John McGhie. He was pursuing his career and painted every day. He walked a lot and always had a sketchbook in his pocket. Some pages have charming and detailed scenes in watercolour, others have quickly scribbled pencil drawings, often with written notes on the colours at that particular time of day.

As well as her athletic pursuits, my mother was expected to model for her father and to do her share of domestic chores.

I imagine those summers of the first three decades of the century as perpetually busy, however there was a hammock and a swinging garden couch with awning, which suggest that there was a certain amount of lounging allowed. I can still remember those two disintegrating items of garden furniture in the thirties when I was a child, though they were soon to be replaced by a Spartan wooden bench, many deck chairs and an inviting little armchair which appeared to be constructed of rough-hewn wooden branches. Its sylvan appearance was entirely false, for it was made of heavy earthenware and it was an uncomfortable and extremely cold seat.

When war was declared in 1939, it seemed likely that Glasgow would be a target for bombing and my mother and I moved to Pittenweem where I attended the primary school.

In fact some of the first enemy action of the war took place in the Firth of Forth, when a convoy bound for Leith was attacked by German planes. My mother witnessed this from the garden.

At another time there, an unexploded bomb fell on James Street, near the west bound bus stop. As a result we had a short holiday from school.

I did not find the four years that I spent in Pittenweem easy. Although I had some very good friends, there were others who were less kind and there was much jeering in the streets. My accent and my clothes were different and I was stubborn enough not to want to change. Children can be cruel everywhere of course.

Like other children of those days I was very active, climbing rocks and jumping off high places were my delight. At school, every game had its own season and while that season lasted one was a specialist at that particular skill. It might be skipping or 'beddies' (hopscotch) or bouncing a ball against the wall in various complicated patterns, or round games which were the least energetic. Whatever it was, one worked at it in all the spare time available and everyone became adept until at some unseen signal, a new fashion arose. Then knitting or crochet was always in hand. Boys and girls were both taught to knit in school and there were certain set tasks, blanket squares for the troops first of all, then a vest, socks and a strange, fat, two-coloured striped tea cosy. We were not tea drinkers, my mother favoured Camp coffee, a sweet, chicory flavoured liquid which came in a bottle and perhaps for this reason I avoided knitting one of those tea cosies. Perhaps I was attempting something more ambitious, such as a cardigan. Those cosies were to be seen in every home for many decades, growing shabbier and stranger each year and I have always had a faint regret that I did not make one.

By the time I reached my teens we had returned to our house in Glasgow but spent all my school holidays in Pittenweem. My grandparents were getting older although John continued painting until I was fourteen. He was now in his seventies and getting gently forgetful. There were no more house guests at 54 High Street, although there was always a stream of Agnes's friends popping in at any time of day for a cup of tea.

My mother suffered from multiple sclerosis and was in a wheelchair from the time that I was twelve. I was her 'carer', although at that time the descriptive word had not been coined nor the role acknowledged

If this sounds like a doom-laden summer holiday, it is not at all how I remember it. I certainly had my chores to do, but swimming was always my great pleasure and as long as I had that, sometimes twice a day, I could deal with anything. Although my grandmother could be difficult and dominating, she could also be very kind, generous and very good fun. She was a complex lady.

Throughout my teens, I was always up early to buy the rolls and give my grandparents their breakfast in bed. Then I could bask in the garden for an hour or so without my grandmother's eagle eye on me. Sunbathing and reading books were not considered appropriate occupations for a teenager.

In my early teens, I occasionally modelled for my grandfather and one photo shows a thin and very disgruntled thirteen year-old, unwillingly holding a basket. I hope I passed through that ungracious stage quickly. My grandfather had always spent a lot of time with me as a young child, visiting parks and museums, reading me stories and as a teenager, I still enjoyed our walks together.

Each week we went to the local cinema. We were well served for cinemas with The Picture House in Pittenweem with three changes of programme each week as well as the Regal and the Empire in Anstruther but I think our visits were mainly to Pittenweem. My grandfather was getting more forgetful and when the advertisements showed Black the grocer in the marketplace or Hughes the chemist at the Toll, he would turn to me, and obviously thinking he was in a Glasgow cinema, say,

"Now isn't that a wonderful coincidence! Fancy Pittenweem shops advertising here and we just happen to see it.".

It was amusing and yet very sad.

As an only child, I was used to being solitary and self sufficient. However each summer my young cousins Eileen and Sheila McGhie, Willie's daughters, would come for a week or two and I would have a chance to practise my maternal skills as they were seven and fourteen years younger than I was. I enjoyed telling them stories and playing make believe games with them. A younger child provides a good excuse for a teenager to shed her dignity and regress. My grandmother was very fond of young children and tended to show her gentle side when they were there.

In my early teens I tended to swim by myself although there were good friends that I would meet up with at the pool sometimes. However I discovered the great delights of social dancing in Pittenweem and through dancing became more a part of the local society. My first military two-step was taken in the market place where a little van arrived to play for two hours every Tuesday and Thursday during the summer months I expect a collection was taken to pay for it but I cannot remember. It was mostly children and young people who danced on the rough uneven tarmac, a surface which shortened the life of even the most robust sandals. Later I graduated to dances in the Pittenweem Legion Hall, now an elegant private home. You walked through Brown's close to the Legion and I can still imagine the excitement of the faint music and hum of conversation coming from the lighted doorway. Such promise of whirling round and round in my long New Look skirt and perhaps meeting someone *really interesting*! By the time I was eighteen, you would find me at Anstruther Town Hall several nights each week throughout the summer. And I did meet some very interesting people. Not many of them were good dancers I am afraid, but we had good conversations and I learned a lot about the world that I was never going to find out in my stuffy, academic High School for Girls in Glasgow.

David from Thornton was the first boy that I met in the marketplace and then finished the evening in the more adult atmosphere of the Legion Hall. He seemed a very good dancer to me and was just as shy as I was. He was leader of a group of Scouts who were camping outside Anstruther and his kilt was an asset in the eightsome reels and Strip-the-Willow. He and his friend invited my friend, Alison and myself to visit their camp for a cup of tea the next day. After our sedate tea and biscuit, we went down to the shore where David and his second-in-command started to dunk the younger boys in the icy sea to "... clean them off a bit ... " It was a cold day and it seemed a very brutal process to me. I was not used to masculine roughness and the howls of the small boys tore at my heartstrings. I wondered what the mothers would think if they knew their children were being so ill-treated. But after all, I spent half an hour in that same chilly sea for pleasure each day myself. Perhaps everyone, in their own way, was showing off to the two girls.

David was an apprentice railway engineer and his father and brothers all worked for the railway. Fourteen years later, Dr Beeching would wipe away the large rail network that centred around Thornton. I wonder what happened to that engineering family. David was athletic and artistic. He had his higher art certificate and had painted some very good watercolours. I have one still. Perhaps he changed direction in later life.

John was a joiner, a pretty good dancer and the top tennis player at the Anstruther club. He had ambitions to join the police force and I think he did. Several times a crowd of us went along to Cellardyke pool for a swim after the dance. It was a very nice pool and the water seemed incredibly warm, much warmer than expected in the chill of the evening. That was a pool that had music playing throughout the day, which was very pleasant and sophisticated I thought. At night of course it was silent and romantic under the stars.

One of my dancing partners was a milkman, I cannot remember his name. I did not see him for a few weeks and asked his friend where he was, only to learn the sad news that he had been 'inside' for a few days.

"Ye ken, that's yin o' the hazards o' a milkman's life."

"What do you mean?" I asked.

"Weel he'd had ower much tae drink. Ye see, ivery hoose he stoappit at wiz offerin' him a dram at the New Year, an' then it wiz his birthday last month an' they wur gien 'm mair booze an' then the polisman seen 'm an' he wiz 'had up' in chairge o' a hoarse, while the waur o' drink. An' that wisnae the first time."

A Cellardyke boy was a very shy, nice boy who seldom danced. He was a baker. My problem with him was that his accent was so strong that I could hardly understand a word. What a struggle! I wanted so much to be kind and polite, but constantly I was forced to ask him to repeat what he had said. Sometimes even at the third or fourth time, I was still puzzled. Very embarrassing! One night I gathered that he had been saving up for something for a long time and was very pleased to have it now. But what was it? It sounded like a 'doocluk' no matter how often he said it and what on earth was a 'doocluk'? At last I asked outright.

"What is that thing you are telling me about?"

He explained that he kept homing pigeons and this was a 'doo clock' or 'pigeon clock' to monitor the exact time of the bird's arrival home. Some years later, I met him. He seemed more confident and I was able to understand him quite easily. He had gone to Edinburgh and got a very good job in McVities' bakeries.

"But y'know, Ah was in chairge o' a lot o' lassies and ye'll mebbe no' believe it, but they didnae ken whit Ah was sayin' an' Ah had tae chinge the wey Ah spoke."

Another fellow whose speech eluded me came from Manchester. I had no key to his broad accent and understood only a tenth of his conversation. Still, he was a nice, very handsome young man and we danced well together all evening. He was a dyer in the cotton industry, I managed to understand that much but our exchange of information was minimal. Though I never saw him again, I still remember him.

By the time I was twenty two, I had a car to drive my mother around. It was good to be self sufficient. Very few people had cars in 1954 and even fewer car-owners were women. I had a large black Vauxhall, almost as old as I was. Usually it was the only car parked in the High Street. Originally it had been a good car and there were still many of that model on the British roads. It is the only car with real leather seats which I have ever owned! Because of its age, it was necessary to 'double-declutch' when moving from third to second and I was proud to be able to do that. Sometimes I drove to Anstruther Town Hall, but really a car was a drawback if one enjoyed walking home with the crowd or perhaps in a romantic twosome. Sometimes I left it to be collected the following day.

One night a slight young man asked me to dance. He had a very bright engaging expression and he made me laugh right away. Ronnie, son of the local Anstruther chemist, was very delighted that he had just acquired a new car, a mini. When he found out that I drove, he insisted that I must have a shot in his new car. I am sure that he thought it was the nicest thing that he could do for me but I was far from enthusiastic. I had not reached that stage of confidence where one can jump into any car and drive it off and his car was as different from mine as it could be, small, nippy and modern where mine was large, cumbersome and almost an antique. Nor did I share that masculine delight in the internal combustion engine. A car was only a tool to me and driving was still a slightly nerve-racking experience. However, Ronnie would not take no for an answer. Off we went in the dark in his precious new car, driving on unknown backroads. I was *terrified* that I would scrape or damage it. What a relief when we parked it and returned to the noisy hall! How I enjoyed a cup of tea and a Blue Riband chocolate biscuit in the basement after that ordeal. There was no alcohol served there in those days. Alcohol was not such a large and seemingly necessary part of life then, certainly not for young people, although some of the men had probably had a beer or two before coming to the dance.

Another 'regular' at the town hall was Jack, an excellent dancer and a marvellous piano player. He was a newly qualified lawyer and came from Edinburgh, though he had Pittenweem connections. His grandfather had been Provost Ogilvie of Pittenweem and his aunt had nearly married my uncle.

Jack had a cousin Drew, who was also a good dancer and a great swimmer. He was training to be an accountant. He bought a little 1929 MG sports car. I was very impressed, for he had taken it all to pieces in Glasgow, put it together again, then passed his driving test first time and that same day, driven through to Fife in this antique car. As I was the only other driver in the crowd, I had a little shot at driving it, very scary and exciting. One sat with one's legs stretched straight out in front to work the pedals. Sadly the wee car lasted only a week till it disintegrated but Drew was philosophical about that as he had learned so much from it. The observant reader of this book will note that I made use of Drew and his car in one of my stories. Drew and I also swam regularly in Pittenweem harbour which was not so industrial in those days.

Before my dancing days in Anstruther Town Hall finished, the Joint Services School of Languages was established in Crail. There, the brightest young men in the three services were being taught Russian in case of serious developments in the Cold War. It may even be that some were being groomed for espionage. This brought new and cosmopolitan faces to the masculine side of the Anstruther dance floor.

I met a young man from Turkey who assured me his parents were English and he certainly spoke the language perfectly and beautifully, as well as French and German. He looked a little different because he had a moustache, which was very unusual. Only my father's and grandfather's generations were moustached. He also dressed impeccably, in well-pressed suits and smartly knotted ties. When I admired his beautiful golden tiepin, which was in the form of a small safety pin, he admitted to me that it was in fact, just a gold safety pin! A fact that no one would have guessed because of his otherwise immaculate style. Without much basis in fact, he was sure that I would be very good at languages and started to teach me the rudiments of Turkish. I still have the notes and exercises that he wrote out for me but it is a difficult language and I did not achieve much, however we had a very nice summer of dancing and swimming. We said farewell regretfully, but no hearts were broken.

Although there were several of my swimming friends that were fishermen, it seems that there are none on my list of dancing partners but I know that I often danced with fishermen.

The summers which my daughters spent in Pittenweem were entirely different again. No swimming! Too cold. No dancing! Dances as I remembered them no longer existed but my daughters were all keen gymnasts and our small garden was often filled by flying limbs, cartwheels, somersaults, straight back leg rolls. Kate was excellent at juggling and what with general dressing-up and experiments with make-up, there was sometimes the atmosphere of a circus.

Also lots of sun-bathing in bikinis.

There was still the possibility of swimming in the old Pittenweem pool in the seventies although it was run down. After regionalisation took place, it was no longer maintained and it quickly deteriorated to a dangerous state. At the top of the braes however were the crazy golf, the ice cream kiosk and the trampolines, the last being a great favourite with my two younger daughters, Sarah and Alice.

All four daughters enjoyed drawing and painting and Sarah was nine when she borrowed my movie camera and made a charming short film of a garden fairy, starring a Barbie doll dressed in flower petals. She is still making films.

In my childhood, because of the comparatively long bus journey, a visit to St Andrews had a unique quality. It was an important excursion and one stayed there all day, shopping and probably having lunch. Nowadays with a car, one can pop up to St Andrews for an hour or less and return home for food. Then it was an all day affair with a certain excitement, now it is just another errand. However in the seventies I had no car for a few years and I also had my invalid mother to care for, so most of our holiday was spent in or around Pittenweem. However each year I would take the children to St Andrews for one whole day and relive that special pleasure that I remembered from my own childhood. We would arrive by the earliest bus that we could manage to catch and first of all visit our favourite shop which sold felt pens, notebooks, fancy rubbers and small necessary tin boxes. Then we would go for a modest lunch in a cafe. Next we would visit the delightful South Street fruit shop, sadly long gone, and stock up with as much fruit as we could carry. Then off to the Step Rock swimming pool for a chilly but refreshing swim. After which we would demolish all the fruit. We might then wander along Market Street, window shopping until the fish and chip shop opened: we were certainly starving by then. The day was finished off by a visit to the cinema before the sleepy bus journey back to Pittenweem. It was such an outing! We all loved it.

One evening it had unexpectedly turned very, very cold and we were still chilled from our swim. The girls were shivering with their bare legs and I wondered if we must forgo our visit to the cinema and just go home but the girls were terribly upset at that idea. All shops where we might have bought socks were closed by this time and yet we still had an hour until the cinema opened. I had a brainwave and went into a newsagents where I was able to buy five pairs of nylon tights very cheaply and we repaired to the Ladies toilet and donned them. They were adults tights and *very baggy* on Alice's little six-year-old legs but it was amazing how warm they made us feel and we were able to enjoy our film.

Sometimes Kate and Esther's teenage friends arrived on motor bikes or by bus and often stayed overnight. Sometimes I had ten to feed. It was like a boarding house! As long as they were happy and I had my swim and a glass of sherry while cooking, all was fine. One of their friends, Eddie, was training to be a chef and we spent some educational time in the kitchen exchanging culinary tips. Twenty years later, when he became a topflight chef in the biggest hotel in Tokyo, I visited him and his beautiful wife Monica and ate a wonderful meal on the fifty fourth floor.

My children mixed less with the local kids than I had done, partly because they had each other and partly because they spent some of their holidays with their father and did not live for long periods in Pittenweem. However my two older daughters, Kate and Esther, were friendly with two Pittenweem boys and went out in a boat with them one day. The girls were utterly amazed at the strength and stamina of these boys as they hauled in one heavy lobster pot after another, all afternoon. Their energy seemed infinite and none of the effete young men of Glasgow's west-end could hold a candle to that sort of endeavour.

When Sarah was fifteen she went several times to a disco in Colinsburgh. Her partner was a teenager from St Monance who was a keen musician, a drummer. He also delivered our milk. He belonged to a band which later did very well and toured the world as the support band to a more famous group.

There is still a healthy and creative interest in music in the East Neuk.

My grandchildren swim in the sea but are clad in wetsuits to enter its iciness. Surfing at St Andrews is something they enjoy very much. They also swim in the indoor pool at St Andrews leisure centre and enjoy the exciting flumes in the Dundee pool. My seven year-old grand-daughter was trying to cajole me into coming to Dundee.

"Oh, you would really enjoy it, grandma, you whirl round and round so fast then drop off a great big height into the water with a splash. *It's great!*"

But I excused myself from such an exciting experience.

The teenage boys nowadays enjoy plummeting into the harbour.

They emerge quickly, clambering up the iron ladder to run and plummet once again, curling themselves up tightly in order to make the biggest splash possible. I saw this taking place on a freezing cold day in March so it was not surprising that they spent very little time in the water.

They also enjoy skate-boarding which is another exciting and dangerous pastime.

I must say how happy I am that I grew up when dancing was so much in fashion. It was an excuse to wear an attractive dress, it was a good way to socialise, and it must have kept us very fit.

Destiny

DORRIE FENSTER LIVED HALFWAY down a wynd with her two sons and three daughters. Shortly after the youngest boy Peter had been born, her husband, with three other fishermen, had perished at sea in one of the sudden storms which will always be the scourge of those brave men who reap the glittering produce of the ocean.

Dorrie and her family were crowded into a very small house with an outside stair at the front and a deep hidden garden full of cabbages and potatoes at the back. There was little money for such a large family but Dorrie was able to turn her hand to most things and she earned many useful pennies from baiting lines or 'turning' an old coat and sometimes she cleaned for the folk 'up the town'. Some people complained that she was slow and careless in her work but she was always there if she said she would be and she did not waste time blethering as some women did. She must have been able to make one shilling do the work of two, for Peter was in his teens before he realised that they were so very poor, poorer even than other fisher families.

Things improved financially when the oldest sister married at seventeen and left home. Soon the other girls left school and started work, one as a maid of all work at the manse and the other as the grocer's message girl. It is true that being young, they earned very little, but Dorrie Fenster commandeered those few shillings and it made a big difference to the family. And there were a few perks attached to these lowly occupations. Sometimes the minister's wife sent home the remains of a semolina pudding or a worn, but still serviceable, tweed skirt, and on a Saturday there might be some bruised apples, over-ripe bananas or a ham bone from the grocer.

Dorrie had few friends, for she was not a local woman. Some said that she had been a gypsy and they whispered it under their breath as though it were a shameful secret. Now, swarthy, shapeless and unprepossessing, always dressed in shabby dark clothes, she showed no signs of the exotic beauty that might have tempted a fisherman to marry out of his caste. Although the women of the fishing community avoided her, they admitted that, "she'd hid an awfy hard row tae hoe and must hae been a marvellous manager, pair sowl, richt enuff."

Tom and his younger brother Peter were quiet boys. Their marks at school were only fair, but they were well behaved and the teachers were happy to ignore them for most of the time and reserve their loud angry voices, their castigations and corporal punishments for the wild or ignorant elements in each class. Most teachers at that time still believed that not only behaviour but also marks could be improved by the liberal application of the belt. Fortunately the Fenster boys generally achieved a five or six out of ten for the various subjects throughout the day and evaded physical punishment, though they did not escape the sarcasm which was also considered a useful educational tool.

Tom loved to draw boats and at this work he was very skilful. His familiarity and observation enabled him to delineate every detail of a working fishing boat. Boats were his only interest and his occasional attempts to draw any other subjects convinced him that he was no artist. On the rare occasions when the little boxes of pastels and the drawing books of grey paper faced with tissue were given out to each child and the jug of limp, wild flowers was set up in front of the class, the sides of Tom's jug were just as badly matched as anyone else's and his flowers just as unconvincing. If it was a picture from imagination, his stick figures or precariously leaning houses showed no more ability or understanding than the next child. It was only in drawing fishing boats that his genius showed. That genius set him apart and he was appreciated by his peers and admired for his 'braw picturs o' boats'. The admiration was never as wholehearted as it might have been, for always there was that feeling that the Fensters were in some way inferior to the rest of the community. The people of Pittenweem have long memories and the mutter of gypsy blood was hard to silence.

Peter, like the rest of his family, was considered 'different' by his classmates, although no one could have explained what this difference was, but it was viewed as a handicap and he was often derided by the other boys. He was a dreamy child who particularly enjoyed the singing class and always learned his poems thoroughly. And though he recited them in the same monotonous sing-song as the others, he never stumbled or stammered or showed embarrassment as he took his turn to deliver an extract from Burns or Shakespeare. He may not have understood much of what he was saying but he appreciated the rhythm and swing of the poetry even if he could not reproduce it vocally. In bed at night he would whisper a poem to himself, taking comfort in repeating it correctly and throughout his life, he would be able to quote every poem that he ever learned in school.

These boys had no other aim in life but to leave school and become fishermen. That was their ambition for that was man's work. And yet they were not seen by others as future fishermen. Perhaps their mother's gypsy blood stood in the way of their acceptance. Their poverty and patched clothes were common to all the children but the Fenster boys had unusually gentle manners, for Dorrie was a stern mother and demanded respect. They were certainly less aggressive and rambunctious than the other boys along the shore. They were considered 'safties' and classmates shouted at them in the street,

"Haw, haw, fearty-gowk! Fearty, fearty Fenster!"

Tom was more ready than Peter to meet these taunts with his fists and sometimes the repeated chant would change to,

"Petey, Petey, teacher's pet!"

And Peter would walk hurriedly homewards with his eyes downcast and his ears scarlet. It seemed horribly unfair to brand him as a pet. As far as he could see, the only manifestation of the teacher's preference seemed to be the negative one of not belting him quite as often as the others.

Whatever it was that set the Fensters apart, Tom was less affected and less troubled by it than his brother. Interestingly, Peter viewed this state of alienation in a very positive light and revelled in being almost an outcast. Peter explained the separateness of his family to himself by the fact that they did not live on the sea-shore beside all the other fishing families. He took a secret pleasure in the fact that their house was more than halfway up the wynd, almost at the top, almost 'up the toon' where the tradesmen and other 'toffs' lived. It was not that Peter aspired to tradesman status, in fact he almost despised anyone outside the fishing community. It was more that he was happy not to be labelled as belonging particularly to either group. He flattered himself that he could speak just as broadly as the shore people or just as 'properly' as the boys whose fathers had shops in the High Street. He might one day be a fisherman or he might be something else. This secret belief in the unique qualities and possibilities of his own family gave him strength to withstand the cruel jibes. Although a quiet lad, his outlook was generally optimistic and he had strong inner reserves.

When Tom left school, he found a boat to take him on. He enjoyed it and was proud to bring his mother home a fine big haddock or half a dozen dabs as well as his small wage. He still drew his detailed boats each weekend and his proportion and finish improved. Sometimes he sold his drawings for a shilling or two, but mostly he enjoyed the compliments he received from the other men.

"My that's an awfy grand drawin', Tom. Thon's jist as guid as a reel airtist wad dae't."

"Man, that's *The Guidin' Light* tae a T. Ah'd ken that boat onywhaur."

"Ye cud get ten punds fur thon in Dundee, Ah'll bet ye cud!"

But Tom did not take them seriously and was content to be admired.

He accepted the fact that he would be a fisherman all his life.

When Peter left school and went to sea, things were less successful for him. Every voyage was a nightmare. Before the harbour was well out of sight, even on the calmest of seas, Peter was helplessly, horribly, wrenchingly seasick and his mother felt tears in her eyes as looked at his white face with dismay each morning when he returned from the night's fishing.

Although he was obedient and quick to learn skills, his sickness made him useless as a crew member and the other men grumbled although the skipper was a kind man and tried to be reassuring.

"Niver you mind, Mrs Fenster, Peter'll be jist grand. The laud's goat a verra weak stoamick. He jist needs tae stick at it an' he'll soon be aw richt whin the spewin' stopes.

But the spewing did not stop and after five weeks, Peter was drawn and emaciated and most of his time at home was spent in bed.

His mother watched him one night as he slowly pulled his big jersey over his head, stopping twice to rest as he struggled with its stiff bulk.

"Ye're no' goin' oot the nicht, Peter. Ye're no' weel enough. Ye're as weak as a bairn."

"Och, Ah'll be aw richt, Ma. Ah'll jist gan . . . "

"Naw, ye're no' gaun. Sit doon an' rest an' Ah'll awa an' tell Robbie Hughes ye're no' able. Sit doon! Sit doon an' rest yersel, ma son."

After two weeks of feeding up on potatoes and cabbage, Peter went back to the fishing in another boat but again he was ill continuously.

It was suggested that he might go to the deep sea fishing as the larger boat might not affect him so badly but he must wait until he was sixteen for that. In the meantime he found a job at the harbour, cleaning up after the market, loading the full wooden fish boxes on to lorries and vans and cleaning the returned empty boxes. In the nineteen fifties before the Fisherman's Mutual Association appropriated all the fish caught in the East Neuk and created the present professional market with its ice factory and continuous stream of collecting lorries, the Pittenweem fish market was a small affair and there was not much work or money for Peter, but he felt useful and enjoyed the company of the old fishermen who hovered around the harbour, smoking their pipes and talking of long gone scandals and the terrible hardships of former days.

His life at the harbour kept him young and more innocent than he might have been had he continued on the boats and entered the swearing, drinking, hard life of the fisherman.

He was shy of girls and did not go to any of the many local dances. The idea of learning to dance never entered his head.

At home he continued to read poetry, and sometimes learned it by heart and he enjoyed browsing through an old *Pear's Encyclopaedia* that his mother had bought at a jumble sale. From this old book he gained many pieces of information, surprising and hardly useful to a fisherlad but pleasing to him. He also picked out words that appealed to him and dropped them unexpectedly into conversation. Without improving his education to any great degree, he managed to give the impression of a broader knowledge, even a hint of erudition that none of his colleagues could match or appreciate and certainly could not understand. Each year, he became, without knowing and without trying, more separate from those around him. There was another lad that helped around the harbour. Jock was a boy who, because of a cruel birth, was less than mentally normal or as the fishermen said "Twa kippers short o' a dozen". Because of Peter's quiet manners, strange words and odd pieces of information it was safer for the other men to bracket him with the unfortunate Jock and the two boys were considered 'simple' and treated with a superior condescension. Peter did not mind because he treasured the feeling of being apart and was quite assured of his own superior knowledge and vocabulary.

When Peter was sixteen, he travelled to Aberdeen and found work on the deep sea fishing boats. He still suffered sea-sickness, but not to such a degree, and pride and necessity kept him working there until he was twenty when a bad bout of fever weakened him and he was forced to return to Pittenweem to recuperate.

He arrived in July during the influx of the Glasgow holiday makers. The High Street was crowded, just as busy as Aberdeen's Union Street on a Saturday. He had forgotten that the summer could be like this and he felt a stranger in his own village. When a fisherman that he had worked with passed him without a smile, without even recognising him, he hurried home to his own house in the wynd.

His home was changed too because Tom had quarrelled with their mother and moved out to a friend's garret while he waited for a council house, for he was to be married soon. His girlfriend was pregnant and the race between bureaucracy and the coming child would be close run.

It seemed to Peter that his mother had aged a lot in four years. She was greyer, slower, stouter and had lost her old enthusiasm for the many summer jumble sales. His sister, Etta was still at home. Etta's dark eyes and curly black hair reinforced the possibility of gypsy lineage. She had got enormously fat since he had last seen her and, inheriting her mother's delight in bazaars and auctions, had filled the house with bags and baskets of old clothes, chipped china ornaments, piles of illustrated magazines, artificial flowers and even dubious old shoes.

"Whit a bloody load o' auld rubbish ye've gethered up. The hoose is a mess an' they shoes are stinkin'."

"Ah dinnae ken why ye cam hame if ye cannae be ceevil." Etta's eyes flashed.

"Noo, noo, dinnae quarrel wi' yer brither. Ah'm that glad tae see ye, ma mannie. The hoose isnae jist the way Ah'd want it but niver mind, there's a steak pie waitin' fur ye. Ye're lookin' jist grand, taller an' broader."

After his meal, Peter walked around the harbour. It seemed so small and insignificant after Aberdeen. The boats, though bigger than the ones he remembered from his boyhood, were like toys.

In the High Street he met a girl who had been in his class at school. He had always liked her for she was kind and funny. Now she was pushing a pram and had a two-year-old by the hand. She looked tired and untidy and nodded to him unenthusiastically. Obviously she did not want to talk.

He saw some others from his class but they either did not recognise him or gave only a brief "Aye, aye, Peter."

He felt very alone but he squared his shoulders and remembered that he never had felt very much a part of this society, so what was the use of regretting? He had not been popular or unpopular with the deep sea fishermen in the last four years. He had not joined in their drinking or their girl-chasing ashore but he had made one or two friends, acquaintances at least, and there was always someone to talk to if he wanted, but he enjoyed his own company and was known as a loner.

He pushed through a crowd of laughing holiday makers. They were queuing outside the fish and chip shop and slightly drunk. They appeared loud, happy and fond of each other and Peter wondered if he would ever be a part of a laughing throng like that. And whether he would want to be a part of it.

He headed for home but there was reluctance in his steps.

As he neared the top of his wynd, he saw another laughing group of people. These were all young and not at all drunk, or drunk only with the delight of youth. Some had tennis racquets and some had bicycles. Peter looked enviously at the bikes. He would have loved a bike but few fishermen could afford such luxuries.

This cheerful group were holiday-makers of a different stamp from the Glasgow crowds, those 'keelies' who had jostled him in the High Street. These were young people whose families owned holiday houses in Pittenweem and came every year for the whole summer. They were known as "toffs" and would arrive at the beginning of July with their parents, in cars packed tight with the paraphernalia for tennis and golf. Their bikes would arrive next day by train. The girls wore Aertex shirts and smart pleated shorts, had many summer dresses and did not scream and shriek with laughter as the 'keelies' did. Peter liked that quiet manner. All the other girls that he had met seemed to scream, either with laughter or mock indignation, at every remark that he made.

Peter knew the family that owned the house at the top of the wynd. There was a boy of his own age in the family and two younger girls and he had watched their arrival every year since early childhood. They had always smiled to Peter, though never talking to or involving him in their games. They might have been of a different race for no words were ever exchanged with the local children or the Glasgow visitors. These children went excursions in the car with their parents or played with the children of the other families who golfed and arrived in motor cars. Peter had never resented this isolationism. He would have liked to speak to the boy and perhaps have had a ride on his bike, but he accepted that they belonged to another world. Perhaps they would not have understood his accent, just as he had had problems with the strong Aberdeen speech. He had never paid much attention to the two girls but now with the lapse of four years, the younger girl, the one with the green eyes and soft brown curls had grown into a woman. Peter knew her name was Celia and he thought he had never seen a more lovely girl. Suddenly the crowd disappeared into the house. As it happened Celia was the last to enter and she saw Peter as he walked towards her. She paused, smiled broadly and said,

"Oh! Hullo!"

It was as though she recognised him with great pleasure and was truly delighted to see him. Peter was overwhelmed and could hardly reply. What a brilliant smile she had! Was she really as pleased to see him as all that?

He hardly slept that night but lay fantasising about how he might somehow meet her and start a conversation, then amuse and astonish her with all the clever things that he knew and eventually marry her.

Could Celia be the person who would appreciate and complete him? Would she appreciate the difference that he felt from the other fishermen? Could she be the bridge to mend his separation from the people around him and bestow that feeling of belonging, of having found his own place in the world? Would she even talk to him? The future was very hazy but completely delightful.

Next morning Peter walked along to watch the fish being landed and saw Celia sitting on the harbour wall, sketching in a small book. It seemed impossible that she should be there, by herself. There was nothing to stop his walking over to her and starting a conversation! Just as he had imagined he might do.

He panicked.

After his dreams of the night before, he found that he had no courage to grasp this unexpected opportunity and he turned on his heel and rushed up the Water wynd to the High Street. Breathless and ashamed of himself, he sauntered aimlessly past the shops, pausing to inspect the garish pink cakes and shining buns in the baker's window, then the socks, braces, handkerchiefs and neat bundles of wool in the draper's window. When he realised that he was standing gazing at the sad furry rabbit corpses hanging above trays of mince in the butcher's, he hurried away with his head downcast.

What a useless idiot he was. He *would* return to the harbour and he would speak to her and have one of those brilliant conversations that he had rehearsed last night.

She could not bite him.

She had seemed so friendly the previous evening when she had said hullo.

He turned down the School Wynd and leaping down the stairs three at a time, he walked purposefully to where she sat.

"Hullo, there, ye're busy."

"Oh, I didn't see you! Yes I am trying to work but people keep coming up and looking over my shoulder."

Peter mumbled an apology and took two steps backwards but she turned and smiled charmingly up at him.

"Oh, I don't mean you. It's *old* people that come and peer at what I am doing then start to tell me what a great artist my uncle George was. He lived here and was really famous and he painted Pittenweem harbour and the fishing boats and sold lots of paintings. He was quite wealthy! I can't tell you how many folk gaze at my drawing for about five minutes and then they will start talking about my uncle George and say what a *marvellous* artist he was. They say absolutely nothing about my picture so it's obvious they don't think it's worth a button. It's pretty dispiriting, I can tell you. I feel quite doleful."

She looked up at Peter and giggled in a very undoleful way.

He had been concentrating so hard on what he might say to her that he hardly heard her words and he was terribly relieved that she seemed so prepared to talk to him. Before he could make any comment on her picture, she started chatting again, explaining that she had finished her first year at Art School and had to fill at least three sketch books and paint several paintings during her long summer holidays.

"My friends and tutors seem to think I'm fortunate coming to this picturesque place but they don't know how tricky it is when you are well known and everyone speaks to you all the time and especially when you have an Uncle George who is known to be a genius. And a *successful* genius! He made such tons of money! That was long before the war of course. But I mean to say I'm just starting out, aren't I? I'm just a tyro, I can't expect to be as good as Uncle George! Not yet anyway. Can I?"

"No. Ye cannae expect it."

He felt this inadequate remark had none of the brilliance of the imagined exchanges of the previous night. However, as she was assuming the entire conversational burden, the encounter was easier than he had expected.

As she continued to chat about her studies, her holiday, her family and the friends that were expected to arrive soon, Peter realised that she used many unusual words, not particularly long words but unfamiliar ones and they sounded strange in everyday conversation. Some words he did not recognise at all and he tried to remember them to look them up in his Pear's Encyclopaedia.

He examined her drawing as she spoke and was surprised to see that the boats were not nearly as good as the ones his brother drew, although the houses and the figures were more realistic than Tom could achieve.

"Ma brither draws boats. He's awfy cliver at it. He's been drawin' boats since he wis a wee laud. He pits in a' the details, ye ken."

"I expect you mean he draws them *far* better than I do. Boats are *very* difficult. God, it's bad enough having Uncle George cast up at me all the time without having your brother's boats to contend with!"

"Aw Ah'm sorry! He's aye been a fisherman, ye see . . . an' it' easy fur him. Ah didnae mean . . . "

Celia laughed and told Peter not to worry but to give her a hand to carry her stuff up the wynd. The stool, easel and wooden box of paints, none of which she seemed to have used that day, were quite heavy but Peter would happily have carried ten times the load.

"Did ye cairt this a' doon here yersel? It's gey heavy fur a lassie."

"Oh, We artists have to be strong."

He looked at her arms and noted the defined muscles of a keen tennis player, under a smooth brown skin adorned with a sprinkling of fair hairs. He could have looked at those arms for hours.

Then she laughed and Peter felt himself more enchanted than ever. He felt terrific strength in his own arms and shoulders, while his knees were weak as water. It was a strange and wonderful feeling to toil up the steep slope of the wynd while in this state of enchantment and he wished the hill was as high as Everest.

At her door she said,

"We're all going up to the wee picture house tonight, it's

Humphrey Bogart, an ancient film but I didn't see it the first time round, are you going? Should be good. We'll maybe see you there? 'Bye."

It was almost as though she had invited him to join her crowd!

Was that what she had meant? He was puzzled.

He could not ask her and he thought about little else that day.

Should he go to her house that night and escort her up the road?

Would she be expecting him? Would she let him pay for her? He had the cash. His mind seemed full of questions that had no answers, yet he felt very happy.

He did go to the cinema and saw Celia sitting surrounded by her friends. She gave him a cheerful wave before the lights went out but as there were no empty seats near her, Peter had no chance to speak to her. He thought the film boring and incomprehensible, just as had found most of the films throughout his childhood except, of course, the cowboy films where the hero rode a white horse while the villain had a black one and the Red Indians were always the enemy. He had always loved those films for you knew exactly what was happening and how they would end.

He left before the Bogart film finished and disconsolately bought himself a fish supper and determined that the next day would be spent in Anstruther where he would not bump into Celia. What was the point, what was the use of pursuing such an unattainable dream. He was just a bloody fool to let his mind dwell on her.

Next morning was wet and he sat around the house dipping into his encyclopaedia at random.

Etta made some scathing remarks about his having nothing to do but his mother assured him he was welcome to have a holiday with them any time.

In the afternoon his mother asked him to buy bread and when he came to the top of the wynd there was Celia and her friends grouped around a strange little red sports car, a very old model.

"Oh it's Peter!" Celia shouted as soon as he turned the corner. "Come and see this! See how clever Drew has been!"

Peter recognised Drew as another of the regular summer visitors. He was tall and very dark and hairy.

"Drew's just passed his driving test *today* in Glasgow and he's driven *all the way through* here in this *amazing machine*. It is so ancient, it's older than *any of us*, 1929. Imagine! And Drew took it all absolutely to pieces and then put it all back together again just like Humpty

Dumpty. He's just *so clever* and look! You have to sit with your *legs straight out in front of you* and Drew says I can have a shot *driving it*."

Peter thought that the affected way she was speaking about the car sounded stupid and embarrassing but at the same time was glad to see that Drew was looking at his little vehicle with too much adoration to pay much attention to Celia.

"It's a braw wee car. Ah've niver seen yin like it but Ah dinnae think ye should drive it. It micht be dangerous. Ah've tae buy a loaf o' breed fur ma mither noo."

He walked quickly along the street and felt how juvenile and inadequate his response had been. There was Celia treating him like an equal and inviting him into her crowd of friends and what did he do? Give her advice as though he was her uncle, advice she didn't want to hear and then run away a message to the baker's, like a wee lauddie. He felt furious with himself and the echo of laughter from the group behind him made his ears burn scarlet. It was no use telling himself that it was unlikely that he was the cause of their laughter, because they were always laughing at something but the jeering sound echoed in his head all along the street and he returned home by way of the harbour in order that he need not again pass that tight little self-satisfied group with their fancy accents.

Peter needed to find some work if he wanted to stay in Pittenweem and though he and his sister had little family fondness for each other, it was she who told him that the Anstruther auctioneer was looking for a strong young man. And it was through his work with the auctioneer that he met Celia's Aunt Lilian. Lilian had bought a large box of miscellaneous china and it was when Peter delivered it that Lilian recognised him as the boy from down the wynd. She asked him to stay for a cup of tea and they sat in the garden as she unpacked the box, exclaiming over its contents much as a child unpacks its Christmas presents. When Celia walked through the garden gate, Peter spilled half a cup of tea on himself but said nothing and nobody noticed.

"This is Peter from down the wynd, Celia. He brought me this wonderful box of goodies that I bought at that roup in Anstruther yesterday. Just wait till you see some of these treasures! We've been having a great time examining them, haven't we, Peter. There's tea in the pot."

"I know Peter very well indeed and I know how strong he is. He carried all my painting stuff up for me the other day. Hullo Peter."

She sat down beside him and poured herself a cup of tea and for the next hour the two women chatted to him as if he were one of the family. Peter felt so relaxed, apart from his wet trouser leg, that he started to speak in a less restricted way. Lilian listened to what he said as though it were really interesting and important and Celia modified her flirtatious, teasing manner. Celia sometimes asked Peter to repeat what he had said but he was pleased to find that his accent was not too difficult for Lilian to understand. In fact she herself often used east coast expressions. They sounded strange on her lips, but he felt she was trying to make him feel at home.

Afterwards he galloped down the wynd with the feeling that he had been witty and successful, telling one or two jokes and casually dropping several unusual words into his conversation, words which he would never have used with his own family or amongst the local people. He had been accepted as a friend and Lilian had told him as he was leaving 'to be sure and pop in again soon'.

He saw Lilian at every auction, she was a dedicated buyer of knick-knacks and she always waved and smiled, sometimes chatted. One day she asked him,

"Do you go for a midnight swim after the dance like those mad creatures or are you more sensible?"

Peter shook his head and smiled vaguely. What did she mean? Did they really go swimming in the dark? At night time? Did she mean that Celia went too? Suddenly he was filled with a protective anguish and he realised how much Celia meant to him. Imagine her in pitch black water with only foolish boys to help her if she got cramp. How could her aunt contemplate allowing her to be so rash. It was irresponsible. What about her brother? Did no one care? He must find out where they went and he would go too. To protect her, to save her if necessary.

The fact that his swimming skills were of the most basic was unimportant, he should, he *must* be there with her in case she needed him.

The next night he went to the dance in Anstruther Town Hall. He had never attended a dance there before and he arrived early. The melancholy strains of the electric guitar echoing around the empty hall startled him. It sounded quite sophisticated, yet seemed out of place in the unattractive civic decor of the green painted walls and the treacly, varnished woodwork. He stood close to the door with a few other awkward looking boys. They were all smoking and Peter realised that it gave them something to do which he lacked. What if Celia and her friends did not come to this dance? Perhaps there was a dance somewhere else. What if he had wasted his two shillings and stood here all night looking stupid.

Eventually Celia and seven of her friends did arrive. It was obvious even to Peter that the dresses that Celia and her friends wore were more expensive than any other dresses in the hall. They were uncrushed and the skirts were fuller, the hems were straighter and the necklines lay prettily. When this group arrived, the men round Peter moved uneasily and stared at these strangers, then turned their backs and started talking loudly.

Celia caught sight of Peter and was obviously surprised, though she smiled briefly before going to the cloakroom. He felt that she was displeased to see him but could not think why.

Celia did not dance only with her own friends. Peter was surprised to see that she danced with the milkman, the joiner, the policeman, several fishermen and even the plumber's apprentice. Peter considered this last person to be very low. She talked animatedly with each of them. Drew, the boy with the sports car danced as many dances as he could with Celia. It was obvious to Peter that Drew was not interested in dancing with other girls. He wondered if Drew had brought his little car with him that night and worried that they could drive off after the dance and he would be left behind with all his terrible imaginings. Would they go to some remote beach to swim? Would Drew look after her properly? Could he swim? Was he a suitable bloke to be in charge of such a young girl? As Peter struggled with these worries he watched Celia continuously. At ten thirty she came over to him. He was so surprised that he did not smile or greet her in any way.

"Peter, are you terribly angry with me?"

"Me? No! Ah'm no' angry at a'."

"Well you've glared at me all night as though you were really furious and not once have you asked me to dance. Not once!"

"No, Ah don't dance. Ah cannae dance. Ah've niver learned. Ah jist came tae . . . ye know . . . tae watch. Has Drew got yon car wi' him the night?"

Celia burst out laughing.

"Oh the poor wee car, it's broken down and I don't think it can be mended. It's just too old. Are you coming along to Cellardyke for a swim after the dance? It's great fun and it's not a bit cold. Warmer than it is through the day, or it *seems* warmer anyway. Are you coming? Please come!"

"Aye, Ah'll come along."

Peter had done an energetic day's furniture shifting and had stood for three hours watching the dancers and the idea of walking a mile to Cellardyke and watching people swimming, for he had no trunks with him, and then walking two miles back to Pittenweem was not at all attractive, but his sense of devotion to Celia strengthened his resolve. He had a strong feeling that without his presence, there would be a disaster and somehow he alone could save his heroine.

"Did ye hiv a grand time at the dancin' last nicht? Are yer feet sair the day?"

His sister's voice was heavily sarcastic and he did not answer her. He felt very weary, it had been a long and boring night and today there was a big auction in a castle in central Fife with a multitude of heavy pieces to be moved and no doubt innumerable boxes of bric-a-brac to be held up and placed aside. Sometimes the small boxes were more trouble than the larger articles.

"Did they a' gan swimmin' at Cellardyke efter the dance?"

"Aye, they did."

"Daft buggers."

Peter rose from the table and left the house. For once, he agreed with his sister. It had seemed cold, silly and dangerous at the pool. Nothing terrible had happened but no one would have been able to see if there had been an accident, for it was almost pitch black. He had stood nervous and alert for forty minutes, his eyes always on Celia, while they jumped and splashed and screamed like a lot of kids. He could see that Celia was certainly the least likely to be in danger as she was a much better swimmer than the others and as she was the only one that he cared about, he determined that never again would he hang about Cellardyke pool at the dead of night. Some of them had been so cold that their teeth were still chattering when they had walked back to Pittenweem. Not Celia of course. She had had a delightful time, flirting first with Drew, then with another local boy Craig. Then when they had finally left the pool and dressed themselves, she had taken Peter's arm and set off with an order to the others to hurry up. Peter was deliriously happy. The long boring evening had been worthwhile if she would walk home arm in arm with him. His joy was short-lived, for after a few hundred yards she broke away from him and joined up with two girls and continued with them until they reached her house in Pittenweem. Craig, Drew and Peter had little to say to each other and trudged doggedly along behind the three laughing girls.

Although he never again joined a midnight swim party, Peter continued to attend any dance where Celia might be. He did not dance but he was not the only man who watched without taking part. He told himself it was something to do in the long summer evenings. He did not repeat his mistake of staring at her throughout the evening, but nevertheless he was aware of her whereabouts in the hall and who she was dancing with at all times. If a face that he did not recognise dared to ask her to dance, Peter would keep a very sharp eye on that man's general behaviour. Unsure just what he would do if an undesirable approached his goddess, Peter was certainly ready to step in and defend her from any rough or uncouth element if necessary. Fortunately it never was necessary. The independent Celia would not have appreciated his interference. Very occasionally she reached the end of the evening without having made any particular boy her dance-partner for that night. Then she would probably avoid the last dance, that dance which is traditionally danced with the boy who will escort the girl home. If Peter saw Celia leaving the hall just before the last dance, he would swiftly station himself at the cloakroom door where she could not miss his intention and willingness. Sadly she had sometimes made arrangements with a girlfriend to walk the dark mile back to Pittenweem but three times in the month of August, she greeted him with a smile and linked arms with him,

"Are you going to be my cavalier and see me safely to my front door, Peter?"

And to Peter, those three times that they walked home alone together were worth all the waiting and watching, all the boredom and all the two shilling pieces.

By the end of August most of Celia's friends had gone home but she would stay for another fortnight until the start of Art School. Peter hoped that she would need his company after every dance but strangely and suddenly she decided not to go to the dances in Anstruther any more, pleading boredom. However she saw a lot of Peter because her Aunt Lilian had a perfect flurry of buying at auctions. She bought larger articles than previously and when Peter delivered them, he was brought in to have a coffee. Lilian would talk most of the time about her vague plans to start an antique shop.

"Just think what fun it would be, kids, I could go and buy everything that I liked and then sell it at an enormous profit!"

Peter was unsure whether to take her seriously and just smiled politely but Celia was more practical,

"You know you would never want to get rid of anything because you like the things you buy too much. You wouldn't make any money at all and your shop would just get crammed fuller and fuller!"

"You are probably absolutely right, my darling!"

When Lilian was there, Peter felt very relaxed and almost like Celia's accepted boyfriend.

One day when he had delivered a very large clock entwined with metal ivy, Celia, who could scarcely speak for laughing, suggested that they should go to the pictures that night.

"It's an old Tarzan film, I used to love those as a kid. I'm all alone now that the gang has gone so do come with me. Dad sent me a tenner today so it's my treat. Will you come?"

Peter was slow to answer. He could not believe his ears. *She was asking him out!*

Lilian interrupted,

"Celia you've put the poor boy on the spot! He probably hates Tarzan films and he doesn't know how to say no to you and by the way if your father sent you a tenner you can repay that thirty bob you borrowed from me last week."

"You're such a Shylock, Aunt Lilian, I thought that was a little tip you were giving a favourite niece, not a repayable loan. You'll only spend it on more dusty old rubbish like ugly clocks that don't even go. And *of course* he likes Tarzan films. Everybody does. They're so kitsch, no one can resist them."

"Did you hear the joke about the two lion-hunters in the jungle?"

"Oh Lilian! Not that old chestnut again." Celia shook her aunt by the shoulders and laughed. Peter was completely confused by now, terribly unwilling to let Celia's apparent invitation to the cinema remain unanswered but the conversation seemed to have zoomed off into realms where he could not follow. Lilian pushed her niece away and turned to Peter,

"I know Peter will enjoy this story because it's so funny!"

Peter had a terrible sinking feeling that he would not even understand a joke about lion-hunters and prepared himself to watch how the others reacted and laugh heartily with them even if the story was completely incomprehensible to him. As Lilian continued her story, he felt his whole future depended on his laughing at exactly the right moment.

"Well, they were in a tent in the jungle and one of them had gone to bed while the other was still outside the tent. All of a sudden the second hunter rushed into the tent and there must have been a flap at either end of the tent which is quite unusual, I suppose . . . "

"*Get on with it* Aunt Lilian!"

"Yes, well the second hunter rushed into the tent, closely followed by a big lion with a great massive, bristling mane . . . "

"*Aunt Lilian!*"

"The second hunter rushed in one side of the tent with the lion close behind him and as he rushed out the other side he shouted to his friend,

"You skin that one, I'm away for another!"

Then Lilian lay back in her chair and laughed loud and long and Peter joined in heartily while Celia smiled wryly and shook her head.

Suddenly Lilian stopped laughing and leaning forward, put her hand on Peter's arm and her face was terribly serious as she spoke to him

"It is a great joke isn't it, Peter, I never cease to find it funny every time I tell it."

Peter agreed politely, while secretly thinking it was all pretty stupid.

That night at the cinema, however, as he sat close to Celia, Peter appreciated the story fully, for coincidentally in the film, Tarzan was being chased by a lion and as he ran, he passed a tent and when Peter whispered "You skin that one, I'm away for another," the two of them fell into such fits of helpless laughter that the manager shone his torch on them reproachfully and eventually came over to them to ask them to be silent or to leave the cinema.

There is a deep bond created between people who have shared uncontrollable laughter and the relationship of the young couple was changed in the last few days that Celia spent in Pittenweem that summer. Because her other friends had gone, she and Peter spent their evenings walking by the seashore and their conversations became more personal and more serious. Perhaps Celia started to realise the depths of Peter's feelings for her. Perhaps she felt that she had not treated this kind and decent fellow as well as she might have done and she stopped flirting and teasing. Sadly this was even less kind to Peter, for her seriousness and honesty gave him unrealistic hopes for the future.

Throughout that winter as he struggled with the hard life of a deep sea fisherman, Peter thoughts often dwelt on Celia and what special friends they had been in that last week of her holiday. He did not think of the life that she was actually leading because he could not visualise that, but he imagined her in Pittenweem in the garden wearing a heavy coat and gloves as it was winter. He pictured her sitting beside her aunt who was also cosily dressed and they held large mugs of steaming coffee and chatted and laughed. Then he would laugh at himself but quite soon the picture would form again in his mind.

Celia worked and played hard at Art School and Peter was only a hazy memory which seldom occurred. When his image nudged her consciousness, he was just one small part of the jigsaw of her Pittenweem holiday.

The following summer Peter again returned to Pittenweem and took a job with the auctioneer, awaiting her arrival with an almost unbearable suspense. Lilian, who was still enthusiastically buying antiques, invited him in for a coffee one day and told him that Celia would spend most of her summer in France that year and it would be late August before she came to Fife. Peter had taken her presence in Pittenweem for granted and his disappointment was like an illness. He hardly ate and his work with the auctioneer seemed boring and deadly. It was obvious that Celia had not looked forward to this summer as he had. By the end of July the whole idea that there could be anything between them now seemed like a stupid boy's dream. He told himself that he should forget they had ever met. As he watched the young people of Celia's 'gang' enjoying their summer holiday, he felt how ridiculous it was that he could ever be a part of their world. They were so relaxed, without a care in the world. They had education and money and cars and bicycles. Their lives were full of enjoyment and fun. He took a Pittenweem girl to the pictures one night but she accused him of being "awfy complainin'" and he realised that he had criticised things about the cinema and the town and probably the people in it.

"Ah like a laugh when Ah'm oot on a date, Peter. Ah hear enough moanin' an' greetin' at hame"

He apologised but he did not ask her out again.

Strangely when Celia did arrive, Peter was not as overjoyed as he

Agnes McGhie is the central bathing belle in this early scene at the Pittenweem Bathing Shelter, which had one communal changing hut for ladies and only the rocks for men. Improvements were made in the thirties with individual changing boxes, springboards, diving-dale, chute and concrete paths surrounding the pool.

Pittenweem tennis courts were popular in the twenties. Annie is third from left.

Before the Fisherman's Mutual Association was formed and before the covered market was built beside the Granary in the fifties, the fish were laid out and sold from the west pier.

Shelling mussels and baiting lines was a relentless daily labour for Pittenweem women. The old man on the left was a basket maker and McGhie painted him at work. The picture is in the Anstruther Fisheries Musuem.

Violet Black is mending nets at her front door in 1932. In the pram is Bill Black whose stories have helped me so much in compiling this book.

Here in 1936 are Agnes and Annie in outrageous garden party outfits, Willie's wife Eileen is seated and much more sportily dressed. Four-year-old Nanzie is longing to get to the pool.

Nanzie first modelled for her grandfather at the age of four, with much bribery of stories and peeled apples. Here she is six and just acquiring knitting skills.

Willie McGhie's two daughters, Eileen and her young sister Sheila spent happy summer holidays in Pittenweem. Here they have a ride on the stuffed crocodile that Agnes bought at a roup. The stuffed Iguana is in the foreground and the studio is in the background.

Pittenweem football team in 1936. Note the heavy leather sea boots which were difficult to put on and as bad to remove.

Aboard the *Learig* with skipper Tom Black in the wheelhouse.

The author at the start of a life-long love affair with swimming. The chute and diving-dale can be seen in the background.

Nanzie at thirteen is not happy about posing and probably thinking of the swimming pool.

Nanzie on the diving-dale at Pittenweem swimming pool, 1951. The pool was always beautifully clean, being refreshed with every tide. In this picture the tide is full and the bar which forms the end of the pool is covered.

Willie McGhie's two daughters, Eileen (left) and Sheila with their cousin Nanzie at the 2002 exhibition which celebrated work of John McGhie.

Agnes McGhie enjoying a wedding at the Craw's Nest in the sixties.

Four generations at 54 High Street in 1961. Agnes McGhie holds ten week old Katy on her lap. Annie suffered from multiple sclerosis and was in a wheel chair from 1944 onwards. Fortunately she kept good health and was a fine painter of flowers and still life.

In the Pageant of 1989, a witch foretells the coming of St Fillan.

Reinhard Behrens is towing his model Spanish galleon across the swimming pool. It would provide a dramatic moment in the 1988 Pittenweem Arts Festival.

A Pittenweem beauty sits at the window of Kelly Lodging in the historic pageant of the twenties.

In the 2004 Arts Festival, a corner of McGhie's studio recalls his work with his easel and some of the clothes which he kept for models to wear.

Below: Nanzie's four daughters and three grandchildren. Back row, Kate, Alice, Esther with baby Lewis. Front row, Grace, Eden and Sarah.

Bottom: The author in the Pittenweem garden with her grandchildren, Grace, Siannon, Lewis in front and Eden behind.

had expected to be. He happened to be walking along the High Street when she alighted from a taxi. She was very tanned and quite a bit plumper than he remembered. She did not smile but briefly fluttered her hand in his direction and walked quickly into her house, without a word.

If she had struck him, he could not have been more hurt. That offhand wave said that she remembered him, but only just. It diminished him and set him where he belonged, just a part of the colourful Pittenweem background. Those special seashore walks of last September might never have existed. What a fool he had been. He felt humiliated and also angry though later he blamed himself more than Celia. He had been the lone dreamer of dreams throughout those winter months and had manufactured a romance in his head which never had and never could exist.

That night Peter phoned the auctioneer and made excuses for leaving him so suddenly and next morning he caught the train for Aberdeen. His mother and sister were surprised at his sudden departure, but when his mother realised that Celia was back in town, she guessed that she was the reason. Dorrie had known from the first moment that her son was infatuated by the city girl and she was sorry for it. Dorrie believed in Destiny and her gypsy instinct warned her that there would be heartbreak of one kind or another for Peter. She could not see her son sharing his destiny with that girl. She had tried to tell him that but of course he would not listen.

On his way to the station, Peter came face to face with Celia in the High Street.

"Hullo, Peter, you're out and about early!"

"Ah'm just away up tae catch the nine-thirty."

"You're not leaving Pittenweem when I've just got here, are you?"

"Aye, Ah hiv tae get back tae the fishin'."

"Oh, I am disappointed."

"Ah well . . . cannae be helped."

"I'll miss you at the dances."

"Ah still cannae dance."

"I know what . . . I wonder."

Peter shifted his heavy bag to the other hand,

"Peter, I wonder . . . would you come to Glasgow in November to my birthday party? Could you get to Glasgow quite early in the day? I usually have a breakfast party and then we'll do something in the afternoon, I don't know what, maybe the theatre or something. It's a

Saturday, could you come? I'd love you to be there and meet my Glasgow friends."

Without much apparent show of enthusiasm, Peter agreed to come to her party and she gave him the address and instructions of how to get to her house. Peter only just caught his train but the significance of her invitation sent a warm glow into every muscle. Although Celia's life in Glasgow was so unknown and so mysterious to him that a breakfast party hardly seemed odd.

He returned to the deep sea fishing, determined that nothing would keep him away from her party on the 26th of November.

Peter left Aberdeen without breakfast and caught a very early train to Glasgow, arriving hungry, cold, and slightly dazed. Glasgow seemed dark and sooty after the clear cut granite of the eastern city. He wandered around for an hour in case he should arrive at her house too early. As he walked through the light drizzling rain, he was surprised at how warm he felt and although strong gusts of wind blew around every corner, he became hotter and hotter. It was unnatural for a winter's day and though his overcoat was thin, he quite soon found himself sweating.

His hot discomfort was aggravated when he was forced to repeat his request to the tram conductor twice before he made himself understood.

"Aw it's Pollokshields School ye wantin'? Aye, sure, mate, aye Ah'll let ye know, soon's we get therr. Mind ye, it's Setterday an' therr's naebody therr the day, 'cept the janny. An' he'll be at Ibrox!"

Then, laughing at his own wit, he strolled back through the tram, jingling his leather bag of coins, patting each seat in a proprietary manner and shouting,

"Ferrs pleezz, ony mair ferrs pleez."

Peter understood practically nothing of this and only hoped that the conductor had understood his request.

As the tram wended its way through the tenement canyons of Glasgow, Peter marvelled at the amount of houses and the number of people that must stay in them. Aberdeen had nothing like this crowded congestion of households. At first he tried to count how many houses were in a block but that was impossible and he gave up. His knowledge of tenements was limited but he had always felt that only poorer people were thus crammed together in tiny apartments, one family piled above another and he had been astonished when

Celia had given him instructions to find her house.

"Take the twenty six tram and ask to get off at the school, it's on a steep hill. There are two schools with a playground between them just at the tram stop. Are you paying attention, because it's really easy but if you miss that stop then you could get terribly lost and I don't want to have to send out a search party. Now opposite the school are lots of tenements and we are at number eighty four. There's a big flight of stairs up to the close . . . and we are the first door that you come to. Ring the bell loudly because we'll be making lots of noise I expect."

"Is *your* house in a tenement?"

"Yes, of course. Nearly everyone I know lives in a tenement in Glasgow. Silly boy."

The conductor remembered to deposit Peter at the school and he found number eighty four and mounted the stairs. The close was narrow and dark and reminded him of the covered wynd at home known as the ghostie wynd.

A large brass handle in the door frame must be the bell, he supposed and he pressed the end of it for some time without any apparent sound. There must be some other method so he gently pulled the handle outwards and heard a faint tinkle from the other side of the door. He pushed it back then pulled it harder. This time there was a loud and imperative ringing which seemed as though it would never stop. He nervously pushed the handle back in and again the bell shouted in a demanding way. Celia came running through the brightly lit hall.

"Peter!" she exclaimed in a loud party voice, "I thought the house was coming down. You're so late! I had given you up completely."

Peter felt repulsed and stood stock-still on the doorstep.

"Come in, come in though, better late than never!" and Celia grabbed his arm and led him through the hall.

Although it was not a particularly large hallway, Peter was aware of a great space above his head. The ceiling seemed incredibly high. He had never before been in any ordinary room that had such a high ceiling. In a cinema or a town hall it would seem normal to have all that emptiness above your head but this seemed strange and foreign. He smiled to himself, thinking what a devil of a job it would be to whitewash a ceiling away up there.

The sitting room was large, with three windows in one wall. A tram was stopped just outside the window and just at first the immense void above his head and the tram seemed the most important things in sight to Peter. Next he noticed the expanse of patterned carpet that covered the floor. The furniture, which with a three piece suite, a table, coal scuttle, and standard lamp, amounted to much the same as his mother had in a room quarter the size, was pushed back against the wall and the other guests were sitting quietly watching his arrival. He realised with a start that there were nine people in the room. The only face that he recognised from the summer was that of Drew and he recognised it with a surprising amount of pleasure.

"This is Peter from Pittenweem and you've all been waiting to meet him. Isn't he naughty being so late. Did you sleep in, Peter? And miss the train? Or did you take the wrong tram and go away to the west end first?"

Everyone laughed and Peter shook his head and wished himself back on the cool east coast again. He should never have come. He felt his navy suit was cheap-looking and ridiculous and his newly-trimmed hair was far too short, for these young men were dressed casually and very differently from himself, in sweaters and slacks, the sort of clothes that he did not possess. Four of them wore beards which Peter had always considered a suitable adornment for old men only. The girls were even more intimidating than the boys. One girl had hair dyed bright red, another was clad in tight trousers printed like leopard skin, another was weighted with immense jewellery and had enough make-up 'to scrape off with a spoon' as his mother would have said. Even Celia was in a weird get-up of many bright colours and her hair had a wide blonde streak in it that he had never seen before.

It is never easy to arrive late at a party which is well under way and there were more than enough other handicaps to overwhelm Peter. He was starving and the girl with red hair offered him some food, but in her wish to be friendly, she filled his plate with many things that he would never eat. The hard-boiled eggs and sausages looked tasty but she covered them with curry sauce, ruining them for Peter. The rice tasted like nothing at all. The olives, gherkins and pickled onions were strange and strong and as for the mussels. Peter had seen mussels used as bait all his life and had never remotely considered them for human consumption. It turned his stomach to think of eating them. He ate two buttered rolls and hid his plateful of alien food on the floor under the couch. Too polite to take a third roll, he drank a cup of coffee and finding a seat beside Drew, determined to stay there as long as possible. Everyone spoke quickly and he found it hard to follow their clipped accents and different inflections. Often there were bursts of unexplained giggles at artistic references, in-jokes and mimicry of the Art school tutors.

Drew was not at Art School and he felt almost as out of place in the group as Peter but both were shy young men and found little to say to each other.

Soon the games were resumed and in order to please Celia, Drew soon left Peter's side and joined in, though Peter, 'like a mule' as Celia said, resolutely refused and clasped his empty coffee cup for the next two hours, watching these supposed adults perform, laugh and make idiots of themselves. There was lots of girls sitting on boys' knees and lots of kissing with every boy having kissed every girl at some time during the morning. There were animal imitations, noisy and physical, there were songs that Peter had never heard before and there was some silly thing called 'miming' which Peter found particularly stupid and embarrassing. When someone pretended to climb into an invisible motor car and drive off or wade into and swim in invisible water he felt the hairs on the back of his neck rise up.

Occasionally Celia would try to persuade him to join in but she was always unsuccessful.

These mad young people, intent on enjoying themselves, seemed so remote and unreal to Peter that they might have been images on a cinema screen. He despised them and yet he watched with a grudging fascination. He watched their antics as an anthropologist might have studied the rituals of some primitive tribe. Each moment enforced his feelings of distance and difference from these folk. The Celia of the summer months in Pittenweem, the Celia that he thought he knew was not here. This girl was so obviously happy and at home in these infantile amusements.

Suddenly the fact struck Peter that Celia was the instigator and driving force of this ridiculous party and for the first time that day he felt cold all over.

At one-thirty Celia served thick lentil soup and after devouring three bowl-fulls, Peter felt less depressed.

"Poor Peter, I don't think you've enjoyed my party at all, have you. You didn't play one game. Did you enjoy watching? I know you're going to have a great time this afternoon though. I have a surprise for you and I bet you have just *a wonderful* time. Wait and see!"

Celia's smile and tender attention still had the power to delight Peter and for a few moments the afternoon seemed as though it might blank out the memory of the morning. He stood in the crowded hall with the other guests, waiting for the surprise announcement of the afternoon arrangements. Celia kept them in suspense as they donned their coats.

"Right folks, out you go and jump on a tram car and get off at the Kelvin Hall!"

"Oh, the Kelvin Hall, what a good idea."

"Oh smashing, the Kelvin Hall!"

Everyone was laughing and obviously delighted while Peter felt ignorant and shut out from any idea of what the Kelvin Hall was. Drew saw his blank expression and whispered,

"It's the Fair. Roundabouts and side-shows. You know."

Peter's worst fears were realised. A fairground was the last place on earth that Peter would have chosen to visit, for his stomach, which had battled so miserably and so unsuccessfully with the waves of the North Sea, was equally unfitted to deal with the swinging, whirling, dipping machines that were the main attraction of such a place.

After a long rattling tram journey, the noisy crowd paid its entry fee and walked into the vast indoor showground. It seemed colder inside than it had been in the street. Enormous brightly painted structures reared up dangerously ahead. The smell of burned sugar and hot fat mingled unpleasantly with several different, raucous tunes. Men and women shouted and cajoled customers with offers of 'Five shots for thruppence' and promises of 'Big prizes for everyone'. Five ugly clowns' heads turned from side to side, each mouth wide open in a silent, anguished scream, awaiting a ball to fall down its throat at just the right moment to win a tawdry prize.

Peter turned away from it all. It was horrible and he felt ill already with the bright colours, smells and frantic movement. Of course Celia could not know of his weakness. He had not discussed it with her, but he blamed her for choosing such an unsuitable amusement. A great wave of anger and a degree of self-pity swept over him. It had been such a wasted, disappointing day and Celia was not the girl he had imagined her to be. It had been expensive, too. More than he could afford, what with the train journey and the entrance fee to this horrible place.

Just then she came over to him and took his arm.

"Peter, I know the party wasn't your sort of thing this morning.

I'm sorry. Come on the waltzer with me, please, please, please. Let's enjoy ourselves. I *love* the waltzer. Don't you?"

Peter looked down at her. In spite of her bleached hair and her strange outfit, she was very pretty and he believed that she was kind, too. She had been the girl of his dreams for a long time and it was hard to relinquish those dreams, but he had been mistaken, for their lives could never flow together. His mother was right, they could share no common destiny.

"Thanks for the party Celia. It wis . . . jist fine. But Ah'll no' come on the waltzer wi' ye, a' that burlin' would be shair tae mak me seek. Ah'll jist stand here a wee while and watch ye enjoyin' yersel' an' then Ah'll awa tae catch ma train back tae Aberdeen.

The Studio

WHEN THE MCGHIES MOVED to Pittenweem in 1905, they rented Croft cottage on James Street, where their son William would shortly be born.

John McGhie liked to paint 'on the spot', as all artists did at that time, and would carry his cumbersome painting gear, which included a large tripod easel, the canvas and a wooden paint box which held the palette, tubes of paint and brushes, to the harbour or shore to work. He must have been very fit as he often tramped a mile or so along the coast with what would be an unwieldy load, for any breeze would catch the canvas, especially on the return journey when the paint was wet.

If he required a figure in the painting, he would ask the model to come to the house where only the garden was large enough and bright enough to serve as a studio. A public footpath skirted one side of the elongated garden and the four foot wall was not quite high enough to provide complete privacy. If his sitter were a self-conscious young fishergirl, the greetings and remarks from passers-by were embarrassing. With more mature and confident models, a distracting conversation was likely to start up when an acquaintance hove in sight. The wall was a convenient height to lean on to enjoy a good crack and the frequent interruptions were frustrating for the artist. The weather was also a handicap for although the East Neuk has much more than its fair share of Scotland's sunshine, most days are breezy and of course rain would put a stop to all painting.

The problem was put to Henry Lawson, the local joiner and cabinet maker, who was also soon to be blessed with a son called William. (The two Williams would become life-long friends.)

Lawson's suggestion was a large garden shed, twenty-four feet long by sixteen feet broad, half of which would be glazed. The highest point of the roof would be nine feet. It would provide privacy and protection from the weather and would be as bright as daylight inside with space enough for the artist to walk back and forth at his easel to get the important 'distant view' in which errors of proportion or tone become more apparent.

It would be a large structure for a small Pittenweem garden and I do not know whether the design and measurements were decided by the artist or the joiner, but it seemed a good solution. There were no planning regulations in those days and the work was immediately put in hand. Lawson also made a large wooden dais, called the 'throne' to raise the sitter above eye level. It was a rough structure about four feet square and much the height of a modern coffee table.

I wish that I could tell you what the costs were but it must have been a marvellously well-made building, because it would be dismantled and moved twice, first to 58 High Street, which John McGhie rented for a few summers. Then in 1911, it was moved to 54 High Street where it stood until 1971. It was always called the studio, although my grandfather also had a proper indoor studio at 54 High Street which was reached by an outside stone staircase and was always referred to as 'the upstairs studio'.

"John is in the studio" meant that he was in the half glazed garden shed.

The studio was not only used for painting because even on a winter's day, it was warm and welcoming. When my grandfather was engaged elsewhere, it was a wonderful place for a child to play, especially if the haar, that poetic but chilling east coast mist, had come down or if too much breeze was blowing for comfort. No doubt my mother and uncle as children made as good use of the studio as I later did.

For me the throne was a wonderful toy. It could become an island, a ship or a castle, certainly a place of safety in imagined danger and many adventures were enacted out, sometimes with other children but most often alone. With the wooden door for a blackboard, my didactic skills were honed and my dolls were thoroughly educated in spelling and arithmetic and my favourite poem, 'The Brook' by Tennyson, was declaimed daily to my dolls.

The studio was a natural repository for lumber and unwanted books. Old books about the First World War gave me, a wartime child, the uncomfortable impression that war was a natural and continuous state for the world and unlikely to change in my lifetime. A newspaper Special Edition related the tragedy of the *Titanic*, with the names of those lost. Thirty old *National Geographic* magazines which my grandmother had bought at a bazaar, no doubt for a few pennies, were a wonderful fount of photographs of unknown places, animals and people and I poured over them, being particularly fascinated by an article on the Aztecs, which was luridly illustrated with the bloody rites and human sacrifices of that ancient race. Recalling those blood-curdling pictures recently, my first thought was how on earth they could have had photographs of such things? But of course they were artist's impressions, but so lifelike that they had lived photographically in my memory.

The studio was over forty years old and visibly dilapidated in my childhood. It had been granted little maintenance. Several panes of glass were missing, the green paint outside was faded and flaking and the untreated wood inside had a grey furry quality. In one corner a crowd of extra large and brilliant montbretia plants forced their way through some of the rotting timbers to enjoy the balmy temperature of the interior. These flowers pleased me particularly. I liked their sturdy impudence.

The adults too, especially on chilly days, made good use of the studio. I can remember my mother perched on a corner of the throne, knitting a fairisle jumper, while my grandmother, reclining on an old horsehair sofa, enjoyed the Sunday papers.

Personally, I detested that sofa and kept my distance from it, for it was aggressively scratchy to youthful, bare legs.

During the Second World war my mother grew tomatoes and cucumbers in the studio. Nothing seemed so delicious as those fresh fruits straight from the vine. When autumn came and there were still green tomatoes to be picked, she followed the advice of the Radio Doctor, a media celebrity of those days, who gave helpful tips to ease the vicissitudes of wartime. As he advised, she wrapped each tomato in tissue paper and laid them carefully and separately in a drawer. I must have been a cynical child for I did not share her faith in the Radio Doctor. I was pretty sure that it was all a waste of time and they would just rot away. At Christmas when they were brought out and unwrapped, their crisp, scarlet sweetness seemed like a miracle to me.

By the early sixties, the neglected glass of the studio was potentially dangerous and as I now had young children of my own, my grandmother had the glazed half of the old edifice removed, leaving a garden shed which was now entirely wooden, still roomy but filled, as one might expect, with a great many *articles,* unwanted furniture and bric-a-brac, as well as all the garden implements. It was no longer a place to play in, but crowded, dark and dusty with a decrepit aspect and walls which were no longer quite perpendicular.

In the summer holidays in Pittenweem, our Siamese cat was the only member of the family who made use of the studio. He was shut in there each night and the local moggies crept into the space below the hut and hurled insults at the imprisoned, blue-eyed stranger.

My grandmother had always hated high winds and throughout the sixties she spoke of how the old building swayed alarmingly in gales.

"I doubt it will just blow right away someday!" she prophesied.

However, even the hurricane of 1968 did not dislodge our studio, though sadly it completely demolished the new community hall which had recently been built on the braes above the swimming pool. This magnificent modern wooden structure, destined for concerts, dances and whist drives, solid and ten times the size of the remnants of our ancient studio, was completely swept away out over the North Sea. Except for the foundations, not a scrap of the hall was to be seen the following day. Incredibly, the unusually fierce winds had just poured through the many apertures of our little shed and continued on their destructive way. Though the shed had danced and shuddered alarmingly for hours, there it stood the next day, only slightly more drunken-looking than before.

My grandmother died in 1971 and it was in the autumn of that year that I, now the owner of 54, High Street, finally had what was left of the studio dismantled and removed. After it was cleared away, the small garden seemed surprisingly spacious and the view of the sea was certainly improved, but the little hut had almost achieved the span of years allotted to man and I found it very hard to get rid of those last pathetic wooden remnants which had so many memories. The shed's contents would furnish material for many another tale, for my grandmother was a magpie. Not only the studio but the house was crammed with objects. It was far beyond the life-long collection of most old ladies and while some of the articles were very fine and others interesting, there was also a fair amount of rubbish and also many things which were not to my taste. I had been very busy for weeks, selling some things, throwing out others and generally making some space in the house.

One night in October I lay awake listening to the high winds howling round the old house that was now mine. It was the time of the equinoctial gales. Of course they were nothing compared to the 1968 hurricane which was, I hope, a once-in-a lifetime experience. These wuthering winds had a sad, evocative sound in the chimney and I thought regretfully of the studio, though I knew that it was all for the best that it was gone. I hoped that the red-tiled roofs of Pittenweem, those roofs that add so much to the town's picturesque quality, were not too ravaged by the attacking forces of nature. Then I started to think of my grandmother and how she had hated high winds. Suddenly, with a start of guilt, I realised that the previous day, the 20th October had been my grandmother's birthday. I had been so busy transforming her house to mine that I had forgotten. She would have been 90 that day, an age which she often assured us she had *no* desire to reach and she would give an imitation of an old crone, bent double and hobbling along, gibbering in a high whine, then she would straighten to her full, elegant height and say a loud and decided,

"NO THANK YOU!"

My relationship with my grandmother was not always an easy or an affectionate one. She liked to dominate and I was used to freedom in my life and also, if the truth be told, used to exerting authority over those around me, being a teacher and a mother of four children. I think that we had a lot of admiration for each other and could each amuse the other, but my grandmother had an uncomfortably spiky side which might surface unexpectedly and wound. She could be very critical and gifts and tasks were found fault with, depressingly often. She and I were at our best together when my mother was not present, as their relationship, like that of many mothers and daughters, was not an ideal one. They were very different from each other and as I was close to my mother, the three generations together seemed unbalanced.

However that night of the twentieth, I felt very disappointed in myself that I had forgotten my grandmother's birthday. I lay and thought of her many kind acts, her independence and undoubted talents and skills and I shed tears for her for the first time since her death seven months previously.

Black Annabell

In summertime my garden becomes my living room,
And as garden manager, my cat knows every bloom.
Smelling flowers so deeply that she often has to sneeze,
As she ticks off her inventory of butterflies and bees.
She also takes the roll call for our community of snails,
Checking paths and walls for their small silvery trails.
Then on a high wall she will perch and with sharp eyes, make a
    thorough search
Of shrubs and trees of various kinds, of adjoining gardens and
    descending wynds,
Of small white houses whose red roofs glow,
Of soaring seagulls and the harbour below,
Where she can espy the fishing fleet as it sets off to catch what she
    best likes to eat.

When her surveillance is finished at last, she joins me as I break my
    fast,
Stretching beside me, nothing loath to peer into the undergrowth.
Enjoying dew sparkles and earthy smells,
Our senses plumbing the deepest wells.
All these delights we love to share,
Annabell and I are a primitive pair.

Our most glorious hours of play are midsummer nights as bright as
    day,
In a garden where all seems to quiver and grow,
And the sea in the distance appears to flow.
When the perfume of plants is musky and rare and only my cat and
    I are there.
When Schubert drifts through the casement wide,

As I sit with a glass of wine at my side,
Watching in dazed romantic trance,
My black nymph create a marvellous dance.

But as chiffon clouds adorn the moon, we know those nights must
        finish soon,
Those nights when only she and I hear echoes of that Panic sigh.
And who can tell,
In that mythical night,
Who is woman?
Or cat?
Or sprite?

Street Sweeper

ANDREW REEKIE CLAMBERED and slipped on the rocks. His big boots with their rows of tackets were hardly suitable for this occupation but as he had never worn any other type of footgear, he was unaware of their shortcomings. The rocks on which he climbed were of particularly beautiful colours, cream, pale and dark ochre with sometimes a stripe of pink shading to dark purple. Without consciously noticing these colours, Andrew was always happy when climbing these rocks, particularly when, as now, they were enhanced by the rays of the evening sun. Other children, more imaginative than Andrew, would transform this rocky part of the coast into a miniature landscape, naming mountains, lochs and rivers and making wooden boats with paper sails to sail complex voyages. But Andrew was content to jump over the rock-pools known locally as 'dubs' and balance ungracefully on the ridges. He knew that he was happy there although he could not have described the power and freedom which he felt. He liked it best when no other children were present and the sounds of the sea and the seagulls and the bright evening glow delighted him in an abstract way. His pleasure might best be described as poetic, certainly the nearest thing to poetry that he would ever experience. Best of all at the 'dubs', Andrew could be sure of hearing his mother call him to supper. He was always obedient to his hard-working mother and her rare smiles filled him with happiness. The complete trusting love which he felt for his mother was something that even in manhood, he would never lose. Their fisherman's cottage was not far away and when his mother's harshly rich voice shouted his name over the bay, the headland to the west would throw the sound back along the whole foreshore. There was no chance of his missing the call.

In that part of Scotland, with its long history of European trade, the pronunciation of Andrew is akin to the French 'Andre', though less nasal.

"Ondray! Ondray!" with a sharply rising inflection on the second syllable, would echo over the water and the boy would hardly have recognised his name in any other form. Even the school teachers with their aspirations to speak correctly, would modify the vowels of his name.

Vowels were a dreadful worry to teachers. The regular visit of the HM Inspectors necessitated some modification of the local pronunciation. One favourite teacher had confused Andrew completely, and no doubt the rest of the class too, with her constant worry about vowels. At least once a week she would say,

"Now children, I do not want to hear you say BURD. The proper way to say it is BERD. It is the same when you say DURT. I hate to hear that. Please always say DERT."

Her insistence and energy were wasted, for if any child had followed her advice, it would have been laughed to scorn in the playground.

As soon as Andrew heard his mother's call, he left the dubs and ran, lanky and awkward, along the shore to his house, climbing up the small stone staircase to the front door. Exquisitely picturesque, these haphazard and vulnerable little houses, with their outside stairs, had been the delight of artists and photographers for more than a century. Andrew accepted that his house had this unusual feature without question, but his parents considered themselves lucky to have an upper floor, for when storms coincided with the high spring tides the lashing waves swept over the dyke and into the ground floor houses, bringing the devastation of seaweed and sand with the surging water. In these houses, furniture and walls bore various tidemarks of flooding and sand lay always between the floorboards.

Andrew's father was a fisherman on the steam drifters and often away from home for long periods, leaving his wife Nan to deal with the practicalities of bringing up three children on a meagre housekeeping allowance. Billy was a year older than Andrew and there was a baby girl, Moira.

Billy was a physically lazy boy and not such a willing helper as Andrew but then Billy did very well at school. He had always found school easy, he liked numbers and he could read when he was six. No one considered Andrew a clever boy, not even his mother. Some even suggested that he was "a herrin' short o' the dozen". All subjects were a mystery to him and school was a thick fog through which he struggled each day between nine and four o'clock. One or two teachers had been very sympathetic, for he was a good boy, a willing boy, never a troublemaker and devoted and helpful to his mother. Other less patient teachers, convinced that he could try harder, used the belt continuously.

Andrew had an inner restlessness which made it hard for him to sit still for the long periods which were then demanded of school children. He would rattle his pencil, bite his rubber and drop his ruler noisily. Sometimes he would jump to his feet at an inappropriate moment. An intelligent teacher would have tried to use the boy's energy wisely, but too often tasks were given as rewards to those who had gained ten out of ten for mental arithmetic or spelling, subjects quite as remote from Andrew's understanding as trigonometry or the Serbo-Croat language. Thus Andrew seldom had the chance to fetch the milk-crate or clean the blackboard or give out the slates, and these all seemed like heavenly and unattainable occupations to the boy.

It was very hard for Andrew to follow his brother through school for the older boy's attainments only pointed up the inabilities of the younger and teachers with the best will in the world, could not avoid comparisons. He was belted at least once on most days and usually several times. For small misdemeanours such as forgetting to put the straw and pasteboard top from his milk-bottle in the rubbish box or for sitting with his legs stretched out into the narrow passage between the desks, he would be punished rather perfunctorily. Then in Miss Blair's class there was strict rule that, when not writing, everyone must sit at all times with arms folded. For a year Andrew continuously forgot this rule and was punished daily, sometimes twice. Then there were the times when the pleasures of playtime put a visit to the toilet completely out of his head and the rule was that a request to "leave the room" before lunch-time would be granted certainly, but the belt would be used on your return to the classroom. There was an alternative possibility in this situation which girls often chose. If a child peed on the floor, it would not be punished but it must mop it up and suffer the humiliation. Perhaps this was deemed punishment enough. Andrew became inured to the belt. He scarcely felt it and it carried no shame for him. It was just another part of the unpleasant daily experience.

However he dreaded the day that he would move into the "heedie's" class, for his brother's constant warnings seemed dire and threatening.

"Jist you wait though" Billy's face wore a ferocious expression as he spoke, "Jist you wait till ye're in the "heedie's" class like me. *Then ye'll get it.* Auld Robbie's a bugger. Ye'll get the belt a' day, ye ken. *Ye'll get the belt ivry time ye dinnae get five oot o' ten.* Ye'll get the belt fur spellin' an' fur sums an' fur mental an' fur readin' so ye wull. Ye'll get the belt a' day. Ah'm tellin' ye. An' ye'll get it if ye drap yur slate pencil or sclaff yur buits. You jist wait'n see. *An' he's an awfy hard belter!*"

Mr Robertson, who, in spite of thirty-five years of teaching experience, believed firmly, almost religiously, that physical punishment would eventually lead every child to become proficient in learning, used the belt as unfailingly as a more enlightened teacher might have used a word of encouragement or gentle criticism.

Wielding the belt was practically his only method of communication with the less successful pupils.

At home it might have seemed to a stranger that his mother was as repressive and critical as his teachers when she spoke to him.

"Ondray, wull ye set doon, *this meenit*. Ye're aye in ma road, lauddie. Get oot, get oot ma wey, wull ye."

But her apparently stern words were always tempered by smiles and kindly looks, for Andrew was her favourite in spite of, perhaps because of, his mental slowness. He knew very well that he was her favourite and in his gratitude he was a good son.

"He's an awfy kind wee laud, ye ken," she would confide to her next door neighbour. "He niver means ony herm an' he's awfy, awfy *willin'*. Ah kin aye trust 'm tae dae ma messages or look efter wee Moira. But ye see Billy, he's no' like that at a'. He's aye dreamin' or readin' his coamics or wastin' his time somewey."

"But Billy's awfy guid at the skill, is he no'? Awfy grand at his lessons, ah've been hearin'. An' he wins prizes."

"Oh aye, he does weel enuff wi' the teachers, Ah suppose. Aye, that's richt enough. But Ondray's an awfy *grand* lad. Ye canny help but be foand o' him."

Billy was too bright a boy not to be fully aware of his mother's favouritism in spite of remarks like,

"Ondray! Lookit yer brither sittin' there readin' his Beano, nice'n quiet. Why kin you no' sit still like that, ye wee nuisance! Ye ken whit yer problim is, ma mannie? Yer erse is ower roond tae sit still. Aye, aye, tak the brush an' sweep the flair if yer mindit. That'll gie ye somethin' tae dae an' ye kin brush doon the front steps an' a', if ye want. An' dinnae bang yer brush against the furniture like that an' dinnae make ower muckle stoor an' ye kin tak the rag rug doon tae the dyke but dinnae whack it ower hard, it's jist aboot fleein' tae pieces. An' dinnae ... "

Though the words seemed negative, they were accompanied with a clap on the shoulder and a smile while an unsmiling look was directed at the inactive Billy and his comic.

Andrew would wield the broom with enthusiasm, cracking against table and chair legs, especially Billy's chair until his Mother would say,

"That's fine noo, ma mannie. Ah'll gether it up wi' ma wee brush 'n shovel. You kin gang oot tae the front steps an' mak them grand an' clean tae. Here tak the tablecloath wi' ye noo, an' gie't a bit shake afore ye sweep doon the stairs"

By the time that Andrew was nine he had extended his sweeping activities beyond the outside stair and across the cobbled pathway which lay between the house and the sea wall. Soon he was sweeping as far as the break in the seawall where three steps led down to the beach, and in the other direction as far as one of the wynds which ascended to the upper part of the town. Old ladies as they passed would remark.

"Whit a grand wee help ye are tae yer mither, Ondray. Ah wish't Ah hud a wee lauddie like you tae help me."

Big Aggie, who walked her minute dog along the shore every day, occasionally gave him a penny, which had been worth something more when she was a child certainly, but Andrew was always properly appreciative and saved them up.

Many summer visitors came to the pretty fishing village and once a man in a brightly coloured fairisle pullover and tweed plus-fours saw the boy industriously sweeping and gave him sixpence. It would be hard to say whether the man's outfit or his gift caused the lad more astonishment. Another story which he often told in later years was about an artist, one of the many who thronged the shore in the summer.

"Ye ken he drappit a hauf-a-croon an' niver noticed! Niver noticed losin' a hauf-a-croon! Niver noticed it! Ah thoucht they artists wis poor. He wis cairryin' an awfy stuff right enough, a big board tae pent oan an' big sticks tae prop up the board an' a big box wi' his pents in it an' a wee stool tae sit oan. It folded up like, ye ken. He wis fair laden doon. Then he drappit a few things an Ah helpit him pick thim up. Then he wis awa up the wynd an' oot o' sight afore Ah seen the hauf-a-croon lyin' there oan the grund an' Ah tried tae find 'm a' that day an' the nixt yin tae, an' Ah niver did. Ah niver seen 'm again. Ma mither said tae tak it up tae the polis an' Ah did but he wisnae at hame that day an' then ma faither said jist tae keep it fur the man wid niver be comin' back lookin' fur't. An' Ah bocht a wee brooch fur ma mither an' she likit it but said next time tae be sure an' haund ony money intae the polis an' aye be hoanest. But she aye wore that wee brooch when she wis dressin' up tae gan oot veesitin'.

When Andrew reached the age of twelve and moved into Mr Robertson's class, it was a very sad time for him. His mother started to develop a painful illness in her joints and her suppressed groans upset her son. It was as though he suffered each pang with her. Billy was doing well at secondary school, enjoying new subjects like mathematics and science. But while his brother established himself as a successful pupil at the Waid Academy, Andrew was belted throughout every day by Mr Robertson for his failures in spelling, reading and writing, arithmetic written and mental, general knowledge and handwork. Billy had been right. Robbie was a hard belter. The other teachers had been amateurs in comparison to his skills as a belt-wielder. After a year of this regime, poor Andrew seemed a worse scholar than ever and was unfitted to leave the primary school along with his classmates to travel to the secondary school one mile away. The headmaster strongly advised Mrs Reekie that it would be a waste of everyone's time and much better if Andrew stayed another year under his care. By that time Andrew would be nearly school leaving age and would not require to start secondary school at all. Mrs Reekie, still believing in the Jovian power of the headmaster, unquestioningly agreed to this suggestion and in her ignorance sentenced her son to suffer another eight months of sadistic cruelty.

Andrew grew taller and taller and became very thin, gaunt almost, and was even more alone and out of place in the primary school. Few children spoke to him and he developed a stoop to appear less obvious. The other boys were so much smaller that he no longer joined in the games of football but lurked unhappily in corners of the playground, before dragging his large and unwilling feet once more into the classroom of torture. Mr Robertson started commenting on Andrew's extreme height and emaciation and not in a spirit of kindliness. It was Robbie's nearest approach to humour and was sure to produce an easy, if uncomfortable laugh from the rest of the children.

Throughout this testing time, Andrew still drew comfort from sweeping. After school, while Billy worked steadily through his mountain of homework Andrew would help his mother with shopping, cleaning windows, peeling potatoes and all the tasks which she was finding increasingly difficult. But his favourite was always sweeping, especially outside his front door. The strength required to wield the broom on the cobbles and the satisfying improvement never failed to cheer him and buttress what was left of his self-esteem. Passers-by, mainly older folk, would speak to him, sometimes with a compliment and sometimes with a story. Sometimes they just needed to have a little grumble and then they would thank Andrew for listening to them. This astonished him and he discussed it with his mother.

"D'ye ken, auld Duncan thankit me fur listenin' tae 'm."

"Did he, ma son? Well Ah expect he wis a wee bit lonely an' it wid be nice fur 'm tae see that ye sympathised wi' him."

"Ah jist listened, ye ken, Ah didnae say onythin'."

"But he needit ye. Auld folks like tae talk tae young yins an' tell thim wee stories. No ivry young yin'll listen nooadays, but you're a braw laddie . . . Ah ken that."

Her eyes filled with tears as she looked at the emaciated boy in front of her. What was happening to him? He was starting to look like an old man himself, and as for herself what was happening to her? Fear of finding out kept her from the doctor as much as the money involved.

"Keep yer shoothers back noo, laddie. Yer're awfy hunched aboot the shoothers. Ur ye feelin' the cauld? Wid ye like a piece'n jam afore yer tea?"

After leaving school Andrew was offered a place on his uncle's fishing boat but seven weeks of seasickness convinced the family that he would never be a fisherman.

"Besides, Nan," her brother was obviously finding it difficult to express himself, "besides, he's no' exactly quick or haundy. He wis aye drappin' things ower the side an' . . . "

"The boy wisnae weel, he wis spewin' maistly, as far as Ah kin make oot."

"Aye, aye richt enough, he wis gey no weel, thur's nae doot aboot that, but there wis things he couldnae really get the hang o' . . . "

"Well it's feenished noo. He's no' gaun tae sea again. He's that tall an' gangly it's a wunner he didnae topple o'erboard hissel . . . "

"Aye it's a wunner richt enough . . . "

Jessie looked at her brother sharply

"We'll get some ither joab fur the lauddie."

"Ah hope so, Nan, Ah hope so."

It was Andrew's little sister, Moira who made the suggestion.

"Ah wis playin' ropes in the High Street when Geordie Dick's dust cairt passed an' Auld Mrs Hughes wis shoutin' at him tae get doon an' sweep up the mess the seagulls hud made. Ye ken they'd dragged all the papers an' the tottie peelins and the fish guts oot the pail afore the cairt cam roond this mornin'. An he wis saying she shouldnae hae pit it oot sae early in the mornin' an' she wis sayin' . . . "

"Whit are ye tryin' tae tell us, ma bonny bairn?"

"Wid that no be a guid joab fur oor Ondray? Sweepin' up? He's that fond o' sweepin' up an' Geordie Dick's gettin' gey auld noo tae be jumpin' aff his cairt a' day. An' his horse is awfy bad-tempered."

"Ye're an awfy wee lassie! Whaur d'ye get a' they ideas frae?"

However Mrs Reekie thought that it was a very good idea and as her uncle was married to Geordie Dick's cousin she very soon arranged something. Of course the Town Council had to approve another employee but it was obvious that Geordie did need some help and so a very small wage was offered to Andrew and he started the career which he was to follow for the rest of his life.

In the next forty years, he saw many changes in the disposal of Pittenweem refuse.

The first big change, and perhaps the most difficult to implement, was to persuade his mother and all her neighbours who lived along the sea front that their garbage should not be dumped on the sea shore. It had been the custom since time immemorial to throw ashes, potato peelings, broken crockery 'ower the dyke' to be removed by the kindly relentless tide. This was in addition to the myriads of mussel shells, debris of the line-baiting, which were also dumped every day. The modest amount of coarse sand on the beach was almost always hidden under this detritus. Although the dust cart came round regularly, old habits die hard and it was many years before this method of rubbish disposal was discarded by those who lived near the beach. There was the sad story of a summer visitor and his son on the last day of their holiday, sitting on the beach in their good travelling clothes, while the wife gave their holiday rooms a last clean out. The old lady next door, came out and without looking, emptied her bucket of ashes and vegetable peelings over the wall, right on top of the unlucky father and son. This was in the 1950s.

Almost as soon as Andrew started work, the 'bad-tempered horse' was replaced by another more equable creature, Harry. He was a tall thin horse with not much brain but a very nice nature, very suited to the slow laborious job. Andrew, who had few friends and had never owned a pet, discovered the pleasures of caring for a loyal, affectionate animal and delighted in grooming the big shaggy creature and rewarding him with apples and carrots.

For many years, Andrew and Harry were devoted to each other and many secrets were whispered into the horse's brown, twitching ears.

Before Andrew was twenty five, Moira was married and living in Dundee, Billy had finished his training and was an engineer in Glasgow and John Reekie had died tragically at sea. Andrew and Mrs Reekie, who was now frail and in almost constant pain, was pleased to have her favourite son with her and to know he was settled in a steady and respectable job. When they were given the chance of a small council house without stairs, 'up the town,' they moved away from the quaint seashore dwelling to a semi-detached bungalow type house. Nan was delighted with the modern kitchen and bathroom and there was no longer the necessity of struggling up and down the steep West Wynd for shopping.

For Andrew, it was a terrible wrench to leave his home. He missed the sound of the sea and the well-known walls and pathways where his feet knew every mound and hollow, even on the darkest night. However he did not speak of his sadness to her or to anyone, for he knew his mother needed to live in a more easily run house if she were to retain her independence. Thursday was his favourite day though, because that was the scheduled day for street sweeping along the west shore and he took particular care around his old home. In fact he was quite often observed working on those few hundred yards on days other than Thursday. He found it cheered him up to return to the familiar, well-worn pathway of his youth and he was never a worker that watched the clock. His job was to keep the streets clean whatever the time of day and he found a familiar enjoyment in striding up and down the wynds. Although still thin and a little stooped, his satisfying outdoor life had strengthened him.

Eventually in the late fifties, much to Andrew's sorrow, Harry and the battered cart were replaced by a truck.

Geordie Dick had retired and it was decided to hire another man, Donald, to drive the truck for Andrew had no ambition to drive and was quite happy emptying the bins and sweeping the streets on the days when the truck did not collect rubbish. Donald was friendly to the shy old-fashioned Andrew in a patronising way. He taught him to smoke and swear and made him laugh with highly improper remarks about the dignitaries of the town and a never-ending flow of vulgar stories. Although not what would be recognised as a good influence on Andrew, Donald introduced him to a more modern and normal way of socialising which gave Andrew confidence. When he modelled his behaviour on Donald's, Andrew lost the shadow of alienation which had always hung over him and started to feel more accepted in the community.

The other half of the Reekie's semi-detached house belonged to the Ferguson family. The father was said to have heart trouble and walked very slowly and with a stick when he went to collect his pension, which was almost his only outing in the week.

The son, Robert, was thin and wasted and had a bad limp and although he worked at the fish market, he had many absences. It was said amongst the fishermen that his disease was, "Awfy serious and thur wis nae betterment likely. Aye, aye, awfy serious."

Then there would be a general shaking of heads and spitting and marching up and down.

Betty, the daughter, was a few years younger than Andrew and had never married. She looked after the two invalids, the house and had a full-time job in the fruit shop. Her walk was fast and determined and unlike the other inhabitants of Pittenweem, she seldom stopped for a 'blether' in the street, for too many tasks awaited her at home. Whether there had been romance in her life, no one knew, but the necessities of survival and family duty had probably been too strong to allow her to contemplate anything as frivolous as a husband. Her one self indulgence was her garden in which brilliant flowers bloomed each year. It was a retreat for her in the long summer evenings and she might be seen working in it in the June dusk until ten o'clock at night.

"Betty next door's an awfy hard worker, mither, isn't she?" Andrew said to his mother.

It was not the first time he had made this remark.

"Aye I see her oot there wi' her sweet peas again."

"She must be gey tired workin' a' day in the shop then lookin' efter they twa pair sowls an' the hoose an' a'. An' she's goat a' that washin' ivry day."

"Aye but she's goat a machine tae help her noo an' you work a' day too an' work hard at hame lookin' efter me, an' *you're* no' complainin'. She micht spare hersel' the gairden if she'd ony sense."

"But it's a braw gairden, mither. Ah like lookin' at it tae."

The Reekie's own garden was mainly concrete slabs around a little grassy plot, with one or two half-hearted shrubs struggling in the corner.

Nan's smile was sarcastic at this innocent admiration.

"Ah see she's oot there the noo, sittin' there, haein' a cup o' tea in the dark. Whit a funny lassie she is. She's aye been a wee bit strange, that yin."

"Ah wid set in ma gairden an' a', an' drink ma tea amangst ma flooers, if Ah hud such bonny yins."

It was seldom that Andrew set his opinion against his mother's and she did not like it.

"Ah think ye're sweet oan her, Ondray Reekie! Awa oot an hiv a bit chat tae her. She's fine 'n handy tae coort."

But his mother's teasing angered him and he stamped off to his bedroom. Although unaware of it herself, her words were tinged with a jealous bitterness of the younger, stronger woman. Nor was she the first to suggest the suitability and propinquity of Betty Ferguson. Andrew's workmates could always be sure of "takin' a rise" out of him by talking of a possible romance.

Betty and Andrew did occasionally speak over the garden wall. The conversations usually started with Andrew admiring some flower or shrub and then for twenty minutes or so they would talk. Betty would have been astonished and indignant at the idea of any romantic interlude between them and always referred to her neighbour as "puir auld Ondray next door".

Because of her work in the shop, Betty was a source of the latest gossip for Andrew to retell to the housewives and retired fishermen that he met throughout his working day. Always hungry for a good 'baur', his listeners enjoyed Andrew's idiosyncratic and outrageous story-telling, liberally sprinkled with the curses which he had learned from Donald.

With Betty, he was more inhibited and said little, speaking mostly of the skills and charms of his horse, for Betty brought home any broken carrots or bruised apples for Harry.

One evening, they exchanged confidences about their secret dreams.

"Noo ye're no' tae laugh, Ondray, Ah ken it wis silly but Ah aye wantit tae dance. Ah jist loved music an' dancin' about tae it. There wis a lassie came tae Pittenweem whin Ah wis aboot nine or ten and she sterted a wee dancin' class doon the shore, near where Ah used tae bide. My, Ah'd hiv loved tae gan tae that class, but ma mither hud nae money tae pey fur't, so I jist keekit in the windae at thim an' then tried tae practise by masel later. Aye an' Ah sometimes made faces at they lucky lassies that were inside dancin' an' Ah chappit at the window an' a'. They must've thoucht Ah wis a richt daftie but Ah wis jist that mad cos Ah couldnae be in there dancin' tae."

Hurriedly she brushed a tear away from her eye, continuing to pat her hair as though the night insects were annoying her.

"Ah bet ye'd be a dam braw dancer, Betty an' Ah'll tell ye whit Ah wid like tae dae, Betty. Ah'd like tae be like thae buggers oan the wireless, tellin' daft stories and hivin' a'body lauchin' at thim. Big crowds lauchin' awa as though they couldnae stope theirsels. That's whit Ah wid like an' Ah bet they get plenty bloody money fur't tae.

"Ondray! ye'll need tae stoape a' that swearin'! But onywey you div have folk listenin' tae ye an' laughin' right hearty. Ah've seen ye often wi three or four wummin roon' aboot ye an' thur a' laughin' awa fit tae burst thur steys. Ye divnae get big money fur't but ye're entertainin' thim a' the same. An' ye ken whit they say, 'laughter's the best medicine'. Ye're like the doactor, so ye ur."

"Aye the doactor, that's richt enuff, Ah'm jist like the doactor!"

They both laughed heartily at this suggestion and said goodnight.

Though their conversations were sometimes weeks apart and the above the most intimate they ever had, they shared a sympathy and kindly feelings towards each other and there was comfort and satisfaction in knowing that the other was just 'through the wall'.

As the years passed, Mrs Reekie became more dependent and eventually it was decided that she must have a woman's care. Arrangements were made for her to stay with her daughter Moira in Dundee.

"Ah'm no' sae sure aboot Moira haein' me."

"Ur ye no' mither?"

"She wis aye awfy smert an' nippy."

"She's a kind lassie, though. She'll look efter ye better nor Ah can."

He was not sure if this were true but it seemed that his mother must go and it was best to look on the bright side.

"Ye cud aye come back here if ye didnae like it there."

She shook her head sadly.

"An' hoo will you manage here a' by yersel, ma son? Ah'm worrit aboot ye, Ondray."

Poor Andrew was also worried about himself living alone, worried about his mother leaving her beloved Pittenweem and whether he was a bad son to let her go, but then looking after her was more of a worry than anything. When the doctor and the district nurse had said his mother should go to her daughter, he had felt relieved and then he had worried about that feeling. He was thinner than ever with all the worry.

After his mother moved to Dundee there was a lessening of household chores but he certainly found the house lonely and strange. It was hard for him to make small domestic decisions. His mother had been the one to say,

"We'll hae mince the nicht, Ondray."

or,

"It's a grand sunny day, Ondray, we'll get the beds strippit and wash the sheets."

But he managed to adapt and bumble on haphazardly, spending long hours each evening in front of the television, eating toasted cheese or hard-boiled eggs or sometimes just a bowl of cornflakes.

However life, like Nature, often seems to abhor a vacuum and after only five months of solitude, he had a letter from his brother Billy in Glasgow.

Since leaving for the city, Billy had seldom returned to the East Neuk and a letter from him was an event that did not happen every year. Andrew painstakingly read it with a feeling of alarm and puzzlement.

Dear Andrew,

This will be a surprise to you. I think you know I have had a few health worries over the years. Well, sadly it has all got the better of me now. I have been advised to take early retirement, in fact they made it pretty plain I had no choice. I'm getting a nice lump sum, but I'll need some of that for a wheel chair. It is very hard to feel you are useless when you are not yet sixty! I hope that you will agree that the best thing I can do is to return to Pittenweem and move in with you. Anyway, I expect you are feeling the house lonely with mum away in Dundee. I should get everything organised here in a week or two and be with you by the end of the month. There is a pal at work will drive me through in a van with my few bits and pieces so no need to worry about that.

Your loving brother, Billy

"Billy! In a wheel-chair!"

Even his mother had never needed a wheelchair. Betty's brother next door was in a wheel-chair. She had to lift him in and out his chair. She sometimes spoke of the constant struggle. Would Billy expect to be lifted? In spite of the signature, there had never been much love lost between the brothers. They were so different and Billy had left home when young. They hardly knew each other. Andrew kept thinking of other people in Pittenweem that he knew better than Billy and liked better too, but to live in the same house! That was different. You might enjoy a blether in the market place but not live in the same house with them. He tried to think of returning from work and his brother always there. In a wheelchair! Needing his dinner! Needing to be looked after! Because of his love for his mother, the demands that she had made on him had never seemed too great. But Billy meant nothing to him. He could hardly remember what he looked like, but he remembered the unhappy atmosphere and the hostility of their boyhood years. Andrew's imagination was unequal to all the possible drawbacks of Billy coming to live in his house, but he felt very strongly that he did not want it. It made him sad and angry to think about how his life was to be changed whether he wanted it or not. Trying to think of the problem tired his mind so much that he slept all night in the armchair in front of the TV.

As he had with the rest of life's problems, Andrew accepted and adapted to Billy's arrival. It was not so terrible as it might have been. Billy was not completely chairbound and the new arrangement worked not badly, though it would be wrong to say that they became close and brotherly in their relations. At best, a comfortable familiarity existed between them and they shared the same tastes in food and television programmes. Billy had changed a lot and he was good at making those small day to day decisions which Andrew found so difficult.

Andrew spent longer hours at work now for his efforts were redoubled in his struggle against the ever increasing litter on the streets of Pittenweem. Crisp bags, chocolate wrappers, cigarette packet cellophane, polythene bags, beer-cans and plastic bottles were lying everywhere, for eating seemed to be a non-stop occupation, with the used packaging immediately discarded. Eight o'clock on Sunday morning saw him sweeping up the Saturday night chip bags and papers in order that the eyes of the early service churchgoers might not be offended.

He was quite happy to spend long hours working, for the street was where his social life existed. It was where he could meet people and make them laugh.

The years passed and life had settled into a rut for the two brothers. Billy had been getting his old age pension for two years now, Andrew collected it each Thursday. Soon Andrew himself would reach retiral age, but this was never in his thoughts. It was impossible for him to think of a life without streets to sweep. Although very thin, he was still strong and fit and out in all the weathers that the fierce east coast could cast at him.

One Friday night towards the end of November, Andrew came home to find the house in darkness. He thought that strange, for it had been dull since two that afternoon.

Billy must have gone for his afternoon nap and overslept. Right enough it was a dismal day.

Andrew walked into Billy's bedroom quite noisily.

"Time ye were up, Billy! It's Friday ye ken. Are ye wantin' tae share a white puddin' wi' me the nicht or will Ah get an extra fish. Are ye hungry, man? C'moan it's time tae get up, lazylump."

As he said the last word, which had been a favourite with his mother when they were sleepy boys, he realised that something was different. The figure in the bed had not moved at all and would never move again, for Billy had died quietly that morning soon after Andrew left for work.

Andrew touched his brother's hand and it was ice cold.

Andrew went and sat in the sitting room, without any light and without pulling the curtains.

He felt unable to think at all and his muscles seemed too tired to move.

At first he closed his eyes and fell asleep for two hours.

When he wakened, very cold, he jumped up, put on the light and TV and pulled the curtains before he remembered his brother in the bedroom. It could not be true.

In a daze he went back to his brother's room and pulled the curtains across the window, catching a glimpse of Betty in her garden as she called her cat in for the night. The sight of her steadied him a little bit.

What would Betty do?

Her father was dead. She would know about dead people and what you did about them. Could he ask her for help? He decided she had enough to worry her although she only had her brother to care for now. Besides, he was not really sure that Billy was dead. He was unable to believe it. It was impossible. Perhaps Billy was just very cold. Andrew put another two blankets on Billy's bed, tucking them well round about him.

He returned to the sitting room. It was now nine o'clock. He felt he must do something. What should he do? Should he get the doctor? The doctor was always kind but it seemed late to bring him out and how would he explain Billy's symptoms over the phone? If Billy was really dead, then there was nothing the doctor could do to help him. No he would not phone the doctor. Tomorrow he would ask Betty or someone else perhaps. Someone that would know what to do.

Besides, Billy might just be all right in the morning. Maybe he had taken some sort of fit that would pass with a good night's sleep.

Andrew sat and watched TV for twenty minutes. He understood none of it, but it helped to take his mind off the terrible problem.

Suddenly he realised that he was very hungry in the way that extremely thin people become all at once.

He bought two fish suppers and a single white pudding, partly hoping that Billy might be ready for something by now and partly feeling awkward at changing his regular Friday night order of the last nine years. If he did that, there would be comments,

"*Jist wan supper*, Ondray? Wha's no' hungry the nicht? Is Billy no' weel?"

"An' whit's wrang wi' him?"

" Is it his stoamack playin' up?"

"Ah aye say there's naethin' like chips tae settle yer stoamick!"

"Aye, tell 'm he's goat tae eat, tae keep his strength up."

Then there would be laughter.

Andrew had a clear perception of the likely banter which would occur and he felt he could not deal with it tonight. Buying the usual two suppers solved that problem.

At home, Billy was still motionless and Andrew ate both suppers and the pudding as he watched incomprehensible television.

Saturday, there was no change in Billy but Andrew was still unwilling to accept that things might not improve. He did some street sweeping in the morning. Although friendly to passers-by as usual, he did not join in any gossip. He took his usual walk to Anstruther in the afternoon, treating himself to a cup of tea and a scone in the Fisheries Museum cafe. Saturday night he went to bed early and slept all night.

Sunday he wakened, absolutely determined to speak to Betty and ask her advice, but by the time he was dressed and brave enough, he saw Betty walking off to church. He meant to speak when she returned at lunchtime, but his courage had deserted him by then.

It was easier for him once the working week began, for he left the problem of what he should do about his brother behind him, when he left the house. Always a fellow who lived very much in the present moment, Andrew found that by concentrating on the job in hand and resuming his friendly chats, he could manage to wipe any thoughts of Billy from his mind for most of the day. The evenings were difficult but he slept much more than he normally would.

When Thursday arrived, he collected Billy's pension as usual, otherwise there would be that questioning of anything out of the ordinary and the resulting speculative comment which is so much a part of village life.

When he got home he divided the money carefully, putting Billy's share of rent and fuel, though not food of course, into his own wallet and adding the remainder to Billy's cash box which already had thirty pounds saved.

After that first week, which would lay down the pattern of Andrew's life for the next three months, Andrew had admitted to himself that Billy must be dead. He was sorry, but not heart-broken and reverted to the life he had led in the interlude between his mother's departure and Billy's arrival. It seemed that by waiting for a week to tell anyone, he had made it even more difficult, impossible really. Who can say what his thoughts about the future were? He just tried not to think about it too much and was quite successful in his waking hours, although he had some strange dreams.

Sometimes when he met Betty in the street, he was reminded that she might have helped him at one time, but it was too late now and he said nothing to her and was in fact much less friendly to her.

A mist, like the east coast haar, drifted into Andrew's brain and he stopped worrying about what he should have done and had not done. The future no longer existed for him and he concerned himself only with each day.

He was aided in dealing with the practical problems of his brother's corpse by the extremely cold weather of the next three months. He opened the bedroom window as wide as it would go, covering the body with as many blankets and bedspreads as he could find, with the vague idea of protecting his brother from the fierce icy draught. Then he locked the bedroom door and did not visit Billy again, it was too upsetting.

When Andrew had been buying his unnecessary fish supper and collecting Billy's illegal pension for three months, he made a change in his story. For whatever reason, he told more than one person that Billy was away visiting their sister in Dundee. Perhaps by then he believed it. No neighbour had seen any sign of any car coming to collect Billy and there was a discrepancy in Andrew's story, for sometimes Billy was supposed to have gone last week, sometimes the week before. Suspicions were aroused and the welfare was brought in. Poor Andrew was taken off to be cared for and Billy was given a decent funeral, while the neighbours spoke to each other in hushed incredulous tones.

How could this have happened three months ago and nobody noticed a thing?

When well-wishers had asked after Billy's health, they had always been told that "he's fine, just the same as ever."

As the brothers had no regular visitors there was no one to disprove the fact.

Only in retrospect did people remember noticing that Andrew was withdrawn and 'not quite himself'.

Betty, in the semi-detached house next door, was most shocked of all and sometimes blamed herself for not being a more caring neighbour. She had wondered about the open bedroom window in the bitter weather, but she was seldom in the garden that hard winter and soon forgot about it on returning to the warmth of her own house.

She wondered if she would ever stop thinking about the poor lonely man and his dead brother, for it was a horrible thing to happen 'just through the wall'.

Mostly she was really sorry for the sad story of the two lonely men. Countless times she asked herself why had Andrew not come to her for help? She regretted that deeply.

I like to remember the wonderful job that Andrew made of keeping the streets and wynds of Pittenweem impeccably clean. It was a daunting task and no doubt his jokes and stories also cheered many a humdrum or sad day.

The Pageant

UNTIL THE SIXTIES, an important part of Glasgow's public transport was provided by a fleet of tramcars. They were brightly coloured, with each different colour denoting a different destination. Although many were very old and dilapidated and rattled along noisily, most citizens felt very affectionate towards them. At night the vehicles were herded into a large building on the south side of the city where they were washed and maintained. After the demise of the trams, this building lay empty until the eighties, when it became a venue for the arts with the structure hardly changed since its previous use. The dramatic productions in the Tramway, as it was called, were very different from those in an ordinary theatre, where the audience sits sedately in the stalls or balcony and watches actors who are safely distanced, behind the proscenium arch. In the Tramway, the audience experienced some very exciting experimental theatre and the actors walked close to us, even amongst us. One time the sprinkler system was used to add a rainy day atmosphere to a sad funeral scene and we were forced to step back hastily out of the realistic drizzle!

Much money has been spent on the Tramway since then and it is more genteel and chic but, personally, I scarcely think it is improved.

In 1988, I saw a marvellous performance there, called 'Border Warfare', which depicted the historic struggle between Scotland and England. It was a production of the talented actors of the Wildcat Company and it was a truly enchanting night. I hardly noticed the fact that I was on my feet for most of the time, for the audience was gently guided back and forth to allow the actors to perform. The actors were constantly close to us and might come from any direction, walking, running and often wheeled on carts, pushed by their colleagues. Sometimes, like a flock of swallows, the audience must all change direction at once to view the next piece of action and once or twice we were ushered to a separate room and allowed to sit for a brief scene. Some scenes were enacted above our head on scaffolding and sometimes a single actor would appear high at the top of a pillar to sing an unexpected song, because there was a lot of wonderful music that night.

It was a great experience and even as I watched it, I visualised Pittenweem, with its many different and picturesque areas, as the perfect venue for a similar production.

I was inspired to recreate historic scenes all over Pittenweem!

How on earth would I go about this ambitious programme?

Fancy dress parades have always been popular in the small towns of the East Neuk.

The ones that I remember best happened during the war years, when, along with bazaars, concerts, lucky dips and raffles, they served the purpose of encouraging the war effort, which was all about fund-raising and exhorting the people to invest in National Savings. For one week each year, there was an obsession with saving and many hundreds of pounds were gathered in to the national coffers. The sum reached would be announced each day of the week. I expect there was competition between the different towns, though I was too young to notice. The highlight of the War Effort week was the fancy dress parade when the standard of outfits and decorated floats was amazingly high, with great ingenuity and artistry shown at a time when cash and commodities were even scarcer than normal. It was a chance for people to explore and exploit their own creativity and drama and it was fun to walk in the parade or to stand and watch it.

One year, dressed as a Victorian child, I was delighted to win the excellent prize of a fifteen shilling savings certificate. There was no thought of cashing it in and spending it! It was a welcome addition to the slow but sure accumulation of certificates that children were expected to acquire by investing a weekly sixpence, perhaps less, at school. The teacher added the skill of banking to her other pursuits and collected these small savings each Monday. It must have been an unwelcome extra task for her, with perhaps fifty bank books to fill in and add up in order to bestow the certificate when, after many weeks, the sum of fifteen shillings had been laboriously reached. Almost certainly it would also be a difficulty for some of the parents to find the regular investment, especially for those who had large families.

Those parades of my youth had an avowed fund-raising purpose and I would later take part in the Glasgow Students' Charities Day when, dressed outrageously and inadequately for the wintry weather, we shook our collecting cans aggressively at our fellow citizens on streets, buses and trams and earned large sums for the hospitals.

Peacetime Pittenweem parades had a more disinterested aim and were for 'the purpose of enlivening the burgh during the Fair' as Eric Eunson notes in his book, *Old PITTENWEEM* There was the fancy dress cycle parade in 1913 and two ambitious, scripted parades in the twenties and thirties, each with a historic theme.

The tradition of dressing up and walking through the streets dates from very much further back and had a religious significance. In every Spanish city and town, devotional Easter processions still take place each year. Preparation must take months and great expense. Then there is the pre-Lenten orgiastic extravagance of Mardi Gras and Carnival in South America and the Caribbean.

If I have digressed from the ambition that I formed that night at the Tramway, it is because a fancy dress parade seemed to provide the best possibility of realising it.

How was I going to reintroduce something which had practically died out? Although there had been a few modest children's fancy dress competitions over the years, I wanted to involve adults in my show, I wanted to use the various picturesque parts of Pittenweem and I wanted *all the inhabitants* to join in. Because June is my favourite month in Pittenweem, I wanted to hold it in June. I had no purpose in view for this creative desire that I had, I just *wanted to do it.*

I came through to Fife in March and found that the Pittenweem Parish Church was celebrating its anniversary of four hundred years. Each month had a different 'happening' a film show, lecture or exhibition, with a committee in charge of each event. I visited Charles Thrower, the minister, whom I knew slightly although I am not a church goer. He was very helpful and said that they had hoped to do some sort of pageant or parade but no one had been pin-pointed to be in charge, as yet. I was so delighted and asked if I could do it and I think he was pleased to find someone who was willing. In fact he was good enough to say that I was heaven-sent.

Yes, it could be on Saturday 21st June.

It all seemed to have been meant to happen.

At the beginning of May, I started dance classes both in Pittenweem and Dunino primary schools and I was very pleased when some ladies joined the classes. I was greatly helped in this by Jessie Lyons, the church organist. I found some suitably ancient music and created simple country dances that could be learned quickly and hoped that no one would question their authenticity. I wanted to incorporate these dancers into a Medieval masque in the Priory grounds and was delighted to find that there was a group of madrigal singers in Pittenweem who would join us and also a drummer and a trumpeter. In Glasgow I had recently produced a show with a Carnival theme and I had made an outsize puppet for the show. Three people, each holding a long stick, manipulated this eight-foot-high puppet. There was also a pantomime horse and a Chinese dragon, which required three children with sticks to manoeuvre its undulations.

In the previous year, there had been a fancy dress race at the Annual Arts Festival and a gang of wild, burly Vikings had impressed me. They are mentioned elsewhere in this book. I tracked them down by some judicious pub-crawling and they gave me their assurance that they would hire the costumes again and take part in my pageant. My plan was to start the whole thing off with a little violence, with the Vikings landing and attacking the Pictish people who were the early residents here.

The church choir at that time had a preponderance of handsome old men, none of them in the best of health but all ready to do their bit. Some old curtains from my Glasgow house were dyed brown and I made habits for six monks. The dying was patchy but this added authenticity, for they looked as though they might have been worn for years of rowing back and forth to the May Island monastery

When the choir rehearsed the hymn, dressed somewhat self-consciously in their habits, I must admit that tears came to my eyes.

I made a rather more elegant and saintly outfit for Charles Thrower to wear as St Fillan arriving in Pittenweem to bring Christianity to the Picts. This would be part of the first scene of the pageant and would take place at the harbour. I was hopeful that he could arrive by sea, however that was not to be. We rehearsed it the previous week but I felt that the sound of the boat's motor as it approached the shore was incongruous. Then when I realised how difficult it would be for Charles to climb over the side of the boat and into the water without hoisting up his skirts and showing his rolled up trousers in an unsaintly sort of way, I changed my plan. Much simpler if he walked along the sea wall.

I arranged with friends to play leading roles, Neil and Trish Anderson as James IV and his bride, Johnny and Heather Cunningham as Charles II and court, Andy Grieg as Victorian father of the bride, his daughter Jackie, with accompanying fiddler, Jack Ramsay, two close harmony singers of old fisher songs, Evelyn Anderson and Catherine Brunton and various others all added to the pleasure of the day. Effie Taylor consented to play Queen Victoria and the milkman's cart was made available for my daughters Sarah and Kate to decorate in swags of royal scarlet cloth to carry her Majesty through the town. Though the other monarchs had certainly visited Pittenweem, Victoria never did. That was artistic licence.

I needed a commentator to give directions and explanations to the audience and hold the occasion together and Tom McBain, very smart in top hat and morning dress took charge of guiding the event through the town.

In the weeks leading up to the pageant, I appealed several times for everyone in Pittenweem to be a part of my plan. I spoke from the pulpit and at the early family service and at coffee mornings. When about the town shopping, I kept encouraging folk to join in. I particularly wanted some traditional fisherpeople but I was unsure right until the last minute whether anybody would take that role.

The night of the 20th, I was sent an apology from the Viking group. The costumes had all arrived but sadly the men, some of whom were fishermen, some long distance drivers, would be working away from Pittenweem and unable to appear. However they would send stand-ins and I was not to worry!

For the six weeks preceding the pageant, the weather was beautiful and I feared that there would be no sunshine left for the 21st.

The day arrived rather overcast and threatening, the pageant was due to start at one thirty. A rainy day would be just too tragic, but by midday the sun was out again and I breathed a sigh of relief.

In the morning there was a buzz of excitement in Pittenweem. Everyone was discussing the pageant.

At one twenty five, a small group of Picts were assembled in front of the Gyles. There were ragged children and adults, living their simple lives and it looked rather good. I was dressed as a fearsome old crone, for there is a long tradition of witches in Pittenweem. There was not much of an audience yet and there was no sign of the Vikings, who were supposed to rush up the slipway from the sea and rape and pillage these defenceless people.

Tom the commentator would arrive at any moment to start proceedings and *no Vikings!*

I could hear the accompanying drummer in the distance.

The audience was growing larger every minute.

I ran to the foot of the Cove Wynd and there rushing down towards me were the Vikings! How delighted I was to see them!

Even the fact that these were not the brawny ones that I had expected, but slender, youthful Vikings, even the fact that the leader wore spectacles and a neck brace surprised, but did not disappoint me.

There they were, ready to strike terror into the heart of the community and though they went about their work in a polite and caring way, the audience seemed to enjoy it.

After their rather apologetic exit, the old crone, pointing and gesticulating, forecast the coming of a great man from the sea. I hope that people understood what I meant.

On cue, Charles appeared from behind the lighthouse, where my daughter Alice had helped him to robe himself, and strode along the seawall looking very splendid. Lifting up one of the Pictish children, he carried her around as he shook hands with all the adults. It looked very good though I doubt if St Fillan did much hand-shaking. Next the saint joined the old men of the choir to sing their hymn. Knowing that one or two of them suffered heart problems, I had wondered if we needed transport to bring them up to the High Street again. However they were fine and marched up Cove wynd into St Fillan's cave with the entire audience following behind!

This was not according to plan and must have been a crush in the small cave, however the master of ceremonies cleverly redirected the crowds to the Priory grounds for the next scene.

I had meanwhile rushed home for a quick change into my medieval pageant master's outfit to take charge of the Masque. The setting was lovely with the ladies and gentlemen of the court ranged against the ancient stone walls. Everyone had made such an effort and looked stunning.

The mature faces of the community council were grave and impressive under their ancient headgear.

Jessie Lyons was spectacular in a Tudor outfit.

James IV and his bride arrived with some pomp, looking magnificent although I know that Trish was feeling very ill that day and I appreciated that she was such a trouper.

My dancers arrived and the puppets and then there was music, dancing and the madrigals. I was proud of my dancers as they whirled and fluttered their ribbons and the singing sounded so sweetly in the open air and really evoked a past time. They looked so good too. I had made about sixteen medieval hats, not too difficult a task and they had dressed themselves wonderfully to match.

At the penultimate rehearsal, the boys who worked the dragon and the horse had not shown the proper professional attitude. In fact they had been, as small boys often can be, right wee devils. So much so that I had told them that I did not need a dragon or a horse. As I could not trust them, I would just cut those items out of the show. However they came repentant to the final rehearsal and promised faithfully to do their best and they did. Their dragon and horse came on stage perfectly on cue and only spoiled the effect slightly by straying into the rose bed and where the horse's tail caught momentarily on the thorns. They very quickly freed themselves and got off again absolutely on time. I was proud of them

Then Charles Thrower, who had made a quick change and donned a large black beard, marched purposefully around the gardens as John Knox, with the audience giving a few boos and hisses.

The next scene took place at Kellie Lodging in the High Street where Charles II and his friends were regaled with Hedderwick bun and good ale just as the original court was said to be. Johnny Cunningham made a perfect king and the effeminate satins, laces and ostrich feathers of this group were outrageous. A handsome Labrador dog behaved beautifully. Joyce Laing, in a lace cap, sat at an upper window, recreating a well-known photograph of a beauty in a previous Pittenweem pageant of sixty years ago.

Next we had what was the most touching scene for me. A crowd of traditionally dressed fisherwomen came up the wynd and grouped outside the bank. There were all ages, one mother carried an infant and there was a toddler, a small boy and a grannie. There were terrible times in the seventeenth century when many of the men in the town were lost in wars and storms, leaving the widows alone with their orphans in the struggle to survive. As I looked at the faces, I felt sure that many of those fine, good-looking features had been handed down through the generations and this group would show similarities to a group of two hundred years ago. Old fishing songs were sung and another time was perfectly recreated.

Next, Jack Ramsay, a fine fiddler, led the bridal party along the High Street to the church, followed by the bride's father, handsome in a top hat, and the bride and bridesmaid glowing in the finery which they had worn only three years before for a twentieth century wedding. At the church, Charles had made another quick change and with some judicial trimming of the Knox beard, had transformed himself into a Victorian minister. The ladies of the church choir, in bonnets, created the right atmosphere by singing "Where e'er She Walks."

The last scene had Queen Victoria being driven past the church to cheers from the audience. The poor horse, used to the quiet morning saunter of his milk round, was taken aback by the cheering crowds and threatened to turn round and go home but, his able driver controlled and calmed him.

Next, everyone formed a procession behind the Queen's carriage and made three circuits of the town.

I had said that it would last for one and a half hours and I am pleased to say that was exactly the time that it lasted.

I am very grateful to everyone for the work that they put into it and although I was tired at the end of that day, not too tired for a glass of champagne in my garden with some of the leading figures of the pageant. I think it was a happy occasion.

My daughter Kate made a video of the whole event which has since been shown once or twice at the Festival.

I had hoped that I might have inspired someone else to organise a similar event, but so far this has not happened.

It would be a shame if this Pittenweem tradition were allowed to die out and I would like to suggest that the breakwater extension to the harbour wall, which was completed in 1993 would make a splendid processional route.

Heading North

SERGEANT MCLEAN AND POLICEWOMAN Fraser were proceeding west on South Street when they spotted the BMW parked on the double yellow line.

"Fiona, jist pull in in front o' that daft bugger an' Ah'll book 'm."

Fiona parked the car neatly. Her face was expressionless but her heart was bitter. Booking badly parked cars on a Saturday afternoon was hardly the excitement she had sought when she joined the force. Everyone was too damned well-behaved in St Andrews. Perhaps they were inhibited by having a prince living in the town.

Certainly Bill McLean knew every aspect of his job thoroughly, but Fiona found it an endurance test to spend four hours with him. He was a big handsome fellow, but he was easily the slowest and most boring police officer in the East Neuk.

A young woman, huddled in a travelling rug, sat in the passenger seat of the luxurious car. After a brief but fruitless attempt to open the electric window, she opened the door, smiling wanly up at the burly policeman.

"I am afraid you must move your vehicle, madam, it is illegally parked."

"It's not my car and I don't have a key and . . . "

Bill stood waiting patiently but the woman hesitated and tears came into her eyes.

"You see . . . the owner has gone off." She calmed herself and Bill noticed she was wearing a light party sort of outfit under the rug, "He's disappeared and I can't think what's happened to him. It's a very long story."

Bill nodded portentously as he considered what he might do next, when some news came squawking through on his walkie-talkie and he turned away from the car to listen. It was very bad news. A serious motorway pile-up on the A90. Three lorries, two buses and a large saloon were scattered across all lanes. Miraculously, there was no loss of life, but several people required hospital treatment.

Nothing he could do about it. He brought out his notebook.

"Now, madam, your name?"

"Elizabeth Bates."

Her age was the same as his own and the address was a small inland town twelve miles away,

"Profession?"

"Teacher, primary school."

"Now I'll just bet that's Colinsburgh school," he smiled broadly and his accent and whole manner changed, "and you're the Miss Bates that my wee niece Diana is always talking about. From what she says I judged you to be some sort of angel! She fair admires you, she really does."

"That's right, Colinsburgh, how nice of Diana, sweet girl." Elizabeth blinked. Diana McLean was a spoiled little chatterbox and often in trouble.

"Now, my lass, ye'd better tell me aboot the missin' car owner, no matter how long the story is. Maybe Ah can help." His speech had lost its official coldness and his manner was now quite fatherly. She appreciated that. She had been feeling very low as well as impossibly stupid and freezing cold.

"I was at a party in Kilconquhar . . . "

"Your hometown?"

"Yes."

"*Earlier today*? Awfy early fur a party?"

"Kilconquhar is like that, lots of elderly folk and they don't tend to stay up late, so it's usually lunch parties."

"Ah'm no' sure if Ah'd be in the mood fur a party at that time o' day. An' that's why ye're wearin' party claes on a cauld nicht like this."

"Yes."

"Mind, it wis nice earlier but it's efter five noo an' that wind's gettin' up. Right enough it's November."

"Could I please continue. I'm awfully cold."

Just then his walkie-talkie broke in with more details of the crash and he turned away.

Elizabeth shut the door and wondered how on earth she could tell the story without appearing an utter idiot.

She had left the boring party early and, feeling restless and dissatisfied with her life in that well-manicured but stultifying village, had marched right past her front door and set off for Elie, two and a half miles away. It was only two-thirty and bright and sunny and she needed the exercise after standing around for two hours. She would have a coffee in the gift shop and take the bus home before it got dark. It was hardly a stimulating Saturday afternoon for an intelligent and educated woman of thirty-five. Not for the first time, she thought seriously about selling her exquisite little cottage and moving back to the city.

There was little traffic on the road for the first mile and she was berating herself for walking that distance in party shoes when a car drove slowly past and stopped just ahead of her. It was a new and glittering BMW. The window slid down and a young man, not particularly handsome, but with an engaging smile and thick blonde hair, looked over and with a mock pathetic air pleaded,

"Can you possibly help a poor motorist in distress?" He smiled apologetically and he had sparkling white teeth. How young he was, compared to those mature, worn faces at the party! Elizabeth was immediately ready and anxious to give him assistance.

"I've been driving round and round these never-ending back roads of Fife for hours, it seems and I'm completely confused. Absolutely flummoxed. I'm already half an hour late for my appointment and I seem no nearer the place than I was when I started! I've been to Cardenden and Cowdenbeath and Pittenweem and the Peat Inn and I don't even know where I should be heading."

She could not help laughing,

"That's the real problem, I'm not completely sure of my destination!"

"That does make it difficult, doesn't it"

They were both laughing heartily when a car passed and blasted its horn angrily as the BMW was parked awkwardly on a curve of the narrow road.

"Look here I'd better shift myself. Is there a town nearby? Is it close? Can I get a sandwich there? I'm absolutely starving. I say, why don't you jump in and show me the way? I'm desperate and I'll bring you back to wherever you want. Presumably not to this godforsaken spot of the highway when you're wearing such a very smart outfit and those shoes. Go on, I'm highly respectable. Honest Injun. Jump in. I'll just throw these in the back."

He chucked a polished briefcase and a copy of the Guardian into the back seat and those two respectable items blotted out a lifetime of innate caution and maternal advice.

Elizabeth had slipped, rather thankfully, into the luxurious leather seat.

But how would she explain this to the policeman who had now returned, opening the door himself this time.

"And you didnae get the gentleman's name. Could you describe him to me?"

"About my age, very presentable, thick blonde hair, tallish, wearing a nice suit and a good watch, though I noticed his shoes were shabby, well-manicured hands, well-spoken, some sort of English accent and he had a good singing voice. He seemed an educated fellow and . . . oh yes, he had very good teeth."

Bill was writing as quickly as he could but he stopped and looked at her searchingly for a moment.

"Nae piercings nor tattoos?".

"Certainly not! He wasn't like that at all, I would say he was a professional man, *very bright.*"

Elizabeth had a tendency to categorize people as the children that they might once have been and he would certainly have been a more rewarding pupil than this stolid policeman.

Bill carefully wrote "BRIGHT" in block capitals at the top of his page.

"You've given me an unusually full description, Miss Bates. Maist folk are no' so observant. Did he tell you where he was headin'?"

"No, at least . . . Anstruther or further north . . . I think."

She had asked him.

"Oh, north, I think would be best."

"North? Seriously, though, what town is it you want."

"Well," he hesitated and wrinkled his nose in a puzzled way, "Anstruther . . . "

"Oh, that's easy, just five miles or so along the coast . . . that's east and you must have been near it when you were in Pittenweem. How on earth did you get here?"

She was still laughing.

"God alone knows, but it's not Anstruther I want to go to. It's north of Anstruther, north . . . because a man in Anstruther has laryngitis . . . it's terribly complicated. Let's wait until we're having coffee and I'll explain. You will join me for coffee won't you. I shall be devastated if you don't."

He turned and smiled with a conspiratorial look, keeping his eyes off the road ahead for longer than she found comfortable or safe. However he was an attractive young man to lock gaze with. She smiled as she said,

"You're just talking in riddles".

Unexpectedly he suddenly burst into song. It was the song, "Luck be a Lady Tonight" and he sang it tunefully, with all the words, no da-de-dums

"That's from Guys and Dolls . . . absolutely my favourite musical. Are you a professional singer? You're really good."

"Just one of my hobbies," he answered modestly," also a clue to the riddle of why I am lost in the wilds of Fife!"

"Then, after you entered the car?" Bill showed no surprise as he wrote deliberately.

"We drove to the coffee shop in Elie and he had two sandwiches and a piece of iced gingerbread."

"And yerself?"

"Just coffee, I was full of crumbly canapés."

Bill coughed politely and let that pass.

"Would you say he was very hungry?"

"Oh yes, he was starving, wolfing it down. It seemed out of character. Although he took a long time choosing between pate and smoked salmon, then changed his mind at the last minute. He was rather fickle and the waitress wasn't pleased. P'raps he was teasing her. Then he decided to go to St. Andrews."

Bill added FICKLE to his notes.

After he'd eaten, he explained to her that he was up in Fife to help out the local amateur dramatic society, whose lead singer had laryngitis.

She said what an excellent group the Fife Songbirds were.

"They have a good reputation, as does my own club in East Lothian. That's why they contacted us because their next show is Gs and Ds and we've just finished a production. An SOS brought yours truly galloping to the rescue from the south, which was a sacrifice. I was forced to cancel one of my little dinner parties. I do so love cooking and I'm supposed to be rather an expert! Then in the rush, I lost the scrap of paper with the outlandish destination and I only get voice-mail on the mobile number. So frustrating!"

"There are an awful lot of little towns in Fife, many of them with strange names. Were you going to a rehearsal hall in this town, wherever it is?"

"Probably. I know I had to stay over for a few days."

"The Songbirds always do their show in the Byre Theatre in St. Andrews. You'd surely remember St. Andrews, it's world famous! Anyway the Byre people could certainly tell you where the rehearsals are . . . or give you a contact number. Good hotels there too."

"St. Andrews . . . is that north of Anstruther?"

"Yes, it is. Why are you so keen to go north?" she was laughing again. She might have known him all her life and this ridiculous hunt for an unknown place now seemed as much her problem as his.

"The north? Well it is dark and true and tender, isn't it? I hope you know your Tennyson."

She shook her head,

"Tut, tut and you a teacher too."

It was cooler when they left the cafe and she shivered a little.

"If you'll just drop me in Kilconquhar . . . "

"Where? I don't want to drop you anywhere! Certainly not somewhere with such a strange name. I want you to come with me in case I get lost again!"

"I'm sorry," and she really was sorry," I can't come with you, I must go home now. Kilconquhar is just about a mile from where you picked me up. You'll get to St. Andrews easily, I'll point you in the right direction, it's well sign-posted."

"And then?"

"I asked him to take me back to Kilconquhar, but he drove right past the turn-off, looking very fierce."

Bill wrote down "FEIRCE", then corrected it.

"What did you say then?"

"Nothing, I was scared. Angry too."

"So you were angry with each other when you reached St Andrews?"

"Not really, we had made up again. He was very charming."

"Aye."

"Then he went off to make enquiries at the Byre and," tears welled into her eyes again but she composed herself with an effort, "I haven't seen him since. I went along to the theatre myself but the people on duty said that no one had been there. They also said that the Songbirds are doing Carousel this year."

"Aye and not until the Spring. My cousin's in the chorus."

Just then an overweight man in his fifties trotted up. He was out of breath and very upset.

"Officer! I wish to report a stolen car. A Mercedes, brand new. Parked it in Market Street only an hour ago!"

"My colleague in the police car there will be very pleased to help you, sir."

The man turned away with a furious exclamation.

Dropping his official accent again, Bill told Elizabeth of the serious road accident.

"Widnae be surprised if that pair auld man's caur's the cause o' that bustup on the A90. They scallywags kin steal big caurs but they cannae drive thim. But let's see wha's the owner o' this lot."

He made use of his communication systems for nearly five minutes, smiling grimly, alternately shaking and nodding his head.

Elizabeth felt cold, miserable and humiliated and longed to return home. Surely there was never such a slow policeman.

Ten minutes of modern technology enabled Bill to report that the BMW belonged to Mr Henderson in Haddington, who had last seen it early that morning.

"Noo, aff the record, Ah'll jist tell ye that close tae Mr Henderson's house was a dented Daimler, missin' from Carlisle since Thursday and in Carlisle there's whit hud been a bran' new 4x4 from a farm in Yorkshire. Burned oot. And that's no' the end o't. See that fellow ye spent the efternoon wi', he's a bugger wi' caurs. Mr Henderson's lucky an' *so are you!*"

"What a damned idiot I have been. I'll never forgive myself for such stupidity."

"Aye an' you a teacher, tae. Ye've shown an unfortunate lack o' judgement the day, but we a' make mistakes. It's only fools that make them twice. But that's the boy right enough. Aye, that's him to a T. We've a' been lookin' fur him up an' doon the country. Great ladies' man! He got away from . . . an open prison it was, near the south coast. He's been on the loose for a while. He comes frae Thurso . . . so he wis aye travellin' north, zig-zaggin' back 'n forrards an' leavin' a trail o' stolen cars behind 'm. That laud kin fairly wreck the caurs he steals, ladies' hearts too, I believe." He gave Elizabeth an old-fashioned wink, "They were puttin' on a wee show in the jail, ye see. Tae keep the lads happy-like and there wis jist a wee bit mair laxity an' he goat away free. Ye really wonder hoo that happens. I believe he hud a nice singin' voice, tae. Why could he no' use that talent tae earn money, instead o' a' they funny tricks he goat up tae."

Unwilling to hear any more details of the 'tricks' he had got up to, she asked if she could please be driven back to Kilconquhar soon.

"Aye, nae bother, ye deserve a reward for apprehendin' a criminal."

Fortunately it was the policewoman, still ignorant of Elizabeth's gross stupidity, that drove her home. Elizabeth could not have endured any more of Bill's heavy-handed remarks.

The following day she put her cottage on the market.

Sergeant McLean watched the police car drive off towards Kilconquhar at the cautious speed that female members of the force used. He considered it unsuitably tentative. Gave the police a bad name.

The wind was cold and setting off at a smart pace for headquarters in North Street, he chose the short cuts through narrow closes that he had used since boyhood.

What a foolish young woman that had been. You could never measure the depths of stupidity of apparently intelligent people. Educated! Responsible for kids! He shook his head as he crossed Market Street. She was nice-looking though. She'd made a fuss about taking the cashmere blanket with her, but her outfit was useless for a wintry night and he had assured her that he would personally see it was returned to Mr Henderson of Haddington in due course. He might just pop down to Kilconquhar himself to collect it.

Funny her not being married.

What a silly bugger she had been that day, but awful lucky.

Extraordinarily and amazingly lucky.

Bill McLean was well aware that he was known in the office for his slow reactions and his infallible honesty. He was teased about it often enough. He would certainly not be the chosen man if instant action or some degree of subterfuge were required.

He smiled to himself with satisfaction for he had been pretty quick that day.

Quick and devious!

Probably a promotion waiting for him now.

Luck had been on his side of course, with all the evidence coming together at the corner of the street like that, but he had spotted the clues, made his deduction and reported it smartly.

Elizabeth's own words had been the key, reminding him of a poem he had learned in school, no idea who wrote it, but 'bright, fierce and fickle' described the south. For weeks, every police force in the country had been after that escapee from the south. Then the man's determination to go north and the trail of stolen cars clinched it.

Not that Harry Power would be much of a danger now. His injuries on the A90 had put paid to a future life of crime.

What pleased Bill best was that he had lied judiciously and plausibly to that vulnerable, young woman.

She was cold, confused, obviously shocked and very ashamed of her own stupidity, as well she might be, but that was no reason to aggravate her state of mind. Quite on the spur of the moment, honest Bill had misled her.

She would hear the truth soon enough.

She would be called as a witness, one of the few, in a very nasty trial, for it was not only car wrecks that littered that northbound trail. As usual, the media would have a field day with all the gruesome details and Elizabeth would hear of other foolish young women, less fortunate than herself, who had accepted lifts from Handsome Harry and she'd learn that the kitchens where he had 'loved cooking' belonged not to an open prison, but to Broadmoor.

Festival Haikus. 2004

CROWDS ARE VISITING THE Pittenweem Festival, in search of culture.
Sun and wine compete to promote frivolity on opening night.
Amazing outfits are worn with beards, beads, shorts, shawls and
wellington boots.
But fickle weather, with impalpable power, dominates the scene.
The hot humid air, so unusual for Fife, is enervating.
The haar envelopes and imbues with poetry the steep, twisting
wynds
In the clinging mist, the red pantiles are faded to a modest blush.
In enfolding fog, the unseen sea extends to distant unseen shores.
Seven fishing boats vanish into nothingness, in a brief moment.
Gazing puzzled cats, whiskers beaded with moisture, watch birds
disappear.
Fireworks are enhanced by the aerial effect of the conditions.
Even thunderstorms cannot disperse the laden clouds and the rain
pours down.
Gutters are flowing, umbrellas open and close and floors are
mopped dry.
Brave people persist, in spite of the fierce torrents, to visit venues.
They are not deterred! Even flooding cannot stop determined
aesthetes.

Pittenweem Arts Festival

THE WEATHER COULD NOT have been more propitious for the very first Pittenweem Arts Festival. The sun shone all day and the evenings had a balmy Mediterranean quality which, while not unknown in the East Neuk, is not as frequently found as one might wish.

The committee was mostly made up of my friends, but I had opted out of it. I thought that Joyce Laing's dream of a festival was a great idea, but someone has to work hard to get great ideas off the ground. My working life in Glasgow was often concerned with staging shows and I did not want my month in Fife turned into a busman's holiday. Besides it was many years since my first, and only, experience of a committee and I had vowed never to join another.

I fully appreciate that if everyone took this selfish attitude, there would not be the amazing annual festival that we have in our little town when, for a week, it is transformed. We owe a debt of gratitude to that first committee because, for twenty three years, their dream has thrived and grown in scope and popularity. Now thousands of people come each year to enjoy the torchlight procession, fireworks, concerts, plays, competitions and around eighty exhibitions of art of all kinds, traditional harbour scenes with boats galore, avant garde abstracts, beautifully framed and prettily coloured little sketches, sculpture, installations and various very fine crafts. For nine days there is a buzz of excitement in Pittenweem, as crowds of visitors from all over the world wander around the wynds and streets, dipping into as many of the exhibitions as their feet will carry them to. In 2003, I estimated that around four thousand people walked through my garden, admired the view, climbed the outside staircase to my studio and studied the exhibition. They came from France, Germany, Italy, Spain, Scandinavia, Japan, Australia and North America and perhaps other places as well. What tickled me was that one busload was from Edinburgh, where the largest arts festival in

Europe was in full swing at that moment.

2003 was another splendid year for weather with continuous sunshine, not a spot of rain and hardly a breeze. Unlike 2004, when it seemed that our luck had run out and the haar, that thick white coastal mist, hovered over the East Neuk for an unprecedented three weeks, blocking the view of the Bass Rock on the other side of the Firth, almost hiding the sea itself. At regular intervals heavy rain fell in determined showers.

'You win some, you lose some.'

And while the numbers were certainly reduced, those that did come, were, as in previous sunnier years, just as enthusiastic, as energetic and as determined to see as much as possible.

Who will deny that the glimpses of the charming and widely varying interiors and gardens of Pittenweem exert almost as great a fascination over the visitors as the art work on display?

That is perhaps unfair, as many come with wallet in hand, ready to purchase and that is very pleasant knowledge for the creative people who have hopefully toiled for months previously.

Before I remind you of some of the festival highlights that I particularly enjoyed, I want to make an apology to each person whose name does not appear in this story. Please forgive me if your name or your work is not included. It would be impossible for me to mention all the different people, quite apart from the artists, who have worked so hard every year, often throughout the year, to make the festival a success. I want to congratulate them and say how much I admire their energy and determination. I am writing this as a tribute to every person who has given their time or muscle power to the Pittenweem Arts Festival.

Indeed the people of Pittenweem, with their sprucely painted houses, sparkling windows and flourishing gardens, tubs and hanging baskets, all play their part in the success of the festival. The conscientious street cleaner should also be congratulated.

Last summer, I walked around the whole town on one of the few good days and no village in Europe could have looked prettier or more perfectly maintained.

Joyce Laing and Reinhard Behrens have been absolutely integral to the festival from the start.

Although Joyce has a misleadingly relaxed attitude, she has a steel will and has accomplished miracles. Her contacts with the Scottish art establishment have helped to bring many interesting names to the festival and her aim was always to create a festival of standing which would invite performers and artists of repute, rather than it should be just a small local celebration. There is no doubt that this aim has been achieved. She has held many exhibitions in her house and introduced many interesting artists. Keith Brockie with his wonderful drawings of nature on the May Island was one of the most popular.

Some people may not remember that in the eighties, when the festival started, Joyce suffered bouts of very ill health. In fact her friends at times despaired. However here she is, still walking her energetic dogs and with a new project in hand. No matter how much we miss Adamson's delicious bread and rolls, the gallery of Art Extraordinary, housed in the old baker's premises, is another attraction for the Pittenweem Arts Festival.

Reinhard Behrens' superhuman energy has been poured into the Arts Festival from the beginning, and his wife Margaret Smyth, has been equally involved. Three or four weeks before the start of the festival each year, I would see Reinhard walk past my window, going slightly faster than his normal impressive stride. As each day passed, the speed would become gradually greater until in the last week, he was running back and forth many times a day, almost too fast to recognise. At night when I brushed my teeth, I could see from my bathroom window that the working lights were on in the Behrens house till very late, perhaps throughout night for all I knew. His work was artistic, practical and administrative, covering a wide range from the hanging of street bunting to the decorative cover of the annual festival brochure, not to mention the exciting exhibitions which he and Margaret were preparing for the actual event. These works range from large imaginative paintings featuring his very personal ikon, a small battered tin submarine, which manifests itself in any number of unexpected places, to small, exquisitely realistic, detailed drawings of objects found on the shore. Margaret has created, in her individual and painstaking technique, an incredible world of supernatural toys suspended in realistic and picturesque surroundings.

Reinhard's first exhibition was an 'installation' in the old Granary before its rehabilitation in 1994. The exhibition was called 'Naboland'. It was the first thing of its kind that I had ever seen and I was fascinated and impressed by its many imaginative aspects. With fine drawings, paintings, a charming 'set piece' of an interior and a great deal of text to read, it created an imagined environment and made it very real to us. Further on, I shall describe my favourite piece of Reinhard's work, which I consider to be the most dramatic item to adorn the Festival in its twenty three years.

It is more than fifty years since I was shown the correctly detailed pictures of boats which the untrained More Horsburgh drew so effortlessly when a young man. I may be wrong, but I seem to remember that he had a chance to train at art school but chose the sea instead. His family have lived in Pittenweem for generations and now his mature work provides a link with the fishing industry and is a wonderful historic comment, much appreciated by locals and by festival visitors.

Bill Stevenson has worked tirelessly and unselfishly for 13 years, alternately cajoling and nagging an ever-changing committee, fighting the artistic tendency to procrastinate, sweet-talking the Arts Council, trying to solve the perennial problem of festival parking and generally making five pounds do the work of twenty. Few would have had his application and his determination to get everything correctly done. As the festival has grown larger in the last few years, the demands on Bill have also increased, and we owe him a tremendous debt of gratitude.

Then there are the many important backroom boys, far too numerous to mention, such as Heather and Johnny Cunningham, whose house provides the electricity to play music for the fireworks each year. I seem to have seen them at every single festival, busily frying hamburgers at the harbour dance, or dispensing wine at more sophisticated gatherings, sometimes in fancy dress but often workaday and *just always there, working* to help things run smoothly. And there are many, many more like them who give of their time and energy.

It really is a wonderful festival and here are some of the scenes which I can always conjure up in my mind with pleasure: happily I have some of them on video-tape.

The first festival was not without mishaps of course, in spite of the wonderful weather. It was something absolutely new that was being attempted and some errors of judgement were bound to arise.

I know that I was not the only one that looked sceptically at Joyce's first exhibition. There was a sundial that the invited artist had designed specially for her, but it was difficult to see how the time was to be told. There was a shabby old oar decorated with graffiti, "Nelson was here" in mediocre lettering which seemed insufficient artistic endeavour to me. I cannot remember other items. However, Joyce assured us doubting Thomases that the artist was "going to be *big*". And she was perfectly correct, for today he is an important member of the artistic establishment in Scotland.

Another item which I considered somewhat esoteric for a festival in a small fishing town, was a brass ensemble, with six trombones, was it? Perhaps a mixture of brass instruments, I cannot remember now. They were to play in St Fillan's cave, which must have sounded romantic at discussion level. When I saw the programme, the music that the ensemble had chosen was *very* early and *very* obscure. I had never heard of the composers.

At seven thirty, I stood outside the entrance to the cave with my ticket, but hesitated. The evening was soft and warm. I might have been in Cannes or Nice, but a torrent of cold, damp air poured from the cave mouth and enveloped me in my light summer dress. Should I go in? Just then the most almighty noise started to blare out of the doorway. It was as loud as only six trombones, if that's what they were, can sound when blown enthusiastically in an enclosed space where all the surfaces are hard rock. I decided immediately that it was not for me.

Then the horrible thought struck, what if all that noise started to loosen and dislodge the ancient stones? After all, an avalanche can be started by a whisper. What if the poor audience, chilly at first, then deafened, should eventually be entombed? In my mind's eye I could see the newspaper headlines:

TRAGEDY STRIKES SEASIDE FESTIVAL

I turned and hurried down the Cove Wynd, to walk around the harbour, rather than witness the disaster.

However audience and players safely and sensibly emerged from the cave at the interval and the second half of the concert was played in the town hall, where I joined them, for I hate to waste a ticket. After more *very* early music, the surprising and enjoyable finale was a rousing rendering of "Mad Dogs and Englishmen". Why had they not kept their whole programme a little bit more accessible? At least they sent us home in a good mood.

The town hall is a very charming Georgian building, spacious but very human in scale and I taught one or two dance classes there that first festival week. It was a great pleasure to teach there.

One memory is of a young lady showing some steps that she had choreographed herself. Somewhat surprisingly, she smoked a cigarette as she danced. Part of the movement involved vigorous shaking of the head and flicking of the hair and a constant shower of ash accompanied her performance. Very unusual.

Though probably not in that very first festival, the town hall was also the venue for the first of the Victorian Soirées that have been a recurring and successful feature. Fancy dress was suggested, although not all chose to wear it. Tea, sandwiches and cake were served and a string trio with singer played suitable music, charming and sentimental. Most enjoyable.

The hall was also used for a much younger audience. It was a 'Storytelling' and I was very impressed by the outfit of the young man. He was dressed as a country yokel in overalls and check shirt. He had a marvellous hat with some sort of furry animal on it, or perhaps it was a bird in a nest, and enormous Doc Marten boots painted a gorgeous apple green. His storytelling was splendid with all the little faces enthralled throughout his performance. Unfortunately his entrance was misjudged and I am sure he would learn from his mistake for future occasions. He came *bounding* in, shouting loudly and galloped from one end of the hall to the other, with his enormous green boots narrowly missing the waiting children, who sat cross-legged on the floor. Though none of the children was mine, I broke out in a nervous sweat at his dramatic and blood-curdling entrance which caused five infants to go into hysterics. They had to be removed from the hall, never to return. However those children courageous enough to remain, really enjoyed his subsequent whimsical, gentle humour.

I was inspired by him and in future years I also gave storytelling sessions to pre-school children in my garden. Dressed in a long frock of many fabrics, with a large straw hat and animal puppets to help me, I billed myself as 'The Old Woman in the Garden'. I was young enough at that time to call myself an old woman.

I later worked with older children, making use of our historic house and improvising imaginary scenes which might have happened there, long before my grandfather bought the house in 1911. At that time probably two families inhabited it, with perhaps an old granny or two. There would be cows in what we call the garage, as there was a dairy selling milk at the street entrance. No doubt potatoes and cabbages flourished where my flowers now grow and hens strutted nearby. The separate building, which is reached by an outside stone stairway and is now a studio and the venue for the family exhibitions, was a joiner's workshop and his initials are still to be seen on the wall. It would be a busy workaday place in those far off days and the children in my improvisational session were each given a character to play and encouraged to explore the interactions, sometimes stormy, of those imaginary folk of long ago. The children were creative and dramatic and truthfully, it was very similar to the games that my friends and I played endlessly in youth. The session finished off with pancakes and syrup in the garden and I know that I had a good time.

Last year a tall, handsome young man was visiting my exhibition. He spoke to me, very interestingly, of his career in the arts. Opera was his special field and he was at present working between London and Venice. Just before he left he admitted, rather shyly, that he had been one of those improvising children. How very satisfying it is for a teacher to meet up with a successful pupil.

1988 was the anniversary of the Spanish Armada. There is a story of the escaping Spanish fleet battling terrible storms as they were forced northwards up the east coast of Britain. When, starving and exhausted, they reached the comparative sanctuary of the Firth of Forth, they applied to the East Neuk for food. There are varying reports of their success but whatever the exact truth is, it seemed a good hook on which to hang the festival that year.

Several events referred to the Armada but my favourite was the miniature Spanish galleon which was constructed by Reinhard Behrens. This little masterpiece was about sixteen feet long and throughout the festival week, it stood in the High Street, on the broad pavement opposite the market place. Almost always it had a crowd of admirers around it.

I would like to put it on record here that I had a small investment in the construction of that splendid little ship, although I was unaware of it at the time. The previous winter, extensive work had been done on our house to combat rising damp. The entire first floor was ripped out and evidently Reinhard had made good use of the discarded wood in my skip to build his model. I was very pleased to learn that fact because it was a beautiful structure.

On the Saturday, the galleon was to be moved to the old swimming pool on the outskirts of Pittenweem. It is not a long walk but the ship was heavy and unwieldy. About eight strong men hoisted it up with grunts and not a few oaths and set off west along the High Street. Reinhard, a rather slight man himself, hovered nervously on the edge of the group, ready with advice if required. Incongruously, several of the burly bearers were in realistic Viking costume, for there had been a fancy dress race earlier that afternoon. The East Neuk has always enjoyed an excuse for fancy dress.

I collected my video camera. This was a never-to-be repeated scene.

Those of you who are familiar with the difficult terrain above the swimming pool will wonder how they managed to accomplish the last hundred yards of their journey. Did they descend by the uneven steps with sharp bends to manoeuvre or did they choose the straightforward way down over the grassy steeps, dangerous but swift? There was a short discussion, with many different suggestions and a lot of cursing. Everyone felt that he knew best and Reinhard stood apart, unheeded and obviously worried. Quite soon the sweating men plunged straight over the slippery, grassy bank with their burden, while Reinhard accompanied them, biting his lip, quite prepared to see his creation end up as a bundle of sticks at the bottom of the hill. The language was hair-raising.

Coward that I am, I switched off my camera and walked away, for I could not bear the stress.

Incredibly, they were successful and shortly the galleon was floating jauntily on the calm waters of the swimming pool.

It was a miracle!

In more ways than one, for Reinhard admitted to me later that he had not even been sure that the ship would float.

That night was the first torchlight procession of the Pittenweem Festival and we were blessed with delightful weather. It was dusk as we approached the bathing pool and pretty Elizabethan music was playing. I cannot remember if there was a moon that night but nothing could have been more romantic and evocative than the galleon, dimly mirrored in the absolutely still water, with the crowding flares also reflected and the music adding an other-worldly effect. Shivers ran up and down my spine.

More was to come!

A light was put to the fuse and almost immediately the fireworks, previously loaded on to the galleon, started to explode.

It was a tremendous sight as every flame, flare and spark on board the vessel had its double in the water. Wheels and rockets spurted in all directions with an uneven quality which made me think it was probably very similar to a real ship's conflagration, with gunpowder and ammunition exploding. As I watched, I lost any sense of scale and it no longer seemed a model, but full size and glorious in its destruction.

It was a beautiful and memorable scene, magnificently exciting, poetic and evocative and sad too, for the lovely little ship was burned to ashes.

That was a spectacular ending to the 1988 festival. Nowadays we have the torchlight procession, followed by the magnificent fireworks display at the *start* of our festival, which publicises the event and is sensible, I suppose. Often we have again been lucky enough to have good weather and a calm sea to reflect the splendid effects of the fireworks. I am able to enjoy the display from the comfort of my garden. Even last year, though heavy mist lay low over the coast, I thought there was something delicate and subtle in the way that soaring rockets eventually disappeared and the bright flares spread colour over the entire firmament.

I should also like to remind you of the year that the *Reaper*, the splendid fishing boat from Anstruther Fisheries Museum was moored in Pittenweem harbour. That night, I stood at the West Braes and watched the procession of bobbing torches wend their way down Abbeywall Road, like a vast glimmering caterpillar. In the harbour, the Reaper's enormous 'barkit' sails were lit from behind in a magical way, their warm reddish-brown colour glowing in the dark.

One more instance of successful lighting effects was created by my daughter Sarah, a film-maker. Cutting together some old film of mine from the seventies with her own contemporary video footage, she made a charming 'short' about Pittenweem and the young people in it then and now. The film was projected on the back wall of the House on the Rock on several festival evenings. It was an exciting image in the dusk and particularly appreciated by local inhabitants.

She was also one of those instrumental in opening up the old Pittenweem cinema at Festival time.

One very personal festival memory for me is of sitting in a hall listening to a story read by the late Nettie MacDonald. She had told me that in writing it, she had used my garden as the setting. However, as she read, I realised that the main character in the tale had much more than a passing resemblance to myself and shared many of my characteristics, physical and otherwise. Nettie may not even have realised that she was recreating me, as imaginative writing is a very strange thing. I grew hot under the collar as I listened but as no one mentioned it to me afterwards, perhaps they did not recognise me.

Perhaps some of those who read this book will recognise themselves with the same faint shock.

What is interesting is that exhibitions of paintings were not a very large part of the festival in the early years, while now they almost threaten to overwhelm it. Before Pittenweem had made its name as an important venue and before the town boasted such a plethora of galleries, there were probably only seven or eight shows. Nor was there a torchlight procession in those first years.

One of my regrets is that I have not always involved myself in the festival. As I have already explained, in my younger, busier days I was determined to have a summer holiday and also the timing of the festival was inconvenient. By the end of the summer, I had to upsticks, close up the Pittenweem house and return to Glasgow for my daughters' new school term. Also I must organise the publicity and intake for my dance school. It was a busy life that I led, so that although there are many scenes of the Festival in my memory, there are also many blanks, for there were several years that I was not even in Pittenweem. Please excuse me if your favourite item is not mentioned.

I am glad to say that in the last few years, my daughters have encouraged me to make use of my grandfather's studio for exhibitions. It is attractive and historically significant. Rather late in the day, I too have become an exhibitor in the Pittenweem Arts Festival.

The first exhibition held in Studio 54 or John McGhie Studio, was in 2001 when my son-in-law, Matthew White, held a successful show of his sensitive sculpture. Esther, his wife, added her unique, literary embroidery and a friend, Maddy Pirn, showed her quaint and colourful paintings.

The following year, Matthew and Esther again exhibited downstairs and mu oldest daughter Kate and I paid tribute to my grandfather in his old studio, with his paintings, drawings and etchings as well as photographs, newspaper cuttings and general snippets of information about his very successful career. I think this exhibition was particularly appreciated by the 'Pittenweemers', many of whom still remember him with affection. I have made video interviews with some of his models who are now very old ladies and have fascinating stories to tell.

A painting of myself as a child sitting knitting inspired a corner display of knitting and crochet by my daughters, Kate and Sarah. This led to many interesting discussions with visitors, for knitting is still a popular skill. One man was extremely knowledgeable and there was a lady who spun her own wool.

In that same year, I became aware that several men who could be considered as the vital 'backbone' of the town, had retired or were about to do so. Seven names seemed to me to be so embedded in the fabric of Pittenweem, that I felt some tribute should be paid to them. I decided to paint their portraits.

In 2003 "Seven Elder Statesmen of Pittenweem" was shown, first in June, then repeated in August at the festival.

Painting those portraits was a marvellous experience for me. They were all such interesting people, each personality with a wealth of facets other than their profession or trade demanded and I tried to incorporate these other interests into the portraits. I shall list them, for their names are a part of the town's history and amongst them, they contributed over three hundred years of service to Pittenweem

Andy Greig, as well as being an electrician, is a skilled musician with a band which must have played music for many thousand dancing feet. It was a challenge, but fun, to paint his splendidly decorative Hohner piano accordion.

Kenneth Adamson, a baker from a long line of bakers, is also very musical and in the painting, although dressed in his work clothes, he holds a violin. His faithful old oven, which nowadays is dedicated to the production of delicious oatcakes, is faintly seen in the background.

Waid Academy teacher Johnny Cunningham, a keen angler, holds his fishing line with his favourite fishing spot depicted in the background.

The minister, Charles Thrower, always an ardent seeker after knowledge, holds a weighty and ancient tome. A faded watercolour of the pretty Parish Church, where he officiated for more than thirty years, is on the wall behind him.

The Bass Rock, a sparkling sea and a glimpse of the old harbour make the background for Bill Black, fisherman and fish merchant throughout his life in Pittenweem. Bill and his wife Chrissie were in school with me all those years ago and he was then a bit of a 'tearaway' but now, burly and wise, a pillar of Pittenweem society, no one could look and live the part better than he does.

John Bowman is the builder who has helped maintain our old house since I inherited it, thirty odd years ago, and whose family has been intertwined with mine in various ways. He holds a short wooden ladder in his hand that he made himself in order to work on those roof ridges and chimney pots that his ordinary ladder did not quite reach. It is a wonderful, well used tool that could just as easily have been carried by a medieval workman. His hobby is breeding budgerigars and his aviary is in the background of his portrait. John was kind enough to bring a fine green bird to the studio to model. His grandmother is the heroine of the story "An Incomer of Long ago".

Then there is Dr Kennedy, the respected and well-loved family doctor of Pittenweem for so many years. It was impossible for me to choose one item from his many musical and athletic skills and interests, his involvement with the church, session clerk for over thirty years, the Philharmonic Society, the ski-ing club, the golf club and the town in general, festival included, not to mention his keen application to gardening. He arrived at each sitting with a present of delicious newly picked vegetables for me. I took the easy way out and painted, predictably, an old stethoscope on the table in front of him and a bunch of traditional, medicinal herbs behind.

Many of my video interviewees have expressed the deep gratitude they feel towards him as a doctor and a supportive friend.

If the festival had brought me only one experience, that fascinating one of painting those seven interesting men would be my choice. As we sat there with the fire crackling and sometimes a patter of light rain on the roof light, the sounds and smells of smoke and oil paints reminded of the many childhood hours that I spent with my grandfather in his studio, where he told stories and peeled apples to my heart's delight.

My seven sitters were all great storytellers too and I was thoroughly entertained as I painted.

I made video interviews with each 'statesman' and my daughter Sarah edited these interviews into a charming film, which was shown at the exhibition and added a rich talking dimension to the portraits on the walls.

With the addition of the wives, we also enjoyed two Grand Openings, a champagne supper and various other social occasions in that glorious summer of continuously warm sunny weather.

Pittenweem was crowded all week in the tempting weather and I had a stream of visitors to my exhibition. I found that especially German and Scandinavian visitors invested a lot of time in my Statesmen, watching the video carefully, cross-referencing it with the portraits and the 'thumbnail sketches' which I had written about each sitter. Those who studied it all most thoroughly were also the most enthusiastic afterwards.

Very gratifying!

In 2004, Sarah had the idea of an exhibition of fashion. Ours is a family which throws nothing away and there were garments from four or five generations right through the twentieth century, evening dresses from the twenties, metallic and shapeless, more elaborate gowns of lace and embroidered satin from the thirties, shawls and shoes of years ago, even some things from the nineteenth century. There was quite an extensive array from my own heyday in the 50s and 60s that evoked memories in the bosoms of older ladies and smiles from young ones.

I still think that bright and pretty print dresses are more fun and more flattering than drab denim and skimpy T shirts!

What will we show next?

Who can tell, but hopefully this book will be launched at Pittenweem Arts Festival 2005.